THE
STORIES

Men and Gods

Greeks and Trojans

The Vengeance of the Gods

FARRAR,
STRAUS &
GIROUX
NEW YORK

OF THE GREEKS

REX WARNER

Introduction

The stories of the Greeks come from many sources, from different periods of history and from different elements in experience. Many of them represent the earliest attempts of man to interpret the bewildering world around him as his consciousness began to penetrate into it and to analyse it; others may derive from attempts to explain or to justify some religious or political institution of which the real explanation has been forgotten; others are approximately true records of events which actually took place in the dim past. Others again have been held to be in some sense or other "archetypal" of the structure, the behaviour or history of the human mind itself.

"Mythology," therefore, can carry us in all sorts of directions—historical, archaeological, anthropological, theological, psychoanalytical, to name but a few; and, understood in the sense of an enquiry into such branches of learning, it certainly deserves its learned suffix. It is true too that part of the fascination which these stories have for us does come from their immense antiquity, from elements in them which are prehistoric and precivilised. Often they seem to remind us of things which we once knew, but have forgotten, of places where we once were, or think that we may have been, of dreams more strangely real than waking life, but which are still dreams. These Wordsworthian intimations come to us from myths, as they come to us from poetry and from nature. It is natural that they should be investigated by the religious and the scientific alike, indeed by all who are interested in man's condition.

It remains true, however, that these stories, in the forms in which they have been known to us for some two or three thousand years, are the work, not of priests or of scientists, but of poets. Whatever their remote origins may have been, it is by poets that they have been shaped and through poets that they are known. And though certain great poets have, as it were, fixed the stories in something like a permanent form, there has still been a great variety of interpretation and of emphasis. Aeschylus, for instance, treats the story of Agamemnon, Clytemnestra and Orestes in a very different way from that of Homer or of Euripides. Shakespeare's "Duke Theseus" is as unlike the Theseus of Sophocles as are some of the characters of Cocteau and Anouilh unlike their Greek originals. The wholly sophisticated and "modern" Ovid, with his genius as a story-teller, would have been regarded by Hesiod, one imagines, as, to say the least, irreverent.

It is right, therefore, in introducing a collection of these Greek stories, to give the reader some indication of where they have come from and for what reasons they have sometimes been altered or adapted.

The first section of this book, "Men and Gods," is mostly taken from the *Metamorphoses* of the Roman poet Ovid. A few of the stories ("Phaethon," "The Great Flood," for instance) are straightforward translations. In many others I have followed the original closely, but altered it here and there, either to avoid very obscure mythological references or in the interests of what I have conceived to be either clarity or brevity. Where I have departed from the original, I have tried to preserve something of Ovid's tone, partly because I do not think that one can possibly do better, and partly because I wanted the book to look, if possible, as if it had been written by one person. I am well aware that Ovid, had he been attempting to do the same thing for a modern audience, would have done it with much greater skill. But that, I am afraid, cannot be helped.

There were several reasons for following Ovid so closely. Many modern re-tellings of the Greek myths have seemed to me to be marred by a kind of sentimentality. Ovid can be pathetic or romantic; he is never sentimental. He is also "sophisticated" in a very modern way. How far he "believed in" the gods and heroes of whom he writes we do not know. Certainly he often writes of them almost with his tongue in his cheek. One may, no doubt, extract from him, if one wishes, what can be called "the deeper meanings." T. S. Eliot may have been doing something of this sort in his long note to *The Waste Land* in which he quotes Ovid's version of the strange sexual experiences of Tiresias. (Hardly to the advantage of the ordinary reader, and with much less justification than Gibbon had on another occasion, he has veiled this account "in the decent obscurity of a learned language.") But Ovid himself is not interested in "the deeper meanings." He is interested in the story itself and in all the drama, excitement and pathos he can get out of it. However brilliantly he may tell it, it is still to him "just a story." Very odd things happen, things that are certainly supernatural. But Ovid takes them all in his stride, accepting them gladly for his own artistic purpose, thoroughly enjoying what he is doing, entertaining us with events which often, looked at in another light, would be simply horrifying. If one compares, for instance, Ovid's treatment of the story of Bacchus and Pentheus with that of Euripides in his play *The Bacchae,* the difference of outlook will be immediately evident. Euripides feels the full horror of a situation where a divine power drives human beings into an ecstasy which can be beautiful, but which can also be appallingly savage and cruel. At the end of his play we feel reverence, fear and some other feelings which may be vague, but which are certainly disquieting. But in Ovid there is nothing really disturbing. All the gruesome details are given us, but in the context of his vivid style and rapid narrative they are not frightening. And as to the questions which might legitimately be raised as to whether the gods can really be good, for Ovid such questions simply do not exist, or, if they do exist, they do not matter. With all his sophistication, his extraordinary skill and his fantastic cleverness, he has, in a sense, a childlike view of things. He sees with remarkable clarity but neither he nor we really *feel* the passions, the lacerations and the brutality of which he sometimes writes; or rather we feel them not as realities but as elements in some midsummer night's dream.

It should be added that from Chaucer onwards most English poets have derived their knowledge of Greek mythology very largely from Ovid's *Metamorphoses*. They have reshaped the material according to the demands of their own temperaments and times, but he, an artist and a reshaper himself, remains the "grand original." This was another reason for following him so closely.

In some cases, however, usually because in his *Metamorphoses* Ovid has sometimes chosen to deal only with part of a story, I have attempted to complete the story in my own words. An acute critic would be able to tell, no doubt only too easily, from internal evidence alone, where I have done so. He would also be able to tell, in this version of the story of Orpheus and Eurydice, what parts are from Ovid and what from Virgil.

And one story, that of Cupid and Psyche, is adapted from another *Metamorphoses*, more commonly known as *The Golden Ass*, the work of the later writer Apuleius. It is of a more obviously allegorical pattern than the other stories, but Apuleius has at least something of the brilliant fancifulness and charm of Ovid, and this story, like Ovid's, is probably from a Greek original.

As the writers from whom I have drawn in this section all wrote in Latin, I have used, as they did, the Latin words for the Greek gods and goddesses (Diana instead of Artemis, Venus instead of Aphrodite).

In the second section, "Greeks and Trojans," I have used Greek names throughout, since, of course, the main source has been the *Iliad* of Homer. Much the longest part of this section is Book Two, which is taken almost entirely from Homer. The action of the *Iliad*, however, takes place in a few days, whereas the Trojan War lasted ten years. The *Iliad*, which ends with the funeral of Hector, naturally makes no mention of the fall of Troy (though some episodes are touched on incidentally in the *Odyssey*). Other well-known stories, such as that of the Judgement of Paris, are only briefly mentioned, and others, such as that of Leda and the Swan, are not mentioned at all. So, for the sake of continuity, Book One describes the origins of the war and Book Three continues the narrative from the funeral of Hector to the escape of Aeneas. Much of Book Three is, of course, from Virgil.

Some of the episodes and views in the sources from which these two Books have been derived are not at all Homeric. For instance, the rather crooked Odysseus of Virgil (and of Sophocles' *Philoctetes*) is very different from the Homeric hero. Again in the interests of continuity, I have attempted to tone down these discrepancies as far as possible. The reader will observe that while Book Two is a dramatic whole, Books One and Three are designed simply to satisfy ordinary curiosity as to "what happened next" or "how did it all start."

In Book Three all the stories are taken from Greek plays, and all, except for "Prometheus" and "Agamemnon," which are from Aeschylus, are from plays of Euripides. I included "Prometheus" because it has proved one of the most powerful myths in Western civilisation, and "Agamemnon" partly because the later story of Orestes (from Euripides) would be less easily intelligible without it, though it is true that Euripides' approach is very different from that of Aeschylus. It is also true that a consecutive prose narrative is something very different from poetic drama. The whole action of Aeschylus' *Prometheus Bound,* in which the central figure never once moves, could be described in one or two sentences. And in his *Agamemnon* the long part played by the chorus (who have little or no place in a prose narrative) is exceedingly important. It may well be asked, therefore, what, if one takes from Aeschylus the poetry, the drama, and the visual effects, exactly is left. And the answer must be, I am afraid, "Not very much." Only, in fact, the bare bones of the story. Yet these bare bones seem in themselves to be capable of life. And if their presentation persuades a reader to go on to Aeschylus himself, my purpose will have been well served.

Much the same disadvantages must be found in a prose version of the dramas of Euripides. Again the chorus must be sacrificed and action be translated to narrative. Here, however, the problem is a little easier than it was with Aeschylus. Of the stories related here, only one, "Hippolytus," is a tragic story. Some of the others ("Helen," for instance) would be better described as romantic comedies. And compared with Aeschylus, Euripides is, as Aristophanes found, "modern."

In this book as a whole, as I have tried to make clear, I have attempted to follow wherever possible, and as closely as seemed possible, a literary original. I did this, not really with any particular theory in mind, but because I liked it that way. There has been no attempt at all at explaining the stories in anthopological or historical terms. There is no pretension of scholarship. The aim has been simply "all for your delight."

REX   WARNER

Storrs, Connecticut

Contents

GREEKS & TROJANS

BOOK THREE

The Fall of Troy ☙

THE VENGEANCE OF THE GODS

MEN &
GODS

PYRAMUS AND THISBE

Pyramus and Thisbe lived next door to each other in the city of Babylon, which Semiramis is said to have walled all round with brick. Pyramus was a most beautiful young man and Thisbe more lovely than all the girls of the East. As they were neighbours they soon got to know each other, and in the end they fell in love. They ought really to have got married, but their parents forbade them to do so. What they could not forbid was that they should be in love, which they were, one as much as the other. They had no one to help them in their secret and could only talk together by nods and gestures; but the more their feelings were hid, the more desperate their hidden feelings became.

In the wall between their two houses there was a small chink which had been left there by the builders. Nobody had noticed this for years and years, but love notices everything, and these two lovers were the first to find it and make it a pathway for their conversations. Safely through this chink they would whisper to each other their loving words, and often, when Pyramus was standing on one side of the wall and Thisbe on the other, listening in turn to the sound of each other's breathing, they would say: "You cruel wall, why do you stand in the way of our love? Perhaps it is too much to ask that you should disappear so that we could really meet; but you might at least open a little bit, so that we could kiss each other. All the same we are grateful to you, and admit that it is because of you that our words can reach the ears that love to hear them."

So they would speak, each unfortunately on the wrong side. At nightfall they would say good-bye, and each would press on the wall opposite kisses that could not go through to the other side.

When dawn next day had scattered the stars and the rays of the sun had dried the dew from the grass, they came together again. First in low whispers they complained, and then they decided that in the silence of the night they would try to escape notice and steal out of doors. When they were out of their houses, they would leave the city too, and, so that they should not have to wander about in the open country, they agreed to meet at the tomb of Ninus where they would hide in the shade of a tree. There was a tree there (a very tall mulberry) covered with snow-white fruit, near an icy-cold fountain. This idea pleased them very much, and daylight seemed to them to last a long time. But finally the sun plunged into the waves, and out of the waves came night.

In the darkness Thisbe cautiously swung back the door on its hinges and went out. None of her people saw her and, covering her face with a veil, she came to the tomb and sat down under the tree. Her love gave her courage. Then suddenly a lioness appeared. She had just been killing cattle and her mouth was all smeared with blood. Now she had come to quench her thirst in the water of the spring near the tree. Far off in the moonlight Babylonian Thisbe saw the lioness, and fled trembling into a dark cave, but as she fled her veil slipped from her neck and she left it behind.

The savage lioness drank deeply to quench her thirst and, on her way back to the forest, happened to find, not Thisbe herself, but the dainty scarf she had left behind her. This she tore up with her bloody jaws.

Pyramus arrived a little later and saw deeply marked in the sand what he knew were the footprints of a wild beast. His face went white, and then, when he found the clothes too, all stained with blood, he cried out: "One night will make an end of two lovers. Of us two she was the one who ought to have lived longest. It is I who was to blame. You poor thing, it is I who have destroyed you, because I asked you to come to such a dangerous place by night and did not arrive there first. O you lions who live among these rocks, tear my body to pieces, bite up my wicked flesh in your terrible jaws! But only cowards pray for death."

Then he picked up Thisbe's scarf and took it with him to the shade of the tree where they had planned to meet. First he wept over the scarf which he knew so well, and kissed it. Then he said to it: "Now you must drink my blood too" and immediately plunged the sword which he carried into his side, and drew it out, dying, from the hot wound. As he lay prostrate on the ground the blood spurted up high into the air, just as when, through a defect in the lead, a pipe bursts and through the little hole the water shoots out hissing in a stream, and leaps up into the air. The fruit on the tree was sprayed with his blood and turned black. The roots too were soaked, and as a result gave a purple colour to the hanging berries.

And now, still frightened, but frightened too of missing her lover, Thisbe returned and looked about everywhere for him, anxious to tell him about the great danger which she had escaped. She recognized the surroundings and the shape of the tree which she knew, but the changed colour of the fruit made her uncertain. She wondered whether this was really the tree or not, and while she was hesitating she saw someone's limbs twitching on the bloody ground. She took a pace backwards, her face turned more white than box-wood, and she shuddered like the sea shivers when a little breeze just strokes its surface. Soon she recognized the body of her love, and then she violently struck herself on her guiltless arms, tore her hair, embraced his body, filling his wounds with tears, mingling her weeping with his blood. She pressed kisses on his cold face and cried out: "O Pyramus, what is it that has taken you from me? Pyramus, answer me! It is your dearest Thisbe calling to you. Listen to me! Raise up your drooping head!"

At the sound of Thisbe's name, Pyramus lifted up his eyes which were already heavy with death, and, when he had seen her, he shut them again.

Thisbe then recognized her own veil and saw that the ivory sheath had no sword in it. "So it was your own hand, unhappy one, and your love for me which killed you? I, too, have a hand brave enough for this, and I love you too. My love will give me strength to make the wound. I shall go with you, and people will say that I was not only the cause but also the companion of your death. Only death could have parted you from me, and now not even death shall have the power to do so. And you, our unhappy parents, mine and his, I pray you in the name of both of us that you will not refuse that we, joined together by fixed love and by our last hours, should be buried together in the same tomb. I pray too, that this tree which now covers with its boughs the sad body of one of us and will soon cover mine as well, I pray that in memory of our blood it may always keep the colour in its fruit and have berries suitable for mourning and be a memorial to both of our deaths."

As she spoke, she fitted the point of the sword, still warm from his blood, under her breast and fell forward on it. But both the gods and her parents were touched by her prayers. The colour of the mulberry, when ripe, is dark red: and the ashes of Pyramus and Thisbe rest in the same urn.

CADMUS

Cadmus was a prince of Tyre. Jupiter had fallen in love with his sister, Europa, had changed himself into a bull and had carried the girl away to the fields of Crete. But her father, Agenor, with no idea of what had happened, ordered Cadmus to look for the lost girl throughout the world, and gave him the punishment of exile, if he failed to find her. In one way this was a fair thing to do: in another way it was unfair, since nobody could keep track of all Jupiter's secret loves.

So Cadmus wandered all over the world and became an exile, keeping away from his own country where his father's anger would await him. Finally he visited the oracle of Phoebus and asked

whether there was any land in which he could settle down. Phoebus gave him this reply: "In a desert place you will meet a cow, one that has never had a yoke on her neck or drawn a hooked plough. Follow her as she goes and in the place where she first lies down on the grass, there you must found your city, and you must call the place Boeotia, or Cowland."

Almost as soon as Cadmus had come down from the cave where the oracle was, he saw a young cow, with no one looking after her, walking slowly along, and with no mark on her to show that she had ever been used for ploughing or belonged to anybody. He walked carefully on after her, and, as he went, he silently gave thanks to Phoebus for his guidance.

The cow went across the fords of the river Cephisus and through the fields of Panope. Then she stood still and, lifting up her head, which was very beautiful with its long horns, she filled the air all round with her lowings. Then she gave a look back at Cadmus and his men who were following her, and sank down on the ground, letting her flanks rest in the cool grass. Cadmus gave thanks to the gods, kissed this foreign earth and greeted the mountains and fields that he had never seen before.

The next thing was to make a sacrifice to Jupiter, and he ordered his men to go and find a spring of living water for the libations. There was an ancient forest nearby which had never been touched by the axe, and in the middle of it was a cave all overgrown with bushes and bending twigs. Stones fitted together there formed a low arch out of which welled a stream of water, and, hidden inside the cave, was a serpent sacred to Mars with a wonderful golden crest. Its eyes sparkled with fire: all its body was swollen with poison. It had three tongues which flickered out and three rows of teeth.

As soon as Cadmus's men came, unluckily for them, to this wood, they let down their buckets with a splash into the water, and immediately, out of the depths of the cave the blue serpent stretched out its head and made a terrible hissing. The buckets dropped from their hands, the blood left their bodies, and a sudden trembling came over their limbs. As for the serpent, it gathered itself up with its scaly coils into rolling circles; with a quick movement it arched itself up and, with more than half of its body upright in the air, it looked right down on the trees. It was as big, if you could have seen the whole of it, as the constellation in the sky which is called the Serpent, and is placed between the Great Bear and the Little Bear. Without a second's delay it seized upon Cadmus's men, and it made no difference whether they were getting their swords ready to fight or were thinking of running away or were too terrified to do either. Some of them it killed with its teeth, some by crushing them in its long coils, some by its deadly poisonous breath.

By the time that the sun had reached its full height and the shadows were at their smallest, Cadmus began to wonder why his men were being so long, and he set out to look for them. He carried a lion-skin shield, and his weapons were a shining iron-pointed spear and a javelin. His own stout heart was worth more than any weapon.

When he entered the wood he saw the dead bodies and, sprawling over them in triumph, the huge body of their destroyer, who now with its bloody tongue was licking their grim wounds. "My faithful friends," Cadmus said, "I shall either avenge your death or share in it."

As he spoke he lifted up in his right hand a great stone. It was a huge stone and he threw it with a huge effort; but, though high walls with their towers would have been knocked down by its force, the serpent remained without a wound. Its scales, like a breast-plate, and its hard dark skin protected it against the blow. However, the skin was not too hard for Cadmus's javelin, which fixed firmly and stuck in the middle of the serpent's coiling muscular back, with the iron head going right down into the flesh. Infuriated with pain, the animal twisted its head back, examined its wounds, and bit at the shaft of the javelin that was stuck in it. Tugging violently at it, it managed, when it had loosened it all round, to tear it out; but the point was still stuck in its backbone. Now indeed it had reason to be more savage than ever before. Great veins swelled up on its throat; a white foam shone round its grisly open jaws; its scales made a terrible rustling sound on the earth; a black breath, like that which comes from the mouth of Styx, made the air filthy and tainted. At one moment it coiled itself up into huge folds; and next moment it shot up into the air erect and high as a tree; then it surged forward in a huge wave, like a flooded river, battering down with its breast the trees that stood in its path.

Cadmus retreated a little, holding his lion-skin shield in front of him, and jabbing with his spear point at the open jaws that were always threatening him. The beast became all the more enraged, as it bit uselessly on the hard iron, fixing its teeth into the point of the spear. Soon blood began to fall from the poisonous roof of its mouth and to stain the green grass around. But the wound was not a serious one, because the serpent kept backing away and withdrawing its wounded neck, and so never gave Cadmus a chance to thrust his blow home. Finally, however, he fixed the spear firmly in the beast's throat and pressed on hard till he had driven it back against an oak-tree. There the spear went right through both the neck and the tree. The tree bent down beneath its weight and the trunk groaned as, in its death agony, the serpent lashed it with its tail.

Then, while Cadmus was standing looking at the enormous size of his defeated enemy, he suddenly heard a voice. He had no idea where it came from, but he heard it saying: "Son of Agenor, why are you looking at this dead serpent? A time will come when *you* will be turned into a serpent, and people will be looking at *you*." On hearing these words he stood in terror for some time, with pale face and uneasy mind. Cold fear made his hair stand on end.

Then suddenly Pallas, his patron goddess, appeared, gliding down to him through the upper air. She told him to plough up the land and sow the dragon's teeth in it, and they would grow up to be his people. He obeyed her, ploughing long furrows as he pressed his plough into the earth. He took the teeth, which were to be the seeds of men, as he had been told, and scattered them. Then, incredible as it may seem, the edges of the furrows began to show signs of movement. First there sprang up out of the ground the points of spears, then helmets with bright-coloured nodding crests. Then above the surface there began to show shoulders and breasts and arms heavy with their weapons. So out of the earth came a whole crop of warriors with their shields.

Cadmus was terrified at finding that he had new enemies to deal with, and he was beginning to take up his arms when one of the earth-born people cried out to him: "Leave your arms alone! This is a war amongst ourselves. Do not join in it." He then struck down with his stout sword, fighting hand to hand, one of his earth-born brothers, and was himself struck down by a javelin thrown at him from long range. Yet the man who killed him lived no longer himself, immediately giving up the life which he had only just received. In the same way the whole crowd of them fought bitterly, each man killing his neighbour, brothers only for a very short time. Soon all these young men, whose life had been so short, were dying in agony on their mother earth, all warm with their blood. Only five were left. One of these was called Echion, and at the command of Pallas, he threw down his weapons on the ground and proposed peace to his brothers. The fighting was over and Cadmus had these five men for his companions in founding the city which had been promised him by the oracle of Phoebus.

ACTAEON

One might have thought now that Cadmus was really happy. His city of Thebes was built. He was given the daughter of Venus and Mars, Harmonia, to be his wife. He had four daughters who were called Ino, Agave, Autonoe and Semele. They in turn had children who began to grow up to be men and women. So one would certainly have expected Cadmus and Harmonia to be happy. However, one should always wait for the end, and no one can be called happy until he is dead and buried.

The first reason for sadness that came on Cadmus and Harmonia in the midst of all this good fortune was the fate of their grandson Actaeon, the son of Autonoe. Deer's horns grew on his head and his own hounds drank up their master's blood. And if you think about the story you will see that this was just because of bad luck, not because he did anything wrong. There is nothing wrong in just making a mistake.

Actaeon had been hunting on a mountain, and all the ground was stained with the blood of the wild animals which he had killed. It was midday and the sun stood high up in the sky, making all the shadows short. Young Actaeon with gentle words called to his hunting companions as they strayed through the bushes and thick-

ets: "My friends, all our nets and spears are wet with blood. We
have done well enough to-day. When to-morrow's dawn brings
back the light in her shining chariot, then we will start our hunting
again. Now Phoebus is half-way across the sky and his rays seem to
split the ground. Let us rest now and take up our knotted nets."
His companions did as they were told and gave up their work.

There was a valley in this forest, all overgrown with pine-trees
and sharp-pointed cypresses. It was called Gargaphie and was sacred to the huntress goddess Diana. At the far end of the valley
there was a shady cave, not specially constructed but made by nature to look as though it was a work of art; for there was a natural
arch there made out of the original rock. From one side came the
noise of a shining fountain which bubbled up from the ground and
formed a pool with grassy banks. And in this pool Diana, when she
was tired from hunting, used to bathe her virgin limbs in the bright
water.

This day, too, she had come there. To the nymph who acted as
her armour bearer she gave her javelin, her quiver and her unstrung
bow to hold. Another nymph held over her arm the dress which
the goddess took off. Two others removed her sandals. Another,
with her own hair streaming behind her, tied in a knot the hair
that fell over the goddess's shoulders, and other nymphs fetched
water in their ewers for the goddess's bath.

At this moment, just when Diana was bathing in her usual pool,
Cadmus's grandson, having stopped hunting for the day, came
wandering with no special purpose through the unknown woods
and arrived at Diana's sacred grove. It was fate that brought him
there.

As soon as he peered into the cave, all shining with the fountain spray, the naked nymphs, seeing a man, beat their breasts and
filled all the grove with their startled cries. They crowded round
Diana and tried to shield her with their own bodies, but the goddess was taller than any of them and stood out head and shoulders
above the rest. As she stood there naked and in view, she blushed
the colour of the clouds when the sun strikes slanting across them,
red as the dawn. With the nymphs all around her, she turned
aside, looking behind her as though for her arrows. But she had no
weapons by her except the water, and, taking up some of this, she
dashed it into the young man's face and poured the avenging
stream over his hair. Then she spoke words foretelling the fate that

would soon come upon him. "Now," she said, "tell, if you can tell, how you have seen me naked!"

This was all she said, but, as she spoke, she made stag's horns grow out of his head which she had splashed with the water; she lengthened out his neck and made his ears pointed; instead of hands she gave him hooves; she changed his arms into long legs, and covered his body with a spotted hide. She also made him frightened. The hero Actaeon began to run away, and, while doing so, was astonished to find that he was running so fast. But when he came to a pool and saw his changed face and his horns in the water, he tried to say, "O how unhappy I am," but found that he could not pronounce the words. He groaned (this was the only way he could speak at all). Tears ran down his cheeks, though they were not really his cheeks. Only his mind and his feelings remained unchanged. What was he to do? Should he go back home to the royal palace or should he hide in the woods? He felt ashamed to go home, but frightened to stay where he was.

While he stood wondering what to do, his hounds saw him. First came Blackfoot and keen-scented Trailer, baying to the others. Trailer was a Cretan hound, Blackfoot came from Sparta. Then the others came rushing up, faster than the wind—Greedy and Gazelle, and Hilltreader, all dogs from Arcadia, strong Fawn-slayer, Hunter and Hurricane, swift Flyer and keen-scented Chaser. There were Forester, who had just been wounded by a wild boar, Glen, who was half a wolf, and more than twenty other strong fierce baying hounds. The whole pack of them, eager for the chase, came rushing over the rocks and broken ground, darting through the thickets and appearing, as it were, from nowhere.

Actaeon found himself being chased over the very ground where he had often chased animals himself. He was running away from his own hounds, which he had trained himself, and longed to cry out: "I am Actaeon. You must recognize me. I am your own master." But, however much he wanted to, he was unable to speak.

A hound called Soot was the first one to fix teeth in his back; then came Barker, and then Mountaineer leapt on to his shoulder and hung on. These had started later than the others but had taken a short cut through the mountains and so arrived first. While they held their master fast, the rest of the pack came up and buried their fangs in his body. Soon there was no room left on his skin for further wounds. He groaned aloud, making a sound which, while it was not exactly human, was not the sound that an ordinary stag would make. He filled all the mountain ridges that he knew so well with his sad cries, and, falling on his knees, like someone begging for a favour, he looked round in silence on his persecutors, turning his face to them, as though he were stretching out his arms to ask for mercy.

But his young friends, knowing nothing of the real facts, kept on shouting to the swift hounds, as they usually did, and urging them on to the kill. They all looked round for Actaeon and were always shouting out his name, imagining that he was not there. At the sound of his name, the stag turned his head towards them, but they just said that it was a pity that Actaeon was not there, that he must have been too lazy to come and see this fine sight of the animal brought to bay. Indeed he might well wish that he was not there, but he was. He might well wish to be watching his hounds and not feeling their savage teeth. But as it was they were all about him, burying their muzzles in his flesh, and tearing their own master to pieces in the belief that it was a stag that they were killing. Not till wound had followed wound, and his life was over, was the anger of Diana, the archer goddess, appeased.

PENTHEUS

Another of Cadmus's grandsons, Pentheus, came to a sad end, though he deserved his fate more than Actaeon did. Pentheus was the son of Echion, the earth-born soldier who had helped Cadmus to build Thebes, and of Agave, the daughter of Cadmus and Harmonia. In Cadmus's old age Pentheus became the ruler of Thebes and he met his death by offending the new god Bacchus, who was, in a way, his own cousin, since he was the child of Jupiter and of Pentheus's aunt Semele.

Bacchus, the god of wine, had been brought up secretly, since Juno, the wife of Jupiter, hated him. First he was worshipped in the east but later came back into Greece with his band of revellers. Women in particular joined in the adoration of the new god, dancing and singing in his honour along the mountains. But there were some men, Pentheus among them, who tried to put down the new religion. These men all came to bad ends.

In Thebes there was a famous blind prophet called Tiresias. Most people honoured him, but Pentheus, who was apt to scoff at holy things, laughed at the old man's prophecies and was rude to him about his blindness. The prophet shook his head in disapproval and his white locks swung as he shook it. "How lucky you would be," he said to Pentheus, "if you too were blind so that you could never watch the worship of Bacchus. For the day will come —indeed I know that it is almost here—when the new god, Bacchus, the son of Semele, will come to this country. And unless you honour him and build temples to him, you will be torn into a thousand pieces, your body will be scattered far and wide, and your blood will stain the forests and the hands of your mother and her sisters. This is sure to happen, for I know that you will not give the god the honour he deserves. Then you will be sorry and say that, blind as I am, I have seen far too well."

Pentheus pushed Tiresias away out of his house while he was speaking, but his words came true, and what he had foretold actually took place.

Bacchus did arrive and soon all the country was full of shouting and revelry. Everyone rushed out of the city, men and women, old and young, rich and poor, to join in the new religion. They danced and sang about the mountains, carrying wands tipped with fir cones, wearing garlands of ivy and the skins of fawns. To those who were not worshippers they might seem like mad people, but they felt themselves filled with the god, and, when they smote the ground with their wands, streams of milk came out from the rocks.

Pentheus alone was indignant. "Children of the serpent's teeth," he cried out, "children of Mars, what is this crazy madness? Are you overcome just by the noise of cymbals clashing together or of those long crooked horns, or by a set of magic tricks, and women howling out, vulgar crowds, drunkenness and empty dreams? You who were never frightened by the noise of trumpets in war or the thought of drawn swords and real fighting! And you, old men who with my grandfather came over the sea to found this city, I am surprised at you. Will you allow Thebes to be captured by an un-armed boy, who has no spears or horsemen and whose only weap-ons are perfumed hair, soft garlands and clothes richly woven with purple and gold? Let me deal with him at once by myself. I shall soon force him to admit that he made up the name of his father and that his new religion is nothing but trickery. Go at once, my slaves, and bring this imposter back in chains! Let there be no hanging back and no laziness in obeying my orders!"

His grandfather Cadmus and all the elders urged him not to speak like this, but to be more wise. Their words however had no effect on him. Indeed the more good advice they gave him, the more stubborn he became. All their efforts to control him merely did harm.

Soon the slaves came back, covered with blood and bringing with them a young man with his hands tied behind him. "Where is Bacchus?" Pentheus asked, and they replied, "We could not find him, but we have seized this man who is a companion of his and a priest of his religion."

Pentheus, with eyes made terrible with anger, glanced at the prisoner. He was hardly able to control himself from putting him to death at once. "You are soon going to die," he shouted at him, "and be an example to others by your death. But first tell me your name and your family and where you come from and why you are busying yourself with this new religion."

The young man, showing no sign of fear, replied: "My name is Acoetes. I come from Maeonia. My parents were humble people. My father could not leave me any fields to plough with strong oxen, or any woolly sheep or cattle. He was a poor man himself and used to earn his living by catching fish with a line and hooks and rods. He had no property apart from his skill, and when he died he could leave me nothing but the open sea. This is the only thing that I can say I got from my father. However, so as not to be always fixed to the same bit of rocky shore, I soon began to learn how to steer a ship and all about the stars used in navigation, about the various winds and about the best harbours and anchorages. So I took to the sea and once, when I was on my way to Delos, I was driven off my course and put in, using the oars, to the island of Chios. There we jumped out of the boat and landed on the wet sand. We spent the night there and, as soon as dawn grew red, I told my men to fetch fresh water and showed them the path that went to the spring. I myself went up a small hill to see what the wind was doing. Then I called to my men and started back to the ship. 'Here we are, and see what we have got,' shouted back Opheltes, one of the sailors, and brought up to me what he thought was a useful piece of booty which he had come across in an empty field. It was a young boy with beauty like a girl's beauty. This boy looked as though he was drowsy with wine. He seemed to stagger as he walked and could hardly keep step with those who were leading him. I looked carefully at his clothes and his face and his way of walking. There was nothing in any of these which seemed to me mortal. I realized this at once and I said to my men: 'Exactly what sort of divinity there is in this body I do not know, but in this body there certainly is divinity.' Then I turned to the boy and said, 'Whoever you may be, I pray you to look favourably on us and help us. And please forgive these men who have captured you.'

" 'There is no need to pray for us,' said Dictys. He was the best of all the men at climbing to the topmost yard and sliding down to deck again on a firmly gripped rope. The others agreed with him, Libys and yellow-haired Melanthus the look-out man, Alcimedon and Epopeus who controlled the rowers' rate of stroke and used to urge them on with his voice. So did all the rest, so blind they were in their desire to make profit out of their prize.

" 'Then I, in any case,' I said, 'shall refuse to allow the ship to be used for such an evil purpose. And here I have authority.'

"I tried to stop them coming on board, but Lycabas, one of the roughest of the whole crew, a man who had been exiled for murder, broke into a rage, seized hold of my throat with his great hands and would have thrown me overboard, if I had not, in my terror, managed to cling on to a rope. The other godless men were all supporting him, when at last Bacchus (for this boy was Bacchus himself) seemed to come to his senses, as though all the shouting had woken him up from a drowsy drunkenness. 'What are you doing?' he said. 'Why are you shouting out? Tell me, sailors, how I came here, and where are you taking me.'

" 'Don't be frightened,' Proteus replied. 'Tell us where you want to go and we will put you down at whatever harbour you choose.'

" 'Then,' said Bacchus, 'take me to Naxos. My home is there, and there you shall have a friendly welcome.'

"Then these deceitful men swore by the sea and by all the gods

that they would do as he had asked, and they told me to get the bright-painted ship under sail.

"Naxos was on the right, and, as I was setting course to the right, Opheltes shouted out, 'What are you doing, you madman? We want to go to the left.' Others frowned and winked at me or whispered in my ear, threatening me.

"I was simply amazed. 'Let someone else take the helm then,' I said. 'I refuse to be used to help your wicked treachery.'

"Then they were all against me and turned on me with angry mutterings. Aethalion said: 'You need not suppose that you are the only one who can steer a boat,' and he came and took my place at the helm, turning away from Naxos and making in the opposite direction.

"Then the god, playing with them and making them think that he had only just discovered their treachery, stared out over the sea from the hooked stern and, looking as though he was crying, said: 'O sailors, this is not the shore you promised me. This is not the land where I wanted to be. How have I deserved this from you? Surely you cannot be proud of what you are doing, all of you against one, men against a little boy!'

"As for me I was in tears already, but my wicked men laughed at my tears and struck the water eagerly with their oars, anxious to make land where they could sell their prisoner as a slave.

"Now I swear to you by Bacchus himself (and there is no god more near to you at this moment than he is) that I am telling a true story, incredible as it may seem. Suddenly the ship stuck still in the water, just as if it were in dry dock. The sailors, in amazement, redoubled the strokes of their oars. Then they began to shake out every sail, hoping that with sails and oars together the ship might move. But ivy began to grow round the oars and prevent their motion. Ivy began to climb up the mast, twining and hanging in folds and spreading its clusters of black berries against the white of the sails. The god himself appeared with a crown of leaves and clustering berries on his forehead and in his hand was an ivy wand. Around him there appeared the shapes of tigers and lynxes: at his feet seemed to be lying the fierce bodies of spotted leopards.

"The men, in madness or in terror, jumped overboard. First I noticed that Medon's body had begun to turn black and that his backbone was bending into a regular curve. Lycabas saw this too and was starting to say, 'O Medon, you are turning into some strange animal,' but, as he was speaking, his own jaws expanded sideways, his nose became hooked, his skin hardened and began to be covered with scales. Libys, while he was still tugging at ivy-wreathed oars, suddenly saw his hands shrinking into things that were not hands at all, but fins. Another sailor, as he tried to pull on one of the twisted ropes, found that his arms had disappeared and plunged backwards into the sea without limbs. At the end of his body was a tail curved like the horns of the moon.

"So they leaped about on every side in the water, scattering the spray, plunging under the surface and coming up again, playing together like a troupe of dancers, rolling their bodies sportively in the waves, breathing in the sea through their wide nostrils and blowing it out again.

"Out of twenty men (which was the number of the crew) I was the only survivor. I stood there trembling and cold with fear, hardly conscious of myself. But the god strengthened me. 'Do not be afraid,' he said. 'Hold on the course for Naxos.'

"When we arrived there I joined the religion of Bacchus and now I am one of his worshippers."

Pentheus heard the story and said: "If you think that this long idle tale will soften my anger, you are mistaken. Quickly, slaves, take this man away. Make him suffer every torture, and so send his body to death in the night of Styx."

Immediately Acoetes, who had told the story, was dragged out and shut up behind strong prison walls. But while his executioners were preparing the cruel instruments of torture—red-hot irons and racks—suddenly the prison doors flew open of their own accord, the chains fell of their own accord from the prisoner's arms, and the prisoner was gone.

In spite of this Pentheus remained obstinate. This time he did not send messengers, but went himself to Mount Cithaeron, which was the special place outside Thebes where Bacchus was worshipped and which was loud with the singing and shouting of his worshippers. As he heard the whole air full of the shouting and the crying, Pentheus's anger boiled up all the more in him. It had the effect on him that the sound of trumpets has on a spirited war-horse.

About half-way up the mountain there is an open space, in full view from all sides, with woods around it. Here Pentheus was spying with his unclean eyes on the sacred mysteries of the new religion. His mother, Agave, was the first to see him. She first was driven mad and rushed upon her son, hurling at him her wand of ivy. "Look, sisters," she cried out, "look at this huge wild boar prowling about in our field. I want to be the one to kill him."

The whole rout of women rushed down upon the one man. All gathered round him and pursued him, frightened now, as he well might be, and speaking in quite a different tone from that one which he had used before. Now he was ready to condemn himself and to admit that he had been wrong. But they tore at his body from all sides. Wounded as he was, he cried out to his aunt, Autonoe, "O, help me, aunt! Remember Actaeon, and have pity on me!"

But she, driven out of her mind, did not even remember who Actaeon was. As Pentheus stretched out his arm to her, she seized it and, with the strength of madness, tore it off. Ino, in the same rage, tore off the other arm. Now the wretched man had no arms to stretch out for pity to his mother. "O mother," he said, "look!" and he turned towards her the stumps where his arms had been. Agave, tossing her head with its streaming hair, and howling at the sight of him, tore off his head and, holding it in her fingers which were streaming with blood, she shouted out: "Look, my friends and sisters! See what I have done and see my triumph!"

Then like the wind after the first autumn frosts quickly strips the insecure leaves from high trees, so was the body of Pentheus torn to pieces and scattered by terrible and ignorant hands. Agave, with her sisters, returned to Thebes and, holding the head of Pentheus, came, still mad, to her father Cadmus and boasted to him of how she had killed the wild boar. Cadmus wept to see her and to see his grandson's fate. Very gradually he persuaded her, as her madness began to subside, that what she held in her hands was not a boar's head, but the head of her own son, who had refused to honour the new god. With such a fate to warn them, the Thebans in great numbers adopted the new religion, burned incense and sacrificed before the altars of Bacchus.

INO

The death of Pentheus was not the last of the misfortunes which fell upon the house of Cadmus. Juno still hated the whole family and she now turned her hatred against Cadmus's daughter Ino, who was proud of her children, proud of her husband Athamas, and particularly proud of the new god, Bacchus, whom, after his mother's death, she had helped to bring up.

Juno looked on her with hatred and envy. She remembered how Bacchus, the child of her own husband by another woman, had been able to change the sailors into dolphins and make Agave kill her own son. "And now," she said to herself, "is there nothing I can do except lament and be jealous? Am I not also powerful? Bacchus has shown me what to do. He has shown only too clearly, by the killing of Pentheus, how strong madness can be. Why should not Ino also be driven mad?"

So she decided to go down to the lower world of the ghosts and seek help from the Furies there.

There is a road going downhill and shaded by deathly yew trees. It leads down in utter silence to the kingdom below the earth. There the sluggish stream of the Styx breathes out its damp mists, and on this road the ghosts of those who have just died go down to their habitations. They come to a wide dreary plain, palely lit and icy cold; and there the shades look for the road that leads to the infernal city and the palace of black Pluto, the King of the Dead. This city has a thousand entrances and gates open on every side. As the sea receives all the rivers of the earth, so this place receives all the dead souls. It is big enough to hold whole nations, and when crowds enter it they are unnoticed. Here the thin bloodless ghosts, without flesh or bones, wander to and fro. Some flit about the open squares, some spend their time in the palace of the King of the underworld, some occupy themselves in ways that are an imitation of the life they used to have on earth.

So great was her rage and hatred that Juno left her home in

heaven and came down to this dreadful place. As she stepped on to the threshold, it groaned beneath the weight of her holy body, and the three-headed watch-dog, Cerberus, raised his heads and barked through his three jaws. Juno called for the Furies, who were children of Night, terrible and implacable goddesses. They sat in front of the closed adamantine prison gates of Hell, and as they sat there, they combed back from their heads the black snakes which were their hair. They rose to their feet when they recognized Juno through the dark mist.

This prison house is called the Place of Wickedness, and here the great sinners are punished. The giant Tityos was here, with his huge body stretched over nine acres. Vultures continually devoured his flesh, which continually grew again. He at one time had offered violence to Latona, the mother of Phoebus and of Diana. There also was Tantalus, who had deceived the gods. He was in continual thirst, with water just at his lips but never reaching them, and with fruit trees hanging round his head but always disappearing when he stretched out his hands to the fruit. Then there was Sisyphus, whose punishment was for ever to roll a huge rock to the top of a hill. Whenever he had pushed the rock to the summit it always rolled back again to the plain and his task had to be begun anew. Ixion, who had dared to attack Juno herself, was whirled for ever on a wheel. There also were the fifty Belides, daughters of a king of Egypt, who had murdered their husbands. They were condemned to fetch water in pitchers from one place to another, but the task was never done, as the water always ran from the pitchers on the way.

On all these criminals, and especially on Ixion, Juno looked with fierce eyes. Then she looked at Sisyphus, who had been the brother of Ino's husband Athamas. "Why should this brother," she said, "have to suffer endless torture, while Athamas and his wife, who despise me, live happily in a rich palace?"

She then told the Furies why she had come and what she wanted —which was the complete ruin of the house of Cadmus and that Athamas should be driven mad. When she had finished, the Fury Tisiphone shook her grey tangled hair and brushed back the snakes that swarmed over her forehead. "There is no need," she said, "for you to say more. What you want will be done. Now leave this loveless kingdom and go back to the purer air of heaven."

Pleased with her success, Juno returned and, as she entered

Heaven, Iris, the goddess of the rainbow, sprinkled water over her to purify her.

Meanwhile the terrible Tisiphone hurriedly seized hold of a torch that had been drenched in blood. She put on a dress, wet also with blood, and knotted round her waist a writhing snake. Then she left the lower world and with her went Grief and Terror and Madness with quivering lips. She took her stand in the doorway of the house of Athamas and they say that the very doorposts trembled at her presence and turned pale. The sun fled from the sky. At the awful sight both Ino and Athamas were overwhelmed with terror and tried to run away. But the terrible Fury stood in the entrance and stopped them escaping. She stretched out her arms which were covered with writhing vipers and shook out her hair which was hissing with snakes that fell in coils over her breast and shoulders, spitting out poison with their flickering tongues. Two of these snakes she plucked out of her hair and flung at Athamas and at Ino. They glided over their bodies, not biting them, but distilling their terrible poison into their minds. Then the Fury seized up her torch and whirled it round her head till it burst into a roaring flame. Her task was done and her victory complete. She returned to Hell and undid the serpents which had girdled her dress.

Immediately Athamas, now raving mad, shouted out in the middle of his palace: "Come, my friends, spread out the nets here in this forest! I have just seen a lioness with her two cubs." Then, quite out of his wits, he rushed after his wife as though she were a wild beast. He snatched from her arms his little son Learchus who was smiling at him and stretching out his hands to him, and dashed the baby to the ground. Ino, herself now mad, either because of the Fury or because of what her husband had done, gave a great cry and seized up her little child, Melicertes, in her bare arms. With her hair streaming behind her and shouting out the name of Bacchus, she fled from the house. Juno heard her cry and laughed. "Your foster-child, Bacchus," she said, "is not going to be of any help to you now."

There was a cliff overhanging the sea. Its base had been all hollowed out by the waves, so that the water surged right underneath it. Its top stood high and sharp over the deep sea. Ino in her madness climbed to the very summit and, with no fear, threw herself and her child right out into the sea. The water foamed and whitened in the place where she fell.

Venus, however, pitied the undeserved suffering of her granddaughter and prayed to her uncle Neptune, the god of the sea: "O Neptune, you who rule the waters, you whose power is second only to Jupiter, my request is a big one, but please grant it. Have pity on these friends of mine! The sea owes me something, since in the depths of the sea I was born from the foam, and my Greek name, Aphrodite, means this."

Neptune heard her prayer and changed Ino and her child into divine creatures. The little boy became a sea-god, Palaemon, and his mother a goddess, Lencothoe.

Cadmus, however, had no means of knowing that his daughter and his grandson had been changed into gods of the sea. He was overcome by grief at all the terrible things that had happened to his family, and he left the city which he had founded, as if it was the bad luck of the place, and not his own, which was hanging over him. With his wife he fled away and came in the end to the borders of Illyria. Here, still grieving over all their sorrows, they were discussing all the misfortunes which had come upon their family. Cadmus was saying, "I wonder whether the serpent, which I killed with my spear and whose teeth bore a crop of men, was a sacred serpent. If it is perhaps the death of this serpent that the gods have been avenging on my family, then I pray that I may turn into a serpent myself and have a long snaky body stretched out on the ground."

As he was speaking, this was exactly what did begin to happen to him. He fell down on to his face; his legs joined into one and then lengthened out into a long pointed tail. His arms still remained, and, with tears streaming down what was still his own human face, he stretched his arms out to his wife. "Come to me, my poor wife!" he said. "Come, while there is still something of me left. Touch me, and take my hand, while I have a hand, before I become entirely snake!"

He wanted to go on speaking, but suddenly found that his tongue had become forked, and he could not pronounce the words. Whenever he tried to say something sad, he made a hissing noise. This was the only voice he had.

His wife beat her breast and cried out: "O stay, Cadmus! Come back to yourself! O whatever is happening? Where are your feet and your hands and your shoulders and your face? Oh, now everything is gone. O gods, why will you not turn me into a snake too?"

As she spoke he licked his wife's face and came naturally to her bosom, as though he knew the place, winding himself round her neck in an embrace. All who saw this were terrified; but she stroked the glowing neck of the crested snake, and suddenly there were two snakes there with their coils twined together. Soon they glided away into hiding in a nearby wood. To this day they are not frightened of men, and do not hurt them. They remember what they once were, and are mild gentle snakes.

BAUCIS AND PHILEMON

Many stories go to show how enormous, and indeed limitless, is the power of the gods. If they wish anything, then it is immediately accomplished. For example, there is a place in Phrygia, among the mountains, where an oak- and a lime-tree, with a low wall round them, are growing side by side. I have seen the place myself, and this is the story of it.

Not far away is a huge lake, which was once land with houses and cities and men and women in it, though now it is the home of coots and diving-ducks. At the time when it was inhabited, Jupiter himself and Mercury, laying aside his wings and his wand of twisted snakes, took on the appearance of mortals and visited the place. They went to a thousand houses, asking for a meal and somewhere to rest, but in all of them the bolts were drawn and no hospitality was offered. There was only one house that would receive them, a poor and humble one, thatched with straw and reeds. In this cottage good old Baucis and her husband Philemon, who was of the same age, had first come to live when they were young and had grown old in it. Their poverty was no burden to them, because they admitted it and bore it with contented minds. In this house there would be no point in looking for masters and servants, since the two old people formed the entire household. Both were servants and both were masters.

When the two gods reached this humble house, and, stooping down, went in through a low door, the old man Philemon pulled forward a bench and invited them to rest their limbs. Baucis hurried up busily and threw a rough covering over the bench. Then she moved aside the warm ashes in the grate, put in leaves and bark and brought to life yesterday's fire by kneeling down and blowing at the ashes through her old lips. When the flame came, she took down from a special place some carefully split kindling wood and dry twigs, which she broke into little pieces and put under the small copper saucepan on the fire. Then she began to chop off the outside leaves of the cabbage which her husband had brought in from his well-watered garden. Philemon meanwhile took a forked stick and lifted down from a smoky beam a side of smoked bacon which had been carefully kept for a long time. He cut a little piece off it and put it into the water to boil. Then they began to pass the time in conversation. So that their guests would be more comfortable, they brought out a couch with legs and frame made of willow-wood, and put their mattress on it. They covered the mattress with coverlets that they never used except on special occasions—though these coverlets themselves were made of old cheap stuff, indeed quite the right thing for the old willow bed. On this the gods reclined and Baucis, with her skirt tucked up and with trembling hands, began to lay the table. One of its three legs was too short, so she put a piece of pottery under it to make it level. Then, when it was steady, she wiped it with green mint, and put on it, all in earthenware dishes, some green olives—the fruit sacred to Minerva —some autumn cornel-fruit that had been pickled in wine, endives, radishes, and eggs lightly done in the warm ashes. Then she put on the table a bowl for the wine, also made of earthenware, and beechwood drinking cups with their insides smeared and polished with yellow wax. Soon the hot dish was ready from the fire, and old Philemon brought out his wine, which was of no great age or quality. Then the dishes were cleared away for the second course, which consisted of nuts and figs and fried dates, plums and sweet-smelling apples in broad baskets and purple grapes just picked from the vine. In the centre of the table there was a fine golden honey-comb, and around the table there were cheerful faces, friendliness and ungrudging kindness.

As the meal went on Baucis and Philemon noticed with astonishment that the wine-bowl, whenever it was emptied, filled up again of its own accord. They trembled at this miracle and both uttered a prayer. Then they asked pardon for the poor meal which was all that they could afford. One other thing they had, which was a goose. This bird acted as a watch-dog for their small cottage, and they decided to kill it for the gods who were their guests. But the goose, flapping about with its wings, was too quick for the two old people and quite wore them out in their efforts to catch it. In the end it seemed to take refuge at the feet of the gods themselves, and the gods told them not to kill it. "We are gods," they said. "As for the wicked people who live in this neighbourhood, they shall be punished as they deserve. But you will not share their fate. Now you must leave your house and come with us to the top of the mountain over there."

The two old people did as they were told, and struggled up the long ascent, with walking sticks to help their feeble steps. When they were a bow-shot from the top, they looked back and saw that all the land below them was covered in water. Only their own house remained standing. And while they were looking in amazement at the sight and weeping for the fate of their friends, suddenly that old house of theirs, which had been small even for the two of them, turned into a fine temple. Columns rose up in place of the forked sticks which had served for door-posts; the straw thatch began to gleam as it turned to gold; on the floor was a marble pavement. Then Jupiter turned to them and spoke, smiling at them: "You good old man, with a wife who is worthy of you, ask me for any gift which you would like to have."

Philemon consulted with Baucis for a few moments and then told the gods what they had decided upon together. "What we ask," he said, "is that we may be your priests and look after your temple. And since we have always lived happily together, let us both die at the same moment, so that I shall never have to see my wife's tomb, nor will she have to attend to my funeral."

The gods granted his prayer. While life was allowed to them, they guarded the temple. And when, worn out with extreme old age, they were standing one day in front of the holy building and talking about their adventures, Baucis suddenly noticed that leaves were growing on Philemon's body and old Philemon noticed that leaves were growing on Baucis too. Bark began to form all over them, but before it reached their faces, they both cried out together and at the same time, "Good-bye, dear wife" and "Good-bye, dear husband." Then the bark closed over them and covered their lips.

To this very day the peasants in this part of the world will show you two trees growing close together with their two trunks wound round each other. I myself have seen the garlands hanging from their boughs and I hung a garland there too, saying, as I did so: "Those who loved the gods have become gods themselves. They worshipped Heaven, and now they must themselves be worshipped."

DAEDALUS AND ICARUS

The wife of Minos, the great king of Crete, was the mother of a strange monster, half-bull, half-man, who was called the Minotaur. Wishing to hide away this disgrace to his family, Minos employed a famous Greek engineer, Daedalus, to make an enclosure so full of winding difficult passages that the monster could safely be shut up inside and would never find his way out. So Daedalus constructed the famous labyrinth, a maze of such size and with so many deceptive paths that, when the work was over, he himself could hardly find his way back to the main entrance. Inside this labyrinth the Minotaur was shut up, and another story tells how every year, as part of a tribute owed to Minos, boys and girls from Athens were sent to be devoured by the monster. In the end Theseus, the prince of Athens, with the help of Minos's daughter, Ariadne, killed the Minotaur and found his way back to safety. But this did not happen for about twenty years.

When Daedalus had finished building the labyrinth, he wished to return to his home in Greece, but he was so useful as an inventor that Minos refused to let him go. So he and his son Icarus were compelled to stay in Crete against their will.

Finally Daedalus, hating his long exile and longing more and more to see his native country from which he was cut off by a long stretch of sea, said to himself: "Though Minos has blocked all my ways of escape by land and by water, there is certainly a way through the sky. That is the way I must go. I admit that he is supreme everywhere else, but he does not rule over the air."

Then he set his mind to work on problems that had never been thought about before, and succeeded in altering the very nature of things. He took feathers and arranged them in a row, beginning with the smallest ones and putting the bigger ones next, so that they looked as though they had grown in the shape of a wing. It was the same method as that by which the country Pan-pipes are made out of reeds of different lengths, fastened together. He tied the feathers together in the middle with twine, and joined them at the base with wax. Then, when they were arranged and fastened, he gave them all a slight bend, so that they looked exactly like the wings of real birds.

While he was working his son Icarus stood and watched him. Sometimes, laughing, he went chasing after a feather that the passing breeze blew away; sometimes he pressed his thumbs into the balls of yellow wax. He did not realize that what he was touching was going to be very dangerous to him, and by his playfulness he kept on interrupting the wonderful work on which his father was engaged.

When Daedalus had given the finishing touches to his invention, he put on his wings, flapped them up and down and hung poised in the air above the ground. Then he gave his son careful instructions about how to fly. "My advice to you, Icarus," he said, "is to fly at a moderate height. If you go too low, the sea-water will weigh the feathers down; if you go too high, the heat of the sun will melt the wax. So you must fly neither too high nor too low. The best thing is to follow me."

While he gave him this advice, he was fitting the strange new wings to his son's shoulders, and, as he did so, tears ran down his aged cheeks and his hands trembled. He kissed his son for what was fated to be the last time, and then, taking to the air, he flew on ahead, anxious for the boy, like a bird which for the first time leads his fledglings out of their high nest into the yielding air. He called out words of encouragement to the boy and taught him to use those fatal wings, constantly looking back, as he flapped his own wings, to see how his son was managing.

On the ground people fishing with long trembling rods, or shepherds leaning on their crooks, or ploughmen bent over their plough handles looked up at them in astonishment and came to the conclusion that, since they were flying through the air, they must be gods.

And now they had left several islands—Delos and Paros—behind them. Juno's sacred island of Samos was on the left, and on the right was Calymne, famous for its honey. At this point the boy began to enjoy the daring experience of flight. Longing for the open sky, he forgot to follow his father and climbed higher and higher in the air. As he came nearer to the sun, the scorching rays began to soften the wax that kept the feathers together. The wax melted and Icarus found that he was flapping bare arms which, without their wings, had no hold upon the air. He fell, and the blue sea, which is still called the Icarian Sea, closed over his lips, as he cried out for his father. Unhappy Daedalus, a father no longer, also cried out. "Icarus!" he called. "Where are you? Where have you gone to?" As he was crying out the boy's name, he saw the wings floating on the water. Then he cursed his own invention, found his son's body and buried it. The land is still called after the name of the buried boy.

PERSEUS

Acrisius, King of Argos, had been told by an oracle that he would be killed by his grandson. He therefore determined that his only daughter, Danaë, should never become a mother and he shut her up in a tower of brass under close guard. But with the gods nothing is impossible. She was visited by Jupiter in a shower of gold and by him she became the mother of a baby whom she called Perseus.

Her father, Acrisius, was, as might have been expected, exceedingly angry. He could scarcely execute his own daughter and grandson, but he came as close to doing this as he dared. He set them in the open sea in a little boat with no provisions, and confidently expected that they would either be drowned or would starve to death. However, the gods willed otherwise. The winds and the waves carried the boat to the little island of Seriphus, and here the mother and child were found by a fisherman called Dictys who, in spite of his poverty, treated them kindly and gave them a home.

The king of the island of Seriphus was called Polydectes, and he, as Perseus grew up, became both jealous and frightened of him. He was jealous because Perseus was stronger, more beautiful and more daring than all the other young men of the island. He was frightened because he wished to make Danaë his wife, against her will, and he knew that, so long as Perseus was with her, he would be unable to do this.

He therefore thought of a plan by which he hoped to get rid of Perseus. He invited all the chief men of the island to a great feast, at which it was understood that each of the guests should give the king some valuable present—a horse, or armour, or some rich ornament. He deliberately invited Perseus too, knowing that he was too poor to be able to afford a present. When all the others had given their presents to the king, Perseus, ashamed at having nothing to give, told the king that, though he was too poor to act as the others had done, he would be glad to use what he had, which was only his courage and his skill, in doing the king any service which he thought fit. "Go, then," said Polydectes, "and bring me back the head of the Gorgon, Medusa."

Perseus rose to his feet and left the banqueting hall. He knew that he must either do what the king had ordered or never show his face in Seriphus again; and he knew that the king was planning to destroy him, since no one yet had seen the Gorgons and lived. The Gorgons were three monsters, one of whom, Medusa, with her snaky hair, had once been a human being. They lived at the end of the world, and all who set eyes on them were immediately turned into stone.

Perseus might well have despaired, but the gods helped him. Pluto lent him a helmet which had the power of making the

wearer invisible. Minerva lent him her bright shining shield. Mercury lent him his winged sandals with which he could fly through the air, and also a curious twisted sword, studded with diamonds and so sharp that it could cut easily through any metal. Minerva also told him the way that he would have to go and some of the dangers which he would have to meet.

So Perseus said good-bye to his mother whom he left in the care of the good fisherman, Dictys. Then he tied his winged sandals to his feet, took his helmet and his sword, and flew over land and sea in the direction of the extreme west.

He came to a country where human beings had never set foot before. The only inhabitants were three old unmarried hags, the daughters of Phorkys and sisters of the Gorgons. They had one eye and one tooth between the three of them, and would make use of them in turn.

Perseus approached them wearing the helmet that made him invisible, and, while one of the old creatures was passing the eye to another, he snatched it from her hand and refused to give it back unless they told him where their sisters, the Gorgons, lived.

Much against their will, and with quavering lips, they told him the way, and again Perseus travelled far through unexplored countries, wildernesses, shaggy woods and sharp bristling rocks, till he came to the country where the Gorgons were. He soon knew that he was in the right place, because all over the fields and roads he saw figures of men and animals which had been turned to stone by one look from Medusa's eyes.

Soon he found in a rocky place the three Gorgons asleep, with their long wings folded about them. He approached them invisibly, and took great care not to look directly at Medusa. Instead he only looked at the reflection of her face and snaky hair in the shield which he carried. Then while sleep held both her and the snakes that coiled about her face, with one blow of his sharp sword he cut the head from the neck, and swift as an arrow, too swift for pursuit, sped away on the pathways of the air.

He put the head, still bleeding, into a bag which he had brought for this purpose. From the first drop of blood that fell on the rocky ground there sprang up a wonderful creature, the winged horse, Pegasus. This beautiful and spirited animal flew through the air to Mount Helicon, where the Muses live, and became their favourite and their pet.

Meanwhile Perseus, on his rushing wings, sped through the light air, carrying the Gorgon's head. As he flew over the sands of Libya, more drops of blood fell to the ground. As they sank into the earth they came to life in the form of snakes, which is why the country of Libya is still infested with these creatures.

And now Perseus was tossed about by discordant winds and storms, driven now here, now there, like a grey cloud. Looking down from his great height he saw the lands beneath and flew over the whole surface of the world. Up to the cold north he was swept and back again to the burning south; often the storms bore him to the sunset and often towards the east. Finally, as night was falling and as he feared to trust himself to the darkness, he landed in the land of Hesperia, the kingdom of the giant Atlas, and asked to be allowed to rest until Dawn rose on the next day.

Atlas was far the most enormous of all creatures in human form. He ruled over the edge of the world where, at Sunset, the sun's tired horses plunge into the gleaming sea. In his gardens there was a tree with golden leaves covering branches of gold and golden apples. Perseus came to Atlas and said: "Sir, I beg leave to rest here. If high birth means anything to you, then let me inform you that my father is Jupiter. Or if you are interested in famous deeds, then I think you will be interested in what I have done. I ask you, therefore, for your hospitality."

Atlas, however, remembered an old oracle which had told him that one day a child of Jupiter would come and steal his golden apples, and for this reason he had built huge walls round his orchard, had put a great dragon there to guard the fruit, and refused to allow strangers in his country. So now he said to Perseus: "Be off at once! All your lies about Jupiter and your great deeds will not be of any help to you here." He then seized hold of Perseus and began to thrust him out of his palace. Perseus resisted and at the same time tried to calm Atlas with polite language; but, when this was of no avail, and when he found that the giant was too strong for him (who, indeed, could be as strong as Atlas?) he said: "Then, if you will not give me such a small favour as this, I will give you a different kind of gift." And, turning his own head aside, he held out in front of him the terrible head of Medusa. Immediately Atlas changed into a mountain of the same vast size as he had been in life. His beard and hair became forests; shoulders and arms turned into long ridges; his head was the summit and his bones turned to rock. Then (for such was the will of the gods) he grew in every part to an even more enormous size, and the whole heaven, with all its stars, rested upon his back.

Next day, at dawn, Perseus put on his sandals again, took his curved sword in his hand and cleft his way through the air. After passing over many lands he came in the end to the country of the Ethiopians, over which King Cepheus ruled. As he looked down towards the coasts of this land he saw chained to a rock a most beautiful girl. She stood so still that he would have thought her to be a marble statue, if it had not been for her hair moving in the breeze and her warm tears running down her face. He immediately fell in love with her, and indeed was so struck with her beauty that he almost forgot to move his wings. He alighted close to her and asked her who she was and why she was wearing those cruel chains. At first she made no answer and would have covered her shy face with her hands; but her hands were bound. Her eyes filled with tears and finally, so that he would not think that she had done anything wrong, she told him her story. She was being punished for the foolish words of her mother Cassiope who had boasted that she was more beautiful than the sea-goddesses, the Nereids. The result of this boast was that Neptune, the god of the sea, had sent a great monster out of the ocean to ravage the land. Her father, King Cepheus, had consulted the oracle and had been told that he must sacrifice his daughter Andromeda (for that was the girl's name) to the monster. Now, in chains, she was waiting for the monster to appear. She had been promised in marriage to her uncle Phineus, but he did nothing to help her.

While she was speaking Perseus saw the king and queen, with many people, coming down to the shore, weeping and lamenting for the fate of the innocent girl. Andromeda herself had more reason to weep, for, at the same moment, a great roar came from the sea, and a huge monster appeared with its broad breast making the water surge away at its sides. The girl cried out in terror. Perseus immediately went to her father and mother and addressed them. "My name," he said, "is Perseus. I am the son of Jupiter and of Danaë, whom my father visited in a golden shower. I am also he who killed the Gorgon, Medusa. I think, therefore, that I am quite worthy to be the husband of your daughter. Now, with the help of the gods, I shall attempt to save her and you by fighting with the monster. Will you promise her to me in marriage, if I can save her life?"

Andromeda's parents, not remembering their previous promise to Phineus, agreed at once, and Perseus sprang from the earth and soared into the air. Now the monster, ploughing through the water like a great ship, was only a sling's shot from the shore. It saw Perseus's shadow on the water and, in its savage rage, began to attack the shadow. But Perseus, like an eagle sweeping from above on a serpent and catching it behind the neck, dived down headlong and buried his sword right up to the hilt in the monster's right shoulder. The wounded beast reared up into the air and plunged down again into the sea which was all purple with its blood. Then it turned and twisted like a wild boar surrounded by a pack of hounds. Perseus on his quick wings avoided its terrible jaws and over and over again darted in to wound it, plunging his curved sword into the great back, which was covered with barnacles, or into its sides or into the place where its fishy tail began. The beast belched blood and water from its mouth as it thrashed about in the sea; the feathers on Perseus's wings grew moist and heavy, but, partly supporting himself on a rock that jutted out from the sea, he thrust his sword three times into the animal's heart. All the shores and the sky resounded with the wild shouts of the people applauding the hero's victory. Cepheus and Cassiope welcomed Perseus as their son-in-law and Andromeda, freed from her chains, was ready to marry him at once.

But before they went to the palace for the wedding feast, Perseus washed the blood from his body and his hands in the waters of the sea. So that the Gorgon's head should not be bruised on the hard rocks, he made a pile of seaweed for the head to rest on. The strange power of the head passed into this seaweed, which became stiff and hard, shrivelling up into something like stone. The sea nymphs were delighted with this miracle and brought more and more weeds and twigs, and, when they were hard, carried them back into the sea. This is still the nature of coral, which remains like a twig when it is under the water but hardens when it is exposed to the air.

Meanwhile Perseus built three altars to the gods who had helped him, and sacrificed on the altars a cow, a young bullock and a bull. Then he claimed his bride, and soon in Cepheus's great golden palace a wedding-feast was spread. The walls were hung with gar-lands; sweet-smelling incense was put on the fires; musicians played on lyres and flutes, or sang to the harp before the Ethiopian nobles who came to witness the wedding.

At the end of the feast, when they had eaten and drunk to their heart's content, the king asked Perseus to tell them the story of his wanderings and of how he cut off the Gorgon's head. Perseus be-gan to tell the tale, but, while he was in the middle of it, suddenly from outside the golden doors came a confused noise of shouting and of the clash of arms, a sound most unfitting to a wedding banquet. The doors were flung open and the king's brother Phi-neus, holding a long ashen spear, strode into the hall at the head of a great company of armed men. Poising his heavy spear in his hand, he addressed Perseus. "Here I am," he said. "I have come to avenge the theft of my bride. Now your wings will not be able to save you, nor your stories of Jupiter changing into gold."

He was about to hurl the spear, but Cepheus sprang to his feet and cried out: "Brother, what are you doing? It is madness to think of such a crime. If you really deserved my daughter, you should have come and saved her when she was chained to the rock. If it had not been for Perseus, she would now be dead. How then can anyone have a better right to her than he?"

Phineus looked at him grimly and seemed to hesitate whether to hurl the spear first at his brother or at Perseus. Finally he threw it at Perseus, who lightly avoided it, and it stuck quivering in the bench where he had been sitting. Perseus sprang to his feet, pulled the spear out of the wood, and would have hurled it back at Phi-neus; but Phineus, the coward, had already taken refuge behind the altar. King Cepheus raised up his hands and cried out to the gods that this act of aggression was against his will and against the laws of hospitality. His brother's men were far more numerous than his own, and there seemed no hope of escape for himself or for An-dromeda or Perseus. But, invisible to all, the warrior goddess Mi-nerva was present, protecting Perseus and strengthening his heart.

Now spears were thrown like rain through the hall, past eyes and ears, or cleaving through breastplates or thighs, or stomach. Per-seus, with his back against a pillar stood, striking to right and left of him with his curved sword, cutting down men like a mower with a scythe in thick grass. The Ethiopian nobles fought at his side, and behind them were the king and queen with their daughter, crying out to the gods and weeping. Soon the whole floor was drenched with blood and the hall full of the cries of the wounded or the dying. Still more and more of Phineus's army came pouring into the palace, and Perseus, fighting like a tiger, began to feel his strength beginning to fail as he saw no end to his enemies. So he cried out: "Since you force me to do it, there is only one thing I can do. Turn away your heads, all who are friends of mine!" And he raised on high the terrible head of the Gorgon.

As he spoke one of Phineus's strongest captains poised his spear and shouted out: "Try your magic on someone else! We are not frightened by it."

He was in the act of hurling the spear, and in the very act he turned to a stone statue, with his poised hand stiff and motionless. Others too stopped still and frozen in their places, some with half-open lips, or wide mouths that had been shouting battle cries; others in the act of turning aside from some weapon; others with looks of astonishment on their marble faces. Two hundred had survived the fighting; two hundred statues, in various attitudes, now stood in the halls.

As for Phineus, he had not seen the Gorgon's head, but wherever he looked he saw his friends and comrades turned to stone. Now, with his head turned aside and stretching out his hands, he said: "Perseus, you are the winner. Take away, I beg you, that terrible face that turns men to stone. I admit that I am defeated. I admit that you deserve Andromeda. I ask for nothing, O great hero, except my life."

So he spoke without daring to look in Perseus's direction. Perseus said to him: "You coward, I will not kill you with the sword, but I will make you into a monument which will last for ages and which will please the eyes of my father-in-law and my wife." Then he carried the Gorgon's head to Phineus and, though he struggled to avoid the sight of it, its power fell upon him. The tears on his cowardly face turned to stone: his pleading hands, cringing back and abject look were all fixed in marble.

Now Perseus was victorious over his enemies and safe in the possession of his bride. He had still to discover what had been happening in his absence to his mother in the little island of Seriphus, and he arrived there only just in time to save her life; for, though the good fisherman Dictys had done his best to protect her, King Polydectes had continued to persecute her, and, when Perseus reached the island, she had taken refuge at the altar of Minerva. Perseus went immediately to the palace, where he found the king still as unforgiving and as bitter an enemy as ever. He threatened the hero with violence and even refused to believe that he had killed the Gorgon. "Then believe your own eyes and let them be fixed in the belief," said Perseus, and, holding the head before his face, he turned the king to bloodless stone and in his place made the good Dictys king of the island.

Next Perseus offered to Minerva in her temple the Gorgon's head, and now the goddess carries it fixed in her terrible shield. As for Perseus himself, he went, with his mother and his wife, back to his ancestral country of Argos, feeling sure now that, after his great deeds, his grandfather Acrisius would forgive him, and being anxious too to help him in a war that he was waging. On his way to Argos he stopped at Larissa, where the king of the country was holding athletic sports. Perseus himself competed in the discus throwing event and his first throw went far beyond the boundaries of the stadium and landed among the spectators. Perseus heard with distress that the discus had killed an old man, but his distress was still greater when he learned that the old man was none other than his grandfather Acrisius, who, hearing that Perseus was returning to Argos and still frightened of the oracle, had left his country, little thinking that he would by accident meet his grandson on the way.

After this event Perseus refused the kingdom of Argos. He lived first nearby in the huge castle of Tiryns on the sea, and later founded the kingdom of golden Mycenae. In Athens a temple was built to him and in the temple was an altar specially consecrated to Dictys who had been kind to the hero's mother.

CERES AND PROSERPINE

The huge three-cornered island of Sicily is piled upon the body of the rebellious giant Typhoeus, who once dared to attack the gods in heaven. Often he struggles to free himself, but his hands and arms are pinned down by mountains and over his head is the weight of Etna, through which he spouts out ashes and flames in his fierce insatiable rage. But his efforts to push off him and roll away the cities and mountains that cover his body often cause earthquakes, and then Pluto, the king of the underworld, fears lest the earth should split open and light be let in to terrify the thin and trembling ghosts of the dead.

It was in fear of such an event that, on one occasion, Pluto left his shadowy kingdom and, in a chariot drawn by black horses, came to the land of Sicily to inspect its foundations and see that all was well. He examined everything and, finding that there were no signs of weakness anywhere, he laid aside his fears.

But Venus, the goddess of love, who is worshipped in the Sicilian city of Eryx, saw him as he wandered through the land. She put her arms round her winged son, Cupid, and said to him: "My dear son, you who bring me all my power and my success, take your arrows, with which you conquer everything, and shoot one into the heart of that god who rules the world below. The heaven and the sea already own the power of love. Why should the underworld be exempt? Besides it is time that something was done to show our power, because in heaven I am not given the same honour that I used to have. Two goddesses, Minerva and the huntress Diana, will have nothing to do with me, and Ceres's daughter Proserpine, if I allow it, will choose to remain unmarried. So, if you want to increase my power and yours, make Pluto fall in love with Proserpine."

Cupid, at his mother's bidding, took his quiver and chose from his thousand arrows the one that seemed to him sharpest and most sure in flight. He bent the bow across his knee and with the barbed arrow of love he struck Pluto to the heart.

Not far from the city of Etna there is a lake of deep water and here, even more than in the smooth gliding rivers of Asia, one may hear the songs of swans. Woods lie like a crown around the waters and keep off the rays of the sun. In the shade of the branches grow flowers of every colour. Here it is perpetual spring, and here Proserpine, with her companions, was playing and gathering violets or white lilies. In her girlish excitement she filled her basket and heaped the flowers in her arms, trying to pick more than any of the others, and suddenly, all in the same moment, Pluto saw her, fell in love with her and carried her off; so violent were the feelings that he had.

Terrified, the girl kept on calling out for her friends and for her mother, especially for her mother. She had, in her struggles, torn her dress at the top and all the flowers began to fall out of it. The loss of her flowers made her cry even more.

Meanwhile Pluto urged on his chariot, calling to his horses by name and shaking the black reins on their strong necks and streaming manes. They galloped through deep lakes, over mountains and past pools streaming with sulphur. Proserpine still cried for help, but only in one case did anyone try to help her. This was the nymph Cyane, who rose waist-high out of the water called after her name, recognized Proserpine and called to Pluto: "You shall go no further! You cannot marry Ceres's daughter against her mother's will, and, as for the daughter, you ought to have wooed her, not seized upon her by force."

As she spoke she stretched out her hands in Pluto's way to prevent him passing, but he, furious with her for obstructing him, urged on his terrible horses and, seizing his royal sceptre in his strong arm, struck the pool to its depths. As he struck it, the earth gaped open and down into the earth plunged the black chariot and horses.

Cyane, however, in grief for the fate of the goddess and at the way in which the rights of her own fountain had been set aside, began to melt away in tears and to dissolve into the very waters of which she was the guardian nymph. You might have seen her limbs becoming soft, her bones beginning to bend and her nails losing their brittleness. First the most slender parts melted away; her dark hair, fingers, legs and feet turned into cold water. Then shoulders, back and breast flowed into the stream. Water instead of blood ran through her vanishing veins, and in the end there was nothing left that you could touch.

Meanwhile Proserpine's terrified mother was searching for her, but searching in vain, through every land and every sea. All day she looked for her daughter and at night she lit two torches from the fire of Etna and continued the search in the cold darkness. It would take too long to tell the names of all the lands and seas where she wandered; but, when she had been everywhere in the world, she came back again to Sicily and passed by Cyane. If Cyane had still been a nymph and had not turned into water, she would have told the mother where her daughter was. Now she had no means of speaking, but she did succeed in making some sign, for, floating on her waters, she carried Proserpine's girdle, which had fallen there as she was carried down into the lower world.

When Ceres recognized the girdle, she tore her hair and beat her breast, as if this was the first news she had had of her daughter being stolen away. She still did not know where she was, but she cursed every land in the world and especially Sicily, saying that they were ungrateful to her and did not deserve to have the fruits of the earth. She broke in pieces the ploughs that turn over the soil; she brought death upon the farmers and upon their animals; she made the harvests fail and put blights and diseases among the young plants. Nothing grew but weeds and thorns and thistles. Throughout the world people were dying of famine or of plagues; and still Ceres was unable to find out where her daughter was.

There is a river called Arethusa, which rises in Greece, then descends into the earth and, after diving below the sea, comes into the light again in Sicily. Now this river Arethusa raised her head from her Sicilian stream, and brushing back her wet hair to the sides of her head, she spoke to Ceres. "O mother of fruit," she said, "and mother of the girl so sought for throughout the world, cease your long labour, and do not be angry with this land which does not deserve your anger, since it did not aid the theft of your daughter. I can give you certain news of her. While I was gliding on my path below the earth, down in the depths of the lower world, I saw Proserpine there with my own eyes. She looked sad certainly, and her face showed that she had not yet recovered from her fear, but she reigns there as the great queen of the dark world, the all-powerful wife of the ruler of the dead."

When Ceres heard these words, she stood still as if she had been turned to stone, and was for long like one out of her mind. Finally grief and pain took the place of horror. She mounted her chariot and went up to the bright shores of heaven. There, with cloudy face and hair all loose, she stood in indignation before Jupiter, and said: "Jupiter, I have come to beg your aid for the child who is yours and mine. If you have no respect for the mother, at least the daughter should touch a father's heart. At last I have found her—if you can call it finding her, when she is still lost to me, and when all I know is where she has been carried away. Let Pluto give her back. Your daughter does not deserve to have a robber for her husband."

Jupiter replied: "It is true that she is our daughter and I can understand your feelings. Yet, if we call things by their right names, we shall find that no great harm has been done. It was love that caused the theft. Then, if only you will approve the match, Pluto would be no unworthy son-in-law for us. To be the brother of Jupiter and to have in his own realm power as great as mine is a big thing. Nevertheless, if you are resolved on separating them, Proserpine shall return to heaven—but only on one condition, only if she has touched no food with her lips while she has been in the world below. This is the decision of the Fates."

So he spoke, but Ceres was still determined to have her daughter back. This, however, was what the Fates would not allow, because the girl had already tasted food. While she wandered thoughtlessly in Pluto's gardens, she had picked a red pomegranate from a swaying bough, had cut into the yellow rind and eaten seven grains of the fruit. The only one who saw her do this was a boy called Ascalaphus, the child of one of the nymphs of the underground lakes of Avernus. This boy bore witness against her and prevented her return. Then Proserpine in anger dashed water in his face and turned him into a bird, giving him a beak and feathers, big round eyes and long hooked claws. He became that unpleasant and ill-omened bird, the sluggish screech-owl.

And now Jupiter in arbitration between his brother Pluto and his sad sister Ceres, divided the year into two parts. Now Proserpine is goddess of both worlds and spends half the year with her mother and half with her husband. Her face became bright again at once, and so did her heart. Before, even Pluto had thought that she looked sad, but now she was like the sun which, after being hidden behind a rain cloud, comes out again into the open air.

PHAETHON

Phaethon's father was the Sun. Once, when he was talking big and boasting of his father Phoebus, a friend of his could endure it no longer and told him: "You are a fool who believes everything your mother tells you. You are swollen-headed because you imagine Phoebus is your father, when he isn't really your father at all."

Phaethon's face grew red with anger, but a feeling of shame prevented him from doing anything. He went to his mother Clymene and told her how he had been insulted. "What will grieve you all the more, mother," he said, "is that I, with my fierce noble nature, had to hold my tongue. What a shame it is that such things could be said and yet could not be proved wrong. But you, if I really am sprung from the blood of the gods, give me a sign of my great birth, give me my place in heaven." Then he threw his arms round his mother's neck and begged her for his sake and for the sake of Merops, her husband, and of the future happiness of his sisters, to give him a proof that Phoebus really was their father. As for Clymene, it would be hard to say whether she was moved more by Phaethon's appeal or by the anger she felt at the insult to herself. She raised up her arms to the sky and, looking towards the light of the sun, said: "By that star that flames there with quivering rays, the sun that hears us now and looks down on us, I swear to you, my child, that he whom you now look at, he, the lord of the world, the Sun, is your father. If what I say is false, then let him withdraw himself from my sight, and let this be the last time that my eyes behold him. But it is not difficult for you to find your father's

house. His dwelling place is on the fringes of our land, at the sunrise. If you are brave enough, go there and he will own you to be his."

As soon as his mother had said this, Phaethon leapt gladly to his feet, his mind brimful of heaven. He went through the country of the Ethiopians, whom he regarded as belonging to him, and the Indians who dwell beneath fiery constellations. Resolutely he approached the land from which his father arose.

There stood the palace of the Sun, lofty, with its soaring columns, bright with dazzling gold and metal work that shone as though it were on fire. Its high roof was overlaid with gleaming ivory and the light of silver radiated from its wide-flung double doors. More wonderful than all this was what art had done; for here Vulcan had made reliefs of the waters girdling the earth, of the whole world and of heaven above. In the water were the sea-blue gods, vocal Triton, and Proteus, who changes his shape, and Aegaeon rising from the waves, pressing down with his elbows the enormous backs of whales. There too were Doris and her daughters. Some seemed to be swimming; others, sitting on a breakwater, were drying their sea-green hair; others were riding on fishes. Their faces were not all alike, nor yet entirely different, but just as sisters should look. On the earth were men and cities, forests and wild beasts, rivers and nymphs and all the other country gods. And above all this was a model of the shining sky. Six signs of the zodiac were on the right-hand door, and six on the left.

Now when Clymene's son had come up the steep path and entered the dwelling of the Sun, he turned his steps straight towards his father's face, but halted while still far off, for he could not bear to approach the light any nearer. Wearing a purple robe, Phoebus was sitting on a throne that shone bright with emeralds. To his left and right were the gods of the Day, the Month, the Year, and the Centuries; and the Hours were there too, standing side by side with the same interval between each of them. Spring was there, with a crown of flowers, and naked Summer, with ears of corn twined into garlands; Autumn too, all stained with the trodden grapes, and icy Winter with bristly white hair. In the centre the Sun himself with those eyes that see everything saw the young man standing abashed by the wonder of it all, and said: "Phaethon, my son whom I am glad to own, why have you made this journey? What have you come to seek from this my citadel?"

And Phaethon replied: "O general light of all the world, Phoebus, my father, if you permit me to call you father and if Clymene
is guiltless when she calls you her husband, then, sir, give me some
sure sign so that I may be recognized as truly your son, and that I
may no longer feel any misgivings over it."

He spoke and his father laid aside the fiery rays that shone dazzling round his head. He bade Phaethon approach nearer and he
kissed him. "It was a true son of mine," he said, "that Clymene
bore, and you yourself deserve to be acknowledged by me. And to
remove all your doubt, ask for any gift you like. I will give it to you,
and you shall take it. This I swear by the lake below, the lake of
Styx that our eyes have never seen, an oath binding amongst gods."

Hardly had he finished speaking when Phaethon demanded his
father's chariot, and that he might be allowed for one day to drive
his winged horses.

Phoebus repented of his oath. Thrice and four times he smote
his gleaming forehead. "Rash, indeed," he said, "were the words I
spoke and which you have seized upon. I wish that we were not
allowed to make promises. Child, I admit to you that this was the
one thing I should deny you. I may still try to dissuade you. What
you desire is dangerous. You are asking for something big, Phaethon, something which is too much for the strength you have and
for your tender years. Your fate is that of a mortal; yet you are
begging for power that belongs to gods. Indeed you go further and
are ignorantly aiming at something which is beyond the reach of
the gods themselves. Much as others might like it, there is none but
I who can ride that fiery car. Even the ruler of huge Olympus, he
who rains thunderbolts from his right hand, even he will not guide
this chariot. And what is mightier than Jove?

"The first part of the road is steep and the horses, though they
are fresh in the early dawn, can hardly make the ascent. The middle of the course is in the topmost height of heaven. I myself might
well fear, my heart might well flutter in my breast as I look down
from that height on sea and land. The last part of the way is downhill, and demands a sure hand on the reins. There the goddess of
the sea, Tethys herself, into whose outspread waves I sink, often
fears lest I may be hurled into them headlong. Remember, too,
that the sky itself turns in a continual revolution, whirling the constellations with it round and round in its rapid course. I struggle
against it and this force, which governs all else, does not govern

me; my swift track cuts across. Now suppose I gave you the chariot. What would you do? Could you steer a course against the rolling poles to prevent the motion of the sky from carrying you off your proper way? Perhaps you imagine that in those parts there are sacred groves, cities of the gods, shrines rich in gifts. Actually the road is beset with traps and runs between the shapes of beasts. Even if you keep in the right path and are not led astray, you will have to be straight between the horns of the Bull, past the Archer's bow and the Lion's savage jaws, past the Scorpion on the one side and the Crab on the other, each stretching wide the cruel pincers of his claws. And it is no easy matter to control those horses, spirited as they are with the flames that burn in their hearts and which they breathe from their mouths and nostrils. Even I can only just make them obey me when their fierce spirits have grown hot, and they toss back the reins from their necks. Child, let me not give you a gift that will bring ruin upon you. Be sensible, now that you have a chance, and ask me for something else. Is it a sure sign that you want? I give you a sure sign by this fear that I feel for you, and I prove myself to be your father by showing a father's solicitude for his son. I wish that you could look into my heart and see there all the anxiety that your father feels. Now look round on all the riches that the world contains, and from all the good things of earth and sky and sea ask something for yourself. It will not be refused to you. It is only this one thing that I am unwilling to give, and it is a thing that is more likely to hurt than to honour you. You are asking me to hurt you, Phaethon, not to help you. Poor innocent, why do you put your arms round my neck to coax me? Have no fear; whatever you desire will be granted (have I not sworn by the waters of Styx?). But, I beg you, be more sensible about what you want."

He had said what he could to restrain the boy, but Phaethon refused to listen, and, burning with desire for the chariot, pressed on with his demands. So his father, when he had delayed as long as he might, led the young man to the lofty chariot, the work of Vulcan. The axle was made of gold, and the pole was made of gold; the rims of the wheels were golden, and the spokes radiated out in silver. Chrysolites and jewels shone in rows along the yoke, and shimmered with the light they got from Phoebus.

With swelling heart Phaethon stood staring at it all and examining the workmanship. Then, while he was so occupied, suddenly in

the glowing dawn Aurora woke, and threw wide the purple doors
opening on to her halls that are full of roses. The stars scattered
and Lucifer, who keeps his station longest, followed in the rear
of their retreating ranks. When he saw Lucifer on his way to
the earth, and the world beginning to blush red, and the tips of the
moon's horns as it were fading away, then the Titan ordered the
swift Hours to yoke his horses to the chariot. Quickly the goddesses
did as they were told. They brought out from their lofty stables the
fire-breathing horses, fed on juices of ambrosia, and they laid over
their necks the jingling reins. Then Phoebus put some magic ointment on his son's face, so that he could endure the rushing flame,
and on his head he placed the crown of rays. He sighed, for he felt a
foretaste of the sorrow that was coming, and it was with great anxiety that he spoke: "My dear boy, try to listen at least to what I am
going to say now. Keep a firm hand on the reins, and don't use the
whip. The horses go fast enough of their own accord. The difficulty
is to hold them in. And don't go straight through all the five zones
of heaven. The track curves across, running only through three of
them, avoiding both the south pole and the bitter winds of the
north. This is your way, and you will see clearly the marks of my
wheels in the sky. Then, so that both heaven and earth may have
the right amount of heat, you must neither drive too low down,
nor make the chariot climb to the top of the sky. If you go too high
you will set the houses of the gods on fire, if too low, you will burn
up the earth. The safest way is between the two. Don't go too far
to the right, in the direction of the writhing Snake, or too far to
the left in the direction of the constellation Altar, but keep straight
between them. The rest I must leave to Fortune, and I pray that
she will look after you better than you have looked after yourself.
But, while I have been speaking, damp night has reached her
boundary on the western sky-line. We can wait no longer. My presence is required; darkness is scattered and the dawn is shining.
Grasp the reins in your hand, or, if only you will change your mind,
take my advice and not my chariot. While there is still time, and
you are still standing on solid ground, not yet swept away by the
chariot you have so foolishly begged for, allow *me* to give light to
the earth, so that you can watch me and be safe."

Phaethon swung his young limbs into the airy chariot, took his
stance and felt a thrill of joy as he fingered the light reins. Then he
thanked his father for the favour that he had granted so unwill-

ingly. Meanwhile the four winged horses of the Sun, Fire, Dawn, Brilliant and Flamer, were filling the air with their whinnying, fiery breath, and pawing impatiently against their barriers. Tethys, who knew nothing of her grandson's fate, swung back the gates, and gave them the freedom of the immeasurable sky, and they plunged out into the road and, cleaving the air with their feet, split through the clouds before them, passing by on their soaring wings the winds of the east that rose with them. But the weight of the chariot was light, too light for the horses of the sun to feel. The yoke did not have its usual weight on their backs; and, like curved ships that are underloaded roll and go unsteadily through the sea because of insufficient ballast, so the chariot without its usual freight swung about in the air, tossing up and down as though it were empty. The four horses, as soon as they realized this, got out of hand, left the well-worn track and set off in a different course. Phaethon grew frightened. He did not know how to handle the reins which he held, nor where the proper road was, nor, even if he did know, could he steer the horses into it. Then the cold stars of the north felt for the first time the heat of the sun's rays and tried in vain to plunge into the forbidden sea. But when poor Phaethon looked down from the height of heaven on the lands lying far, far, beneath him, he grew pale and suddenly his knees began to tremble in panic. Through all that light a mist rose before his eyes. Now he would give anything never to have touched his father's horses. He wished that he had never known whose son he was, and never had his prayer answered. He is willing enough now to be called the son of Clymene's mortal husband, now that he is carried along like a ship in a hurricane, when the helmsman has dropped the rudder and can do nothing but pray. What is he to do? Much of the sky is behind him, but much more is in front. He measures both distances with his eyes, looking now towards the region of the sun-set, which he is fated never to reach, now towards the region of the dawn. Not knowing what to do, he stands there stupefied, without letting go of the reins, yet without the strength to hold them properly. He does not even know the horses' names. He sees too, scattered over the coloured heaven, strange wonders, and stares in terror at the shapes of huge beasts. There is one place where the Scorpion stretches out the pincers of his two claws; with crooked arms and tail his shape extends over two of the zodiac's signs. When the boy saw him covered with black poisonous sweat he thought he was going to sting him with his menacing curled tail. He grew cold with fear, lost all control, and dropped the reins.

As soon as the horses felt them lying loose along their backs, they rushed off headlong. With no one to hold them in, they went through the unknown regions of the air, and wherever their fury carried them, there they rushed unchecked. In the height of heaven they run among the fixed stars, tearing the chariot along through trackless ways, now climbing high into the air, now hurtling headlong again towards the earth. The Moon saw with amazement her brother's horses running below her own. The clouds caught on fire and smoked. The mountain tops broke into flame, and the earth, with all the moisture dried out of it, split into great cracks. The grass turned white in the heat; trees with all their leaves burnt up, and the crops took fire all the more easily because they were ripe. Worse still, great walled cities were destroyed. The flames burnt whole nations to cinders. The forests and the mountains were on fire. Athos was blazing and Cilician Taurus and Tmolus, and Oeta, and Ida with its many fountains dry at last. Helicon, where the maiden muses go, and Haemus was ablaze; the fires of Etna roared into the sky with twice their usual strength. The two peaks of Parnassus, Eryx, Cynthius and Othrys were blazing; now at last Rhodope must lose her snow; Mimas, Dyndyma, Mycale, and religious Cithaeron all burn. Arctic weather does not protect the Scythians. Caucasus blazes with Ossa and Pindus and Olympus, greater than both, the airy Alps and cloud-rolling Apennines.

Wherever he looked Phaethon saw the world on fire. He could no longer support the heat. The air he breathed was like a blast from the depths of a furnace. He felt the chariot grow white-hot beneath his feet; he could not hold his head up against the cinders and flying sparks; hot smoke rolled all round him, and this pitchy shroud prevented him from knowing where he was or whither he was going, dragged along at the sweet will of the flying horses. It was at this time, they say, that the Ethiopians got their black skins, because all the blood was drawn to the surface of their bodies by the heat. Then too Libya was drained of moisture and this was the origin of the Sahara desert. The nymphs let their hair flow loose and wept for their fountains and their pools. Rivers are lucky enough to have banks wide apart, yet this did not preserve them. Steam rose from the middle of the Don's stream. Babylonian Euphrates is aflame and Orontes and rushing Thermodon; Ganges, Phasis and Danube; Alpheus boils; the banks of Sperchius are blazing; the gold that the river Tagus carries in its sand is liquefied by the flames. The swans that live in the Cayster, and used to sing in throngs along the banks, are scorched in mid-stream. The Nile fled in terror to the end of the world, and even now no one has discovered where it hid its source. Its seven mouths lay empty and filled with dust, seven channels and no water in any of them. The same thing happened to the rivers of Thrace, the Hebrus and the Strymon and to the streams of the west, the Rhine, the Rhone and the Po and that river which was to have the mastery of the world, the Tiber.

The whole earth split into fissures and through the cracks light pierced down into Hades to frighten the king and queen of the dead. The sea shrivelled up so that what had once been an ocean became a plain of dry sand; and now the islands had their number enlarged by the appearance of mountains which previously had lain deep down beneath the water. Fish went for the bottom and the arched dolphins no longer dared to leap up into the air as they used to do. Dead bodies of seals, belly up, floated on the surface. The story goes that Nereus himself and Doris with her daughters, hiding in the caves of the deep sea, could not even then keep cool. And Neptune, looking furious, three times raised his arms out of the ocean, and each time was unable to stand the fiery atmosphere.

But Mother Earth, who was surrounded by sea, between the waters of ocean and her own streams, which had shrunk and run for hiding into the dark recesses of her body, raised her stifled face, scorched though she was. As she drew her hand across her forehead the earth quaked and settled down lower than it was before. Then the holy mother spoke: "King of Heaven, if this is what you will and what I have deserved, then why is your lightning idle? If I must die by fire, then let it be by the fire *you* throw. Death would be more bearable if I knew that it was from you that it came. As it is I can scarcely open my mouth to say what I am saying" (for the smoke was choking her). "See how my hair is singed and how the sparks are pouring into my eyes and over my lips! Is it for this that I am fertile and hardworking, that I bear the furrowing of curved ploughs and the scraping of hoes, and am hacked about all the year round; that I provide good nourishing fodder for cattle, corn for the race of men, and frankincense for you? Even supposing that I deserve to be destroyed, what harm has the sea done, or your brother Neptune? Why are the waters that he won by lot shrinking away and sinking ever lower from the sky? And if you cannot feel for me or for your brother, then at least have pity on heaven, which belongs to you. Look around you. Smoke is pouring from each of the two poles. If once the fire eats well into them, your own palace will collapse. Look at Atlas and see what trouble he is in. He can only just carry on his shoulders the white-hot firmament. If sea and earth and the kingdom of heaven perish, we shall fall back again into original chaos. O snatch away what is still left from the flames, and save the universe!"

So the earth spoke, and then, since she could bear the heat no longer and could say no more, she sank into herself and into the caverns nearest to the ghosts below.

Then the Almighty Father called all the gods to witness, and particularly him who had given Phaethon the chariot, that, unless he acted, the whole world would perish miserably. He climbed up high to the top of the heaven, to the place where he goes when he spreads clouds over the world, or stirs up the thunder, or shakes out lightning through the air. But then he had no clouds to spread and no rain to let fall from heaven. He thundered, and balanced a thunderbolt in his hand; then, letting it fly from beside his right ear, he shot it at Phaethon and hurled him out of the chariot and out of life as well, quenching with his own raging fire the fire that Phaethon had kindled. The horses panicked and sprang apart from each other, tearing their necks from beneath the yoke and leaving the reins snapped in mid-air. The harness, the axle with the pole torn from it, spokes of the broken wheels, and various fragments of the shattered chariot he scattered far and wide.

As for Phaethon, flame raged through his red hair. Over and over he fell headlong in his long descent from heaven, like a shooting star, which, though it never actually reaches the earth, looks as though it is going to do so. He fell into the river Eridanus far from his native land, in a completely different quarter of the globe, and the river water washed over his smoking face. The Nymphs of Hesperia took the body still smoking from the forked flame, and buried it. On the tombstone they wrote this verse:

> Phaethon rode the sun, and here's his tomb.
> His daring was the reason for his doom.

THE GREAT FLOOD

There was such wickedness once on earth that Justice fled to the sky, and the king of the gods determined to make an end of the race of men. Then Jupiter let loose the South Wind, and the South Wind came with drenching wings. He veiled his terrible face in pitchy darkness; his beard was heavy with the storm and his hair was streaked grey with rain. Clouds sat upon his forehead; water poured from his feathers and the folds of his garments. He squeezed in his fist the hanging masses of cloud, and there was a crash. Thick vapours fell from the air, and Iris, the messenger of Juno, dressed in rainbow colours, carried water to feed the clouds.

The crops were battered to the ground and farmers wept for their fallen hopes; for all the year's work had turned out to have been useless.

Jupiter's anger was not confined to his province of the sky. Neptune, his sea-blue brother, sent the waves to help him. He summoned the rivers and when they had entered the palace of their lord, he said: "No need for many words. Just pour out the whole of your strength. That is what I want. Open all your doors, let nothing stop you, but give free rein to your flowing streams!" So he commanded, and they went away. Then the springs ran unchecked and the rivers rolled unbridled to the seas. Neptune smote the earth with his trident and the earth shivered and shook, giving free passage to the waters under the earth. The rivers broke their bounds and went rushing over the lowlands, dragging along with them fields of corn and orchards, men and beasts together, houses and religious buildings with all their holy images. If there was any house left which could stand up against the flood without crashing down, yet its roof was under water and its turrets were hid by the waves eddying above. Soon there was no telling land from sea. The whole world was sea, except that this sea had no shores.

You could see the men, one getting up on to a hill, another sitting in his curved boat, using oars now in the very place where he had been ploughing only a moment before. Another man is sailing over corn fields or over the roof of some great submerged house; yet another is catching fish among the topmost boughs of an elm. Perhaps their anchors grapple the green grass of meadows, or the curved keels scrape over vines growing under water. And where the light-limbed goats used to crop the turf, now ugly-looking seals go flopping about.

Under the water the sea-nymphs Nereides are staring in amazement at woods, houses and cities. The forests are now full of dolphins who dash about in the tops of the trees and beat their tails against the swaying trunks. You might see a wolf swimming with a flock of sheep, yellow lions carried away by the water, and tigers too. The wild boar, though he is strong as a thunderbolt, cannot help himself, nor is the stag's fleet foot any use to him. He too is swept away; and the birds, after they have wandered far and looked everywhere for a place to alight, fall into the sea too weak to move their wings.

The sea, in its boundless power, had flattened out the smaller hills, and waves, never seen there before, were lapping round the crests of mountains. Nearly all the men perished by water; and those who escaped the water, having no food, died of hunger.

There is a place called Phocis, a rich land, while there was any land, but at that time it was part of the sea, just a huge plain of hurrying water. There is a mountain there whose twin peaks seem to aim at the stars. It is called Parnassus and its summit is above the clouds. All the country round was under water, but Deucalion with his wife, in a little boat, got to this mountain and landed. There was no man more good or more devoted to fair dealing than Deucalion, and there was no more reverent woman than his wife, Pyrrha.

Now when Jupiter saw that the whole earth had become one lake of running water, and that from so many thousands of men and women only this one man and this one woman were left, and that both of them were innocent, both good decent folk, then he dispersed the clouds, made the north wind roll away the rain, and unveiled again the whole vault of heaven. The sea no longer raged. The ruler of the deep laid aside his three-pronged spear and calmed the waters. He called for sea-blue Triton and soon Triton's head rose out of the deep and his shoulders all overgrown with barnacles. Neptune told him to blow on his horn of shell the signal for retreat to waves and rivers. He took up his bugle, a spiral shell, twisted at the mouthpiece and opening out wide at the other end. When he draws in his breath and blows into this bugle the sound goes out from the middle of the sea to the ends of the world. So now as soon as the shell had touched the lips and dripping beard of the god and the blast had been blown calling the retreat, the sound was heard by all the waters of earth and sea, and they obeyed, one and all. Now the sea has shores again, streams run brimming their channels, rivers go back to their beds, and the hills begin to appear. The earth emerges; land grows as water shrinks away, and as time passes woods appear below the naked summits of the hills, though mud still sticks to the leaves of the trees.

So the world came back again. But when Deucalion saw it all empty, and all the countries lying desolate in a tremendous silence, tears came into his eyes and he spoke thus to Pyrrha: "My sister, my wife, you, the only woman left, once it was our family, our birth and our wedding that brought us together, but now our dangers are another bond. We two are all the inhabitants of all the lands that the sun looks on when it rises and when it sets. The sea has the rest. And even now we cannot be sure that we are safe. The terror of those clouds still sticks in my mind. Poor creature, what would you feel like now, if you had been preserved from fate without me? How would you endure terror, if you were alone? Who then would be trying to console you? As for me I am sure that if you had been drowned I should go after you and be drowned too. Oh how I wish that I had the skill of Prometheus, my father, and could get all the people back again and pour life into moulded clay! As it is the whole race of mankind is comprised in us two, and we seem to have been preserved just as specimens of humanity. Such was the will of heaven."

So he spoke, weeping, and then they decided to pray to the powers above, and ask for help from the holy oracle. Together they went straight away to the waters of Cepheus, which were not yet running clear, but they knew where the shallows were and so passed through them. They took water from the stream and sprinkled it on their heads and garments; then they went to the shrine of the holy goddess and saw the roof of the shrine shining with foul sea-slime, and the altars with no fire burning on them. When they reached the steps of the temple, they both fell on their faces and reverently kissed the ice-cold stones. Then they spoke: "If the powers of heaven can feel anything or be at all moved by the prayers of the just, if the anger of the gods is not inflexible, then tell us, O Themis, what skill there is by which we can repair the ruin of the race. Lend thine aid, O most merciful one, to the drowned!"

Moved with compassion, the goddess gave her answer: "Go forth from the temple. Veil your heads and unloose the girdles of your garments. Then scatter behind you on the ground the bones of your venerable mother."

For a long time they stood still in amazement, till Pyrrha first broke the silence, and said that she could not do what the goddess had bidden them. Her lips trembled as she begged for pardon; but how could she dare to wound her mother's ghost by throwing her bones about? All the time they pondered within themselves and revolved in their minds the difficult words of the goddess's reply, so dark to understand.

Finally Deucalion found soothing words to calm his wife. "Oracles," he said, "are good things and could never tell us to do anything bad. Now, either my usual intelligence has gone astray, or else 'our venerable mother' is the earth. And by 'bones' I think the oracle must mean the stones that are in the body of the earth. It is stones that we are told to scatter behind us."

Pyrrha was certainly impressed by her husband's interpretation, but still they hardly dared to hope. So mistrustful were they both of the commands of heaven. Still there was no harm in trying, so they went out of the temple, veiled their heads, girded up their tunics, and, as they had been told, scattered stones behind them as they went. Antiquity is our evidence for what happened next. Otherwise I doubt whether anyone would believe it. For the stones began to lose their hardness. Little by little they grew soft, and as they softened they began to take a new shape. They went on growing; something less hard than stone was stirring within them, something like humanity, although it was not quite clear yet, but more like pieces of sculpture that have only just been begun, which are more or less like what they are meant to be, but are not yet quite rounded off. All the earth and mud which stuck to the stones became flesh; the solid core became bones; veins in the mineral were still veins, but now they had blood in them. And in a short time, by the power of the gods, all the stones which Deucalion had sown

grew up into men, and women sprang from the stones which Pyrrha scattered.

So we human beings are a hard stubborn race, well used to labour; and that is how we prove that this story of our birth is true.

JASON

Jason, who won the Golden Fleece, was the first man to build a
ship. He was also the first to lead an expedition of Greeks against
the East. His father, Aeson, had been driven from the throne of
Iolcos by Pelias, his half-brother, and had been forced to live in a
poor house, with all his wealth and all his honours taken away from
him. At this time Jason was a small boy, not strong enough to
defend himself, and Aeson feared for his son's safety. He therefore
put the boy in the care of the wise centaur, Chiron, half-man and
half-horse, who lived in the wooded mountains around Iolcos. In
music, medicine and archery Chiron was the most famous of
teachers, and in all these subjects Jason quickly became himself an
expert.

As he grew to manhood his beauty, his intelligence and his
strength were alike remarkable, and Chiron, proud of his pupil,
advised him to consult the oracle as to what he should do with
his life. "Return to Iolcos," the oracle replied to his question, "and
demand from Pelias the kingdom that rightfully belongs to your
father."

Jason therefore said good-bye to Chiron and came down from
the mountains to the plain. He carried spear and sword, and was
dressed in a leopard skin. On his way to Iolcos he had to cross a
river which at this time of year was swollen with rainwater from
the melting snow on the mountain peaks. When Jason reached

this river he saw waiting on the bank an old woman who asked him to help her across. This he readily agreed to do, but, when he was in mid-stream, he was surprised to find that, in spite of his strength, the old woman seemed to weigh him down, as though she were heavier than the size of her would suggest. As he struggled through the river, one of his sandals slipped from his foot and was swept away by the stream.

When he reached the other side, he set the old woman down and turned to look at her, but, as he turned his head, she had disappeared, and he knew that he had been visited by one of the gods. It was in fact Juno, the wife of Jupiter, who had been neglected by King Pelias, and who, ever afterwards, helped Jason and supported him.

After addressing a prayer to the goddess, Jason went on his way to the city, and here his yellow hair, his strong and beautiful appearance soon attracted attention. Among those who looked with interest at the stranger was King Pelias himself, but he looked at Jason not only with admiration but also with fear. This was because an oracle had told him that one day he would have his kingdom taken from him by a man wearing only one sandal. He immediately summoned Jason to him and asked who he was and what was his business in Iolcos. Jason boldly and in front of all the people gave his name and said that he had come to claim the kingdom that had been wrongfully taken from his father. As he spoke the people admired the young man's courage and showed plainly that they were on his side. All that Pelias could do was to attempt to gain time. He therefore said to Jason: "If you are indeed worthy of what you claim, you must prove your worth. You are young, and you should have some noble deed to your credit before you can be acknowledged fit to rule. What I wish you to do is this—to avenge the death of our relative Phrixus and to bring back to Greece the Golden Fleece."

Jason knew the story of Phrixus, since he had been told this and other stories of gods and heroes by the centaur Chiron. He also knew that Phrixus had been related to him, since his own grandfather had been the brother of Athamas who in the end had been driven mad by Juno, but who had had by his first wife, Nephele, two children who were called Phrixus and Helle. Later Athamas had married Cadmus's daughter Ino, and Ino, jealous of her stepchildren, had plotted to kill them. But the boy and girl were saved by a ram with a golden fleece, which was given to them by Mercury. On this animal's back they escaped from Thebes and even crossed the sea. The girl Helle grew tired on the way and fell into the sea which is still called the Hellespont after her; but Phrixus arrived safely at the court of King Æetes who ruled over the land of Colchis at the far extremity of the Black Sea. Little at this time was known of Æetes except that his father was the Sun and that he was a wizard with strange powers. Instead of treating Phrixus hospitably, Æetes had murdered him in order to have the golden fleece of the ram which Phrixus had sacrificed when he arrived in Colchis.

Many people would have shrunk from what appeared to be so desperate a task as the recovery of the Golden Fleece, but Jason, though he knew that King Pelias hoped and expected that this adventure would cost him his life, determined nevertheless to undertake it. He let it be known throughout Greece that he intended to lead an expedition to the east, and from all over Greece young men and heroes came to Iolcos, eager for the glory of sharing in the ambitious enterprise. In the end fifty-three men and one woman sailed on the *Argo*, a miraculous ship built by the craftsman Argos. It had in its prow a beam cut in the oak woods of Dodona. This beam was capable of speaking in a human voice and pronouncing oracles.

The ship was launched to the music of the famous singer, Orpheus, who went himself on the expedition. Tiphys was the steersman. Other heroes who sailed with Jason were Hercules, the son of Jupiter, Lynceus, whose eye-sight was so keen that he could easily see quite small objects at a distance of nine miles, Aesculapius, the great doctor, Calais and Zetes, the winged sons of the North Wind, Meleager of Calydon and many others. The one woman who sailed was Atalanta, famous as a huntress and as a runner. All these heroes are known as the Argonauts, since they were sailors in the *Argo*.

The Voyage of the Argonauts

Very many adventures took place on their way through the sea to Colchis. First they landed at the island of Lemnos and were surprised to find not a single man in the place. It was governed entirely by women under their queen, Hypsipile.

The reason for this unusual state of affairs was the anger of Venus. The women of the island had neglected to sacrifice to the goddess of love, and Venus determined to be revenged on them. So she brought it about that they were all afflicted with a most unpleasant smell, which made them not only unattractive, but positively disgusting to their husbands. The result was that their husbands took other wives, either from among their slaves or from among the women of the mainland opposite. In great anger at having been treated in this way the women of Lemnos met together and contrived a cruel plot—that each of them should, in one night, murder her male relations, so that there should be no more men left on the island. This terrible plot was actually carried out, except that the queen Hypsipile spared the life of her father Thoas.

It was not long after this murder of the men that the Argonauts landed in Lemnos, and found that the women, now restored to their usual condition, were very glad to see them. In particular Queen Hypsipile fell deeply in love with Jason, and Jason promised her that after he had won the Golden Fleece he would return to Lemnos and make her his wife. As we shall see, he did not keep his promise and, in the end, Hypsipile was forced to leave the island, was captured by pirates and sold as a slave. But so hospitably were the Argonauts received at Lemnos that they stayed there for a whole year. Others besides Jason made promises of fidelity to the women who had entertained them, but none of these promises were kept.

After a year's stay at Lemnos, the *Argo* put to sea again and at Cios, where they had landed to find a fresh supply of water, Jason lost the services of one of the strongest and bravest of his companions. Hercules was devoted to his young page Hylas, a beautiful boy who, with the others, took his jar for carrying water and went into the woods to find some fountain or pool. Wandering further than the rest he came in the silence of the midday to a beautiful pool of clear water, with poplars growing near it. Over the pool hung dewy apples that no one had cultivated, growing on trees that few if any eyes had seen before. All around on the cool turf grew white lilies and red poppies. It was a place sacred to the nymphs called Dryads, and Hylas, loving the beauty of the scene, enchanted with the flowers and the bright water, forgot his task and busied himself

with picking the flowers. In the end he lay down beside the lake and, propping himself on his right elbow, leant down to the water to drink. The nymphs of the lake saw him as he leaned towards them and wondered at his beauty. Raising their heads and their wet arms above the surface, they gently drew him below the lake to be their play-fellow. Hylas, as he felt himself being drawn under, cried out for help, and his friend Hercules, though at some distance away, heard him. Then for a whole day Hercules and the rest searched the woods and the glades which resounded to the cries of "Hylas! Hylas!" No trace, however, could be found of the missing boy. There was a long journey to go and the Argonauts determined to leave; but Hercules refused to go with them. As they set out again into the sea he remained behind and for long he sought in vain for his friend. The boy was never found; but to this day, in memory of his loss, the people of this country go every year through the woods calling out "Hylas! Hylas!", as though there was a hope of discovering him.

Among the Argonauts were the two brothers Castor and Pollux, sons of Zeus. Pollux was particularly skilful as a boxer, and this skill was of great service to his companions when, after leaving Hercules behind, they came to the kingdom of King Amycus, the son of Neptune, whose custom it was to challenge all strangers to a boxing match. Those who lost the match (and so powerful was the king that he had never been defeated) were compelled to serve him as slaves or else were put to death. The Argonauts, having chosen Pollux as their champion, watched anxiously as the two boxers fastened to their hands the great gloves of leather with iron bars along the padded knuckles. With such gloves it was not impossible for a man to be killed. They and the followers of King Amycus stood in a circle to watch the fight, and soon it was evident that, though perhaps Amycus was the stronger of the two, Pollux had the greater skill. He lightly avoided the king's enormous blows and, leaping inside his guard, raised great red marks on his ribs and stomach as he struck with the heavy gloves. He manoeuvred carefully, so that the king would have the sun in his eyes, and now, changing his tactics, he began to strike at the face and soon his opponent was spitting out blood and teeth mixed together. Finally, growing desperate, Amycus seized hold of Pollux's right arm with his left and, while he was so held, smashed a blow at him which, if it had landed, would certainly have killed him. But Pollux slipped his head aside and, striking out from the shoulder, struck Amycus such a blow on the temple that the bones cracked and the king fell to the ground in a heap. Pollux might well have killed his enemy, but instead he made him swear a great oath never again to molest strangers with his bullying ways.

Next the Argonauts came to the court of the blind King Phineus, who was gifted with prophetic powers. The king indeed attempted to entertain them hospitably, but, no sooner were they seated at the tables and the food was set out than there swooped down from the air three terrible monsters called the Harpies or "Snatchers." These creatures had women's faces and the bodies and wings of large vultures. They pounced upon the tables, flapping their huge wings, fouling everything with the mess they made, knocking over the goblets of wine and filling their greedy and disgusting mouths with whatever they could take up. So Phineus, in the midst of all his riches, had not been able for years to eat one meal undisturbed. This was a punishment which had been sent him by the gods, because he had used his prophetic power to reveal secret things. Now, however, the day of his deliverance had come, for among the Argonauts were the two winged sons of the North Wind, Calais and Zetes, who were, indeed, his brothers-in-law, since Phineus had married their sister Cleopatra who had not lived to see her husband blind and persecuted.

Now the young children of the North Wind drew their swords and sprang into the air, since they were winged. The Harpies fled away, turning and twisting to avoid the thrusts of the brothers' pursuing swords, and the chase went on over land and sea till, high in the sky above a group of islands that lay like jewels in the blue water, Iris, the goddess of the rainbow, appeared and said: "Cease your pursuit, Calais and Zetes! It is not for you to destroy the Harpies. But Jupiter promises that never more will they come to afflict Phineus. Now return, and ask the king to tell you of the dangers that lie in front of you and Jason and your friends."

The brothers obeyed her and, lightly turning in the air, flew back to the palace of Phineus where, for the first time in years, the king was able to enjoy an unmolested meal.

When the meal was over, Jason turned to the king and said: "We have been glad to help you to escape from your persecution. Now we ask you to help us. Tell us, if you will be so kind, what other dangers we are to expect before we reach the land of Colchis."

Phineus turned his blind eyes in Jason's direction. "Your greatest dangers," he said, "will be in the land of Colchis itself, and of these I may not speak. What I can tell you is that, before you enter the Black Sea, at its very gateway, you will have to pass between two blue rocks that are called the Symplegades, or Clashers. Those rocks guard the straits. At one moment they move apart from each other; at the next they dash together with such violence that anything, whether it be a bird or a ship, that is caught between them is immediately crushed and broken to pieces. When you reach these rocks, what I advise you to do is to take a pigeon and let it go free. If the pigeon succeeds in flying unscathed between the rocks, that will be a sign to you that the gods are not unfriendly. Watch the rocks carefully, and, when they move apart, row with all your might. If you pass through safely, you will have done a glorious thing, for you will have made a road for ever from Greece into the eastern sea."

Jason and the Argonauts listened to him with astonishment, and not without fear. This was a danger which they had never imagined. Nevertheless they had not come so far only to turn back again, and, after sacrificing to the gods, and having enjoyed for some days the hospitality of Phineus, they again set to sea. The winds favoured them, and it was not long before, on the distant horizon, they saw what appeared to be sheets of water spouting into the air. As they drew nearer they were aware of a noise like thunder, and soon they could see clearly the two blue and craggy rocks that intermittently leapt apart and sprang clashing together, sending up clouds of water as they met, and deafening the ears with the roar of their impact. Beyond them was the surface of another sea, and there was no way to reach it except between these clashing mountains.

Jason took his stand in the stern so that from there he could urge on the rowers. First, he prayed to all the gods and especially to Juno, and liberated a white dove. All watched the dove closely as it sped straight as an arrow between the rocks. It flew fast, but, as the rocks closed roaring together, it looked as though the dove had been caught and crushed between them. The next moment, as the spray subsided, the Argonauts raised a shout of joy. One of the dove's tail feathers indeed was swaying up and down on the water, but the dove itself, as they could see, had flown through in safety and was already winging its way over an unknown sea.

Jason called to his companions and urged them (not that there was any need of urging) to use every ounce of their strength when he gave the word. Again the rocks clashed together. Then, as they parted, Jason shouted out the word of command. The rowers bent over their oars and the ship's timbers seemed to shiver as she leapt through the rough and foaming water. The steersman, Tiphys, held her on a straight course, and she seemed to move as though some divine power had given her wings. With a tremendous splintering crash the two rocks came together again; but the *Argo* was through. A piece of the rudder had been smashed to pieces, but the ship and all aboard her were safe and sound. The Argonauts looked at one another with wide and startled eyes, hardly believing that they had escaped so great a danger. Friend embraced friend and offered up prayers of thanksgiving to the gods. Then they looked back in astonishment at the sudden silence that had fallen on the sea. The two rocks, which never before had made way for any man or any ship, now stood motionless, one on each side of the channel. So they stand to this day, giving an easy passage to sailors from the west. The Argonauts, keeping the northern coast of Asia upon their right, sailed on to Colchis at the limit of the sea.

The Golden Fleece

In the end they reached the swift and muddy waters of the river Phasis. This is the land from which pheasants came in the first place. Rowing up the river they reached the court of King Æetes, and there, surrounded by his brave companions, Jason explained the reason of their coming and asked that the Golden Fleece should be returned to the kinsmen of Phrixus.

The king, seeing so many and such brave champions in front of him, was, for the moment, at a loss for a reply. Finally he spoke: "I admit that your claim is just, but I can grant it only on these conditions. To-morrow at sunrise, you must yoke my bulls to the plough.

You must plough a field and then sow there the teeth of a dragon. If you are successful in these tests, you may take the Golden Fleece, but you must take it yourself and single-handed from the serpent who is its guardian. These are my terms. Tell me if you will accept them."

The gods made Jason bold. "They have helped me so far," he thought. "Will they not help me to the end?" He looked resolutely at the king. "I accept your conditions," he said. "But if I do my part you must do yours."

The king smiled as he agreed. Only he and his daughter Medea, who was sitting at his side, knew that the tasks he had proposed were beyond the strength of any mortal man. As for Medea, her mind was carried this way and that way as she looked now at her father, to whom she owed her loyalty, and now at the brave and beautiful stranger whom she was seeing for the first time. "What I feel," she said to herself, "is either love or something like what people call love. I cannot bear the thought of this stranger perishing and I want to save him. Yet, if I do so, I shall be betraying my father and my native land. I know that I should support my father; yet, though I see clearly what I ought to do, my feelings lead me in exactly the opposite direction. Would it not be cruel to allow this young man to feel the fiery breath of my father's bulls, to fight with an army springing from the earth, or to be given as a helpless prey to the terrible dragon? Yet these things must happen to him if I do not help him. But then, when he has the Golden Fleece, what will become of me? I cannot bear to lose him. If I can help him, he must take me with him to Greece and make me his wife. I should have to leave my father and my home, but I should be the wife of a great hero and I should be renowned myself for my magic arts and for saving all the best of the Greeks."

So she thought to herself, and in the evening, when she was on her way to sacrifice to Hecate, the great goddess of witches and enchantresses, she met Jason in a wood and fixed her eyes on his face as though she were seeing him for the first time. Jason took hold of her right hand, and, in a low voice, begged her to help him, promising that, if she did so, he would take her away with him and marry her. She burst into tears and said: "I know that what I am doing is wrong, but I shall do it. Only swear that you will keep your promise."

Jason then swore by Hecate, by the all-seeing Sun and by all the gods that he would be true. Medea gave him the magic herbs and told him how he must use them in the perils of the next day.

When dawn came crowds flocked to the sacred field of Mars and stood all round it on the heights above. King Æetes, in a purple robe and carrying an ivory sceptre, sat on his throne with Medea at his side and his people all round him. Suddenly into the field came the bulls. They had hooves and horns of brass, and through their iron-hard nostrils they blew out fire and smoke. The grass shrivelled and caught on fire as they breathed on it, and the noise of their breathing was like the noise of a roaring furnace. Jason went to meet them, and, as he approached, they turned their terrible faces upon him, pawed the ground with their brazen hooves and shook their metal horns, filling the whole air with fiery bellowings. The Argonauts, as they watched, stood stiff and silent in terror; but Jason went up to the bulls, and, so great was the power of the magic herbs that he had received, did not feel the burning of their fiery breath. With one hand he boldly stroked their swinging dewlaps; then he put the yoke on their necks and forced them to draw the heavy plough and furrow up the field that had never felt iron before. The men of Colchis gazed at him in astonishment. The Argonauts raised a great shout and added to his courage by their applause.

Next Jason took the dragon's teeth from a brazen helmet and began to sow them in the ploughed field. The teeth, steeped as they were in powerful magic, grew soft in the earth and began to swell up into new forms. Just as a child grows gradually inside the mother's body, and does not come out into the world until it is a fully-shaped human creature, so these seeds grew under ground and did not emerge to the surface of the earth till they had taken on the shapes of fully-grown men, complete with weapons which they clashed together. When the Greeks saw this army of warriors preparing to hurl their sharp spears at Jason's head, again their faces fell and again their hearts failed them. Medea herself was frightened and grew pale as she saw one man surrounded by so many enemies. Silently, as she sat there, in case the charms she had already given him should not prove strong enough, she began under her breath to mutter other magic spells. But Jason took up a great rock and hurled it into the middle of the earth-born army. This had the effect of turning all their rage and anger upon themselves.

Man fought man until the whole lot of armed men had perished by each other's hands.

Then the Argonauts thronged round Jason, embracing him and cheering and congratulating him on his victory. Medea, too, would have liked to embrace him, but was afraid of what people might say. All she could do was to look at him with silent joy and thank the gods who had given her such powerful spells.

All that remained now was to face the terrible dragon that guarded the Golden Fleece. It was a creature with a great crest on its head, a three-forked tongue and curving hooked teeth. It was coiled around the stem of the tree where, through the thick dark leaves, glowed a gleam of gold, showing where the fleece was. Jason sprinkled on the dragon some juices from herbs of forgetfulness which Medea had given him. Then three times he recited a spell strong enough to make stormy seas calm or to force swollen over-flowing rivers back into their beds. Gradually and for the first time sleep came over the dragon's eyes. Jason threw the heavy fleece across his shoulder and, fearing some treacherous attack from King Æetes, hurried to his ship with the Greeks and with Medea, who had saved him. Quickly they went aboard and quickly sat down at the rowing benches. They were sailing down the river almost before Æetes had realized what had happened.

When, however, the king discovered that his daughter had fled with Jason, he determined to overtake them and sailed in pursuit with his whole fleet. Once more Medea saved her husband and the Greeks, but she only saved them by doing a terrible deed. She had taken with her her little brother Absyrtus. Now she killed the boy and threw on the water pieces of his body, so that King Æetes would delay his pursuit in order to collect the fragments of his son's body for burial. Thus the Argonauts reached the open sea in safety. In their peril no one of them had blamed Medea for her cruel act, but afterwards many were to reproach her for it. Now, their task achieved, they sailed joyfully back to Iolcos.

Jason and Medea

One might have expected that now Jason, who had performed the most noble exploit, and his beautiful wife Medea, the greatest of enchantresses, would have been happy; but, whether because of the cruel murder of Absyrtus or for some other reason, events were to turn out far otherwise.

When first the Argonauts returned in triumph to Iolcos the city was full of glad crowds and everything that could be done was done to celebrate the safe and glorious return of the heroes. Incense was heaped on the flames of the altars. Great feasts were held, and bulls with gilded horns were sacrificed to the gods. But one man was unable to take part in all the rejoicing. This was Jason's father, Aeson, who was now so old and so close to death that he could not leave his house. In pity and distress Jason spoke to Medea. "My dear wife, to whom I owe my safety, you have given me everything already; but, since your spells are so strong, can you not perhaps give me one thing more? Can you not take away some of the years that I myself am fated to live, and give these to my father, so that he may live longer?"

Medea remembered how she had deserted her own father, and she was touched by Jason's love for the old Aeson. "Certainly, Jason," she said, "I would not, even if I could, take away any years from your life. But, if Hecate will help me, I will try to do something better still. I will try to make your father young again."

In three nights' time it would be full moon. When the third night came, and all the earth lay white beneath the moon's round and complete splendour, Medea put on a loose flowing dress and went out of doors. She was barefooted and her hair was loose on her shoulders. Men, beasts and birds were sunk in deep sleep; there was no movement in the hedge-rows; the leaves hung motionless on the trees; the dewy air was still and silent. Only the stars twinkled, and, stretching her arms towards the stars, Medea turned round in a circle three times (since the gods of witchcraft are pleased with uneven numbers), three times sprinkled fresh water on her head, and three times pronounced a howling cry. Then she kneeled down on the hard ground and prayed: "O Night, you who hide our mysteries, and Hecate, you who are the goddess of witches and enchanters, and Earth, you who provide us with our magic herbs, now I need your help. Already by my spells I have made rivers run backwards, drawn the moon down from the sky, up-rooted forests and mountains, and compelled the ghosts to rise from their tombs. Now I have need of drugs which will turn old age back again to youth, and now I know that I shall find them, for the stars flash out their reply to me and I see my chariot, drawn by winged dragons, coming to me through the air."

As she spoke her magic chariot came to her out of the night. She mounted it and, after she had stroked the dragons' necks, she flew away to the plains of Thessaly and for nine days and nine nights plucked from river-beds and forests and open ground the herbs and grasses she needed. Some she pulled up by the roots and others she cut with a bronze sickle. Finally, after wandering far and wide, she returned in her chariot. The dragons that drew it had only smelt the magic herbs, but even so their old gnarled skins changed into new skins of the most brilliant colours.

When Medea reached her home, she would not yet go indoors or allow her husband or anyone else to touch her. She built two altars out of turf, one to Hecate and one to Youth. By each altar she dug a ditch and filled the ditches with the blood of a black sheep which she sacrificed. On the top of the blood she poured bowls of wine and of warm milk.

Then she ordered her servants to bring old Aeson out of the house. They carried him on a stretcher, since he was too weak to move and indeed on the point of death. Medea, by her spells, put him into a deep sleep and laid him on a bed of herbs. Then she told Jason and all the rest to retire. None must be allowed to wit-ness her secret rites.

They retired and she, with her loose hair streaming behind her, went from altar to altar, kindling the flames and dipping the wood that she burned in the pools of blood. Then in a bronze cauldron she began to mix her magic brew. Into the cauldron went the roots that she had cut in the valleys of Thessaly, together with seeds and flowers and pressed juices. To these she added some pebbles from the far east and some sand from the stream of Ocean. Then she put in some frost which had been collected under the full moon, also the wings with some of the flesh of the hideous screech-owl, and the entrails of a were-wolf—the animal that can change from a wolf into a man. There, too, in the cauldron was the scaly skin of a water-snake, the liver of a stag, the eggs and head of a crow that had lived for nine generations. All these and a thousand other strange things were mixed together in the pot, and, as the pot began to simmer, Medea stirred it with an old dry branch of olive. This old dry stick, as it touched the hot liquid, first of all began to grow green, then put out leaves, and then was covered with fresh grown olives. And whenever drops of the mixture bubbled over on to the ground, the earth where the drops fell became green and flowers began to grow there.

As soon as Medea saw this, she drew her sword from its sheath and cut the old man's throat. She let out all the old blood and instead of it filled his body, partly through the lips and partly through the wound, with her magic potion. As the new blood spread in his veins, Aeson's grey hair and beard began to turn black; his thin scraggy limbs put on flesh; his pale neglected cheeks flushed red; the wrinkles disappeared, and he rose to his feet in all the strength of youth. As he looked in amazement at himself, he remembered that this was what he had been like forty years before.

Unfortunately, however, Medea was not content with this act of mercy. She determined to use the fame which she had won to revenge herself cruelly on Pelias, who had taken Aeson's kingdom from him and who had refused to surrender it to Jason. In order that she might carry out her plan she pretended that she and Jason had quarrelled and she went to the house of Pelias where she was kindly received by his daughters. These girls were naturally interested in all Medea's magic powers, and Medea was constantly telling them of how she had made old Aeson young again. The daughters of Pelias asked her whether she could not do the same thing to their own father. Medea craftily pretended to hesitate, so that in the end they would be all the more willing to do as she told them. After appearing to ponder things over in her own mind she said: "It is necessary for you to have confidence in me, and so that you may really feel confidence, I ask you to bring me the oldest ram in all your flocks. You will see that my charms will make him into a lamb again."

At once the daughters of Pelias brought a woolly ram so ancient that he could scarcely stand, with great horns curving round his hollow temples. Medea cut his old throat, hardly staining her sword, since the blood was so thin, and then plunged the body into a bronze cauldron where powerful herbs were boiling in the water. These herbs made the body shrink and made both the horns and the years of the animal disappear. A thin bleating noise came from inside the cauldron and, while they were still wondering at this noise, out skipped a lamb which, after stumbling a little on its unsteady legs, ran frisking away to look for some udder to give it milk.

After having seen this, the daughters of Pelias were all the more eager that Medea should try her arts on their father. This was exactly what Medea wanted for the success of her treacherous plan.

Night came and she put over a fire a cauldron of boiling water. Into the water she put herbs which had no magic powers at all. Then she led Pelias's daughters into the bedroom where their old father was asleep. "Why do you hang back now?" she said to them. "Draw your swords and let out the old man's blood, so that I may fill him with new blood. If you love your father, do as I tell you."

They indeed shrunk from such a deed, but in the end, feeling that their father's future happiness depended on them, they plunged their swords into his body. The old man, mortally wounded, woke from his sleep and began to cry out, "My daughters, what are you doing to me?" Then Medea cut his throat with her sword and plunged the body into the boiling water which immediately extinguished any life that was left.

So terrible a revenge pleased neither Jason nor the people of Iolcos. In spite of Jason's great fame, both he and Medea were forced to flee from the country. They went to Corinth, the city between two seas, where, after the voyage of the Argonauts, Jason had brought the *Argo* ashore and dedicated it to the gods. Here for ten years they lived happily, and two children were born to them. This happiness, however, did not last.

Whether because of Medea's savage nature or because he wished to gain advantage by being related to the King of Corinth, Jason decided to leave his wife. He forgot the promises which he had made to her when she saved his life at Colchis, and he asked Creon, the king of Corinth, for the hand of his daughter Glauce. Creon was glad that his daughter should marry the famous leader of the Argonauts, but he was frightened of Medea. He therefore decided to banish her and her children from Corinth.

After he had told her that she must go, Medea, with great difficulty, persuaded the king to allow her to stay for one day in order to make her preparations. What she prepared was a terrible revenge. She pretended that she was not angry either with Jason or the princess Glauce, and she sent her children to the palace with a beautifully woven robe and a golden diadem as a wedding present. The young princess hurried to try on the fine clothes. She put the diadem on her head and dressed herself in the beautiful dress. But both dress and diadem had been steeped in terrible poisons. As the princess walked about her room, now and again stretching out a foot to see how the folds of the robe hung, she suddenly gave a cry of pain. The dress was clinging to her flesh and burning it. Her head was all on fire and, as she shook her head to get rid of the diadem, the fire blazed out all the more fiercely. No one dared touch her until her old father Creon, hearing her cries, came to her and embraced her as she lay dying. Then the fire settled on him too. For all his efforts he could not tear himself away from his daughter's body which clung to him like ivy round a tree. Both of them lay dead, killed by Medea's enchantments.

Meanwhile Medea had done a deed even more dreadful than this. Determined to make Jason suffer in every way, she killed her two children and, when Jason, in rage and misery at the murder of his bride, came to her palace, she appeared before him in her winged chariot with the bodies of the children in her own keeping. She would not even allow him to touch the bodies or give them burial, but flew away to the land of Athens, where the old king Aegeus sheltered her.

As for Jason, in spite of the great fame of his youth, his later years, deprived of his kingdom, his wife and his children, were miserable. One day in his old age he was sitting beside the sea in the shadow of his old ship, the *Argo*, which had been drawn up on land to be a monument. But now many of the timbers had rotted away, and, as Jason sat there, a great beam from the prow broke and crashed on his head. So Jason was killed by the very ship which had made him famous.

ECHO AND NARCISSUS

The famous Theban prophet Tiresias gave many true answers to those who sought his advice. Among these answers was one that he gave to a nymph, the mother of a beautiful boy called Narcissus. She had asked the prophet whether her son would live to old age, and the prophet replied: "Only if he never knows himself." For a long time there seemed to be no meaning in the reply, but in the end the death and the strange falling in love of Narcissus showed that the old prophet was right.

For when the boy had reached his sixteenth year he was loved by very many young men and very many girls. But in his beautiful body there was so much pride that he would have nothing to do with any of them.

Once in the forest when he was driving the frightened deer into his nets, a nymph called Echo saw him. Echo was neither able to begin a conversation nor to keep quiet when others were talking. At this time she had a body and was not, as she is now, just a voice; yet her speech was just as it is now. She could only repeat the last words that others spoke. Juno had made her like this, being angry with her for engaging her in long conversations in order that she would not inquire too closely into what her husband Jupiter was doing.

Now, when she saw Narcissus wandering in the pathless forest she immediately fell in love with him, and, hiding herself, she followed in his footsteps. How much she longed to speak to him and say soft things in his ear! But this she could not do. She had not the power to speak first and could only wait for him to speak so that she could use his own words.

It happened that Narcissus had become separated from his companions and he called out: "Is there anyone here?" Echo answered him, "Here!" and he looked all round him in amazement. "Come to me then!" he shouted out and at once came Echo's reply: "Come to me then." Again he looked round and, as no one appeared, he called out: "Why are you avoiding me?" Again the same words came back to him. He stood stock stiff, wondering what this answering voice could be, then cried out: "Let us meet here!" "Meet here," Echo replied and never gave a reply which delighted her so much. And, following up her own words, she came out of the woods where she had been hiding, went up to Narcissus and wished to throw her arms round his neck. But he fled from her and, as he fled, he cried out: "Take your hands off, and don't touch me. May I die before I let you have your way with me!"

"I let you have your way with me," she answered, and then she could speak no more. Spurned, she lay hid in the woods, covering her blushing face with leaves, and ever afterwards lived in lonely caves. Her love however remained and indeed, through pain at what she had suffered, grew even stronger. In sleeplessness and worry her body wasted away. She became thin and wrinkled: all the moisture in her body vanished into the air: only her bones and her voice were left. Her voice still remains. Her bones, they say, were turned to stone. Still she hides in the woods and is seen no more in the mountains. But everyone can hear her, since her voice, and only her voice, is still alive.

Not only Echo, but many nymphs of the water and of the mountains, were despised by Narcissus. So too were the companies of young men. In the end one of those who had been treated so proudly prayed to the gods: "May he fall in love like this himself, and not gain the thing that he loves!" It was a just prayer and the goddess Nemesis heard it.

There was a bright pool with shining silvery water, a place where no shepherd had ever come or goats that feed on the mountains or any other cattle. No bird or beast or even a bough falling from a tree had ever ruffled its mirrored surface. There was grassy turf round the margin, cool and soft from the water, and there were thickets interlaced that kept away the heat of the sun. Here, tired-out with hunting, Narcissus came and, pleased with the place and with the spring of water, he lay down beside the pool to quench his thirst. But as he did so, he was filled with a different kind of thirst. Seeing himself in the water he looked with amazement at himself and stayed there motionless, with the same expression on his face, like a statue, staring into his own eyes, at his smooth cheeks, his neck like ivory, the white and red of his beautiful face. Without knowing that what he saw was himself, he fell in love with what he saw, and as he looked with love at his own reflection, the face into which he gazed looked back at him with love too. Often he vainly plunged his arms into the water, trying to clasp the neck that he saw there. Never did it dawn upon his foolish mind that the image which he pursued would turn away if he turned away himself, that what he longed for was only a shadow.

Neither hunger nor desire for sleep could tear him away from the place. Stretched out on the shady grass he continued to gaze with eyes that could never be satisfied at that deceitful image of himself. His own beautiful eyes brought him to death. He raised himself a little from the ground and stretched out his arms to the surrounding trees. "O you woods and forests," he said, "you who have witnessed so many loves, has anyone been more unfortunate in love than I? I see, but I cannot touch what I desire. And it is not as though there was a great ocean between us, or long roads or mountains or city walls. We are only separated by a little water. And the face I look at looks back at me with love, smiling when I smile, weeping when I weep. Why then does it always escape me?"

So he spoke and, half out of his senses, looked back again at the image in the water. As his tears fell on the surface, the reflection seemed to shiver and break, and over and over again he cried out: "O do not leave me!" So, lying there, he began to pine and waste away, like yellow wax in the heat or like frost in the rays of the morning sun.

Echo, though she was angry with him, and remembered how he had treated her, was sad when she saw him. When he cried out: "Alas!" she repeated the word after him. His last words as he stared into the water were: "Farewell, face that I have loved in vain!" and Echo replied to him: "I have loved in vain." Then he let his tired hand drop on the green grass. Death closed the eyes that had wondered at their own beauty. Even when he was received into the lower world of the dead, they say he kept gazing at his face reflected in the dark pool of Styx.

The nymphs of the forests and of the rivers mourned for him and Echo answered their cries. They were making ready his funeral with torches and a pile of wood for burning. But the body was nowhere to be found. In its place they found a flower. It has a yellow centre with white petals surrounding it.

MELEAGER OF CALYDON

Meleager was the son of the King of Calydon. The three Fates, Clotho, Lachesis and Atropos, were present at his birth. Clotho foretold that he would be a great hero; Lachesis said that he would be gifted with enormous strength; Atropos declared that his life would last as long as the piece of wood now burning on the fire.

His mother, Althea, when she heard this, immediately took the log from the fire, plunged it in water and kept it carefully, knowing that on it depended the length of her son's life.

As Meleager grew up, all that the Fates foretold came true. He was one of the heroes who sailed with Jason in the *Argo*. His courage and skill saved his country and his father from many enemies. But he is chiefly remembered for the hunting of the Calydonian boar, a noble exploit, though one which was to prove disastrous to him.

Meleager's father, at a great Harvest Festival, had sacrificed grain to Ceres, wine to Bacchus, and olive oil to Minerva. To all the other gods also he sacrificed as was proper. But he neglected the goddess Diana and left her altars without incense or offerings. The gods feel anger like men do. "I may be unhonoured," Diana said, "but I shall not be unavenged," and she sent into the fields of Calydon to avenge herself an enormous wild boar, as big as the bulls one finds in northern Greece and bigger than the bulls of Sicily. His eyes flashed with blood and fire; his neck was like a solid ridge; the bristles along his back stood stiff like the shafts of spears; hot foam flecked his shoulders as he roared and grunted; his tusks were as long as those of the Indian elephant; lightning came from his mouth; the grass shrivelled up when he breathed on it.

He trampled down the young corn as it began to show; he ravaged good crops that farmers were ready to harvest. Threshing floors and granaries were empty. Heavy bunches of grapes with their long green tendrils were thrown down and trodden under foot; so were the branches and trunks of the ever-leafy olive. Then

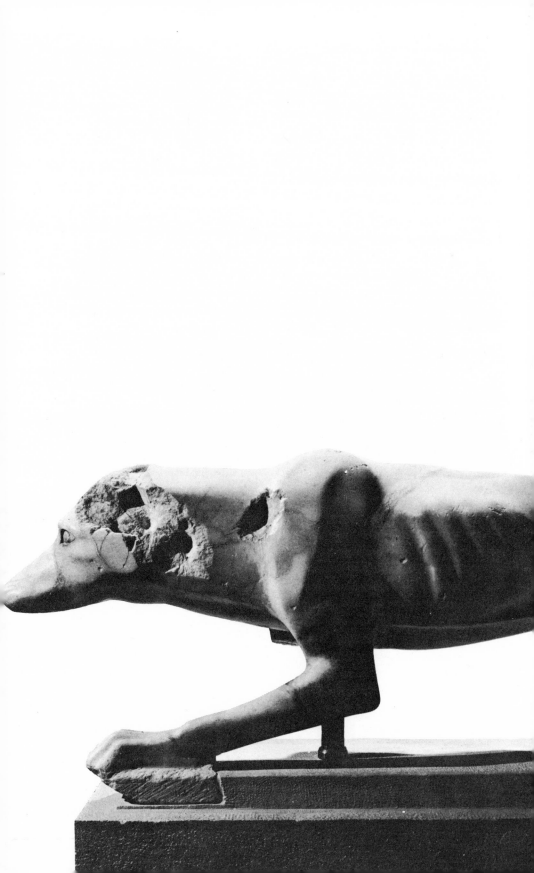

he turned his rage on the farm animals. Shepherds and sheepdogs could not protect their flocks, nor could fierce bulls preserve their own herds. The country folk fled in all directions and did not consider themselves safe unless they were behind city walls.

Meleager now summoned together from all over Greece a band of young men who were eager for the glory of killing this boar. Many of the heroes who had sailed with Jason in the *Argo* came now to Calydon. Among them was Jason himself, Castor and Pollux, and many others. There was Peleus, the father of Achilles, Nestor, a young man who in his old age was to fight in the Trojan War, Laertes the father of Ulysses, Theseus with his great friend Pirithous. There also came Atalanta, the famous huntress of the Arcadian woods. A brightly polished brooch secured her dress at the shoulder; her hair was done simply, tied in a knot behind her head; from her left shoulder swung an ivory quiver which rattled as she moved; in her left hand she carried her bow. Her face was of the kind that might be called boyish in a girl and girlish in a boy. As soon as he saw her, Meleager fell in love with her. "Happy indeed," he said, "would be the man that this woman should think worthy of her!" His own modesty and the importance of the occasion prevented him from saying more. The time had come for the great conflict with the boar.

There was a forest where the trunks of trees stood close together, untouched for ages by the axe. It started from the plain and, rising up the hills, looked down on the fields that sloped away from it. On reaching this forest, some of the hunters began to set out the nets, others loosed their hounds, others followed tracks worn on the ground, all eager to meet danger. So they came to a deep valley into which flowed the streams of rain water from the higher ground. In the bottom of the valley grew willows, sedge, marshgrass, bulrushes and various kinds of reeds. Out of all this undergrowth they roused the boar, which charged down upon its enemies like lightning struck out from the shaken clouds. The trees and bushes were laid flat as he rushed forward; there was a crash of falling boughs as he swept through the forest.

The young men raised a shout, gripped their spears firmly, and held them poised, with the broad iron heads pointing ready to throw. The boar charged on, with deadly sideways movements of the head scattering the barking dogs that tried to hold him. The first spear thrown missed its mark and grazed away some of the bark of a maple tree. The next one, thrown by Jason of Iolcos, seemed certain to stick in the animal's back, but it had been thrown with too much force and went too far. In this first volley only one spear hit the boar and from this spear as it flew Diana tore the point, so that only the wooden shaft reached its mark. Even this blow roused the animal's anger. It rushed on like a thunderbolt. Its eyes glared and it seemed to breathe out flame from its mouth. Like a rock hurled from a catapult comes whirling through the air at walls or towers with soldiers on them, so this bloodthirsty wild boar charged down relentlessly on the young men. It knocked over two of them at the right of the line, but their comrades picked them up and carried them to safety. Another hunter, Enaesimus by name, was not so lucky. As he turned to run away he fell down with the muscles behind his knee ripped through by the boar's tusks. Nestor of Pylos would never have lived to go to the Trojan War if he had not used his spear as a jumping pole and leaped up into the branches of a nearby tree. Safe in the tree, he could look down on the enemy he had escaped. The boar sharpened his tusks on the bark of an oak and then, still furiously raging, made a great gash in the thigh of another hunter. Then the twin brothers Castor and Pollux ran forward, both easily to be recognized on their snow-white horses, both poising their spears together and hurling them through the air. Indeed they would at least have drawn blood with their weapons, if the bristly creature had not plunged into the thick woods out of reach of weapons or of horses. The heroes followed after, and now Atalanta fitted a swift arrow to the string and shot it from her curved bow. The arrow sped over the top of the boar's back and stuck behind his ear. Blood began to ooze over the bristles. Meleager was just as pleased with her success as she was herself. He was the first to see the blood and the first to point it out to the rest. "You shall have the prize that your courage deserves," he cried to her.

The men meanwhile blushed with shame at being outdone by a woman. They urged each other on by shouts, gaining courage themselves from the noise they made, and hurling their spears in no proper order, so that their throwing missed its effect. There was one of them called Ancaeus who was armed with a double-headed axe. He ran in front of the others and spoke boastfully to them. "Now look my friends," he said, "and I shall show you how much better a man's weapons are than a girl's. Leave it all to me. Let

Diana herself, with her bow and arrow, try to protect this boar; whether she likes it or not he will fall by my hand."

So, puffed up with pride, he spoke, and, digging his toes into the ground, he stretched up with his axe held above his head, ready to bring it crashing down upon his enemy. But the boar rushed straight at him, aiming his tusks at the lower part of the stomach where wounds bring death quickest. Ancaeus fell with his stomach ripped open. Streams of blood soaked the ground.

Then Theseus threw his heavy spear with its bronze point. It was well aimed, but on its way caught against the leafy branch of an oak and missed its mark. Jason again hurled a javelin, but had the bad luck to miss the boar and strike an innocent dog, which the spear pinned to the ground.

Meleager himself had a different fortune. He threw two spears, the first of which stuck quivering in the earth. The second one however fixed firmly in the middle of the boar's back. Then he sprang forward and, while the enraged animal turned round in circles, spouting out blood and foam, he pressed on his attack and finally plunged his shining spear right into the beast's shoulder. His friends shouted aloud to show their joy and hurried up to press him by the hand. Then they gazed in wonder at the enormous body lying stretched out over so much ground. Even now it seemed scarcely safe to touch it, but they all dipped their weapons in its blood.

Meleager stood with his foot on the boar's terrible head, and said to Atalanta: "You were the first to wound the boar, and you must have the prize that you deserve. I should wish my glory to be shared with you." He then gave her the trophies of the chase, the skin with its stiff bristles, and the head with its huge tusks.

She was delighted with the gift, and delighted too with the giver, but the others were jealous and resentful. Angry murmurs were heard on all sides.

Two of the hunters, Plexippus and Toxeus, were uncles of Meleager, being brothers of his mother Althea. These two, shouting and waving their arms, cried out: "Put the prize down, girl, and don't think that you can escape with what belongs to men! Don't think either that your beauty is any advantage. Meleager may be in love with you, but will not be able to help you." So they deprived her of her gift and him of the right to give it.

This was too much for Meleager. He bit his lips in rage and cried out: "You that take what belongs to others, I will show you the difference between boasting threats and real action." Immediately he turned on Plexippus who was expecting no such thing, and plunged his sword into his heart. Then, while Toxeus hesitated what to do, his thoughts balanced between the wish to avenge his brother and the fear of sharing in his fate, Meleager cut his hesitation short and thrust the sword still warm from the blood of one brother into the body of the other.

Meanwhile Meleager's mother Althea was bearing gifts to the temples of the gods in honour of her son's victory. But as she was on her way she saw the two dead bodies of her brothers being carried into the city for burial. Then she beat her breast and filled all the place with her cries. Instead of her golden robes she put on black. When, however, she heard that the murderer was her own son, her grief fell away. She now turned from weeping to the desire for vengeance.

In a secret part of the house there had been kept for a long time the log of wood which had been on the fire at the moment of Meleager's birth and which, by being kept safe, had kept Meleager safe himself. Now Althea brought this log out from its hiding place, and told her servants to put pine branches and small kindling wood together and light the unkind fire. Four times she started to throw the log on the fire; four times she stopped herself in the moment of doing so. Her feelings as a mother and her feelings as a sister were on different sides and pulled her in different directions. Sometimes her face looked like the face of one in anger, sometimes like the face of one who feels pity. And when fierce burning of anger seemed to have ended her tears, then the tears would come again. So, like a ship driven one way by the wind and another way by the tide feels both forces and moves now this way now that, Althea was swayed in opposite directions, laid aside her anger and again took it up.

Finally her love for her brothers overpowered her feeling for her son. As the fire grew hot, she took the log and said: "These hot flames must now devour my own flesh. I hate the deed that I do, yet how else can I satisfy my brothers' ghosts who are crying to me for vengeance? My son deserves to die, yet why should I be the one to bring him his death? And by killing him I shall be killing myself.

Yet in front of my eyes are my dear brothers' wounds. I do what I must do."

So she spoke. Then turning away her face, and with her hand trembling, she threw the fatal log into the middle of the fire. It groaned or seemed to groan as the flames fastened on it and the unwilling fire burnt it up.

Meleager far away in the forest and ignorant of what was happening felt himself burning in the same flame. He felt fire raging through his body and in strong endurance he tried to force down the pain. Still he was sad that his death was coming to him not in battle but in this unmanly way, and he called Ancaeus happy for dying as he did. On the point of death, he cried out, groaning with pain, for his old father, his brothers and loving sisters, and his wife. No doubt he cried out for his mother too. As the fire increased so did his pain. They both died down together, and as Meleager's spirit vanished into the thin air, so the white ashes settled on the hearth.

Now high Calydon was brought low. Old and young, rich and poor joined in the lament, beating their breasts and tearing their hair. Meleager's father lay stretched on the ground, complaining that he had lived too long. Now he had lost his wife too, for Althea, in horror at her deed, had punished herself by thrusting a sword through her own heart. No one could describe the grief of Meleager's sisters. Crying and wailing, they kissed over and over again their brother's body, and, when the body was consumed by the funeral fire, they gathered up the ashes and pressed them to their breasts. For long they wasted away in mourning at his tomb, till Diana, who was satisfied with her vengeance, took pity on them, put long wings upon their arms, gave them beaks instead of mouths, changed them into speckled guinea fowl and sent them into the air.

THE STORY OF THESEUS

His Journey to Athens

Not far across the sea from Athens lies the city of Troizen. To this city once came Aegeus, King of Athens, and there he and Aethra, daughter of the King of Troizen, had a child who was called Theseus.

Aegeus returned to Athens but, before leaving, he took his sword with its ivory sheath and put it under a great rock. Then he said to Aethra: "When the boy is strong enough to lift this rock, let him take his father's sword and come to me in Athens."

By the time that Theseus was sixteen, he was not only strong, but intelligent and ambitious. When his mother showed him the rock, he easily lifted it up and took from beneath it the sword, still bright and shining in its close-fitting ivory scabbard. His next task was to visit his father in Athens. Instead of going there by sea, which was the safe and easy way, he decided to travel by land. This meant a journey through narrow mountain passes and rough ways, through a country infested with robbers and wild beasts. Not for a long time had anyone from Troizen dared to go this way.

The first part of the road lay along the sea-shore, and Theseus had not gone far before he met a giant called Periphetes or "Famous", who was the son of Vulcan, the god of fire, and carried a huge iron club with which he would beat out the brains of all travellers who attempted to pass him. Like his father Vulcan, he limped in one foot, but he was immensely strong and quite without mercy. Theseus was well trained in the use of the sword, and, being nimble on his feet, avoided the great swinging blows of the giant's club, thrusting his sword over and over again into his enemy's body. So he slew him and went on his way along the solitary road, carrying with him as a trophy the great club.

The road to Athens went north to the Isthmus of Corinth, where two seas are separated by a narrow strip of land. Near here lived the brigand Sinis, called "the Pine-bender", because, when he seized upon a traveller, he would bend down two pine-trees and, after tying their tops to the arms or legs of his miserable victims, would let the trees go, thus tearing limb from limb the men or women who had fallen into his power. This notable robber attempted to overpower Theseus so that he could treat him in the same way as he had treated so many others. But Theseus smote him to the ground half-stunned with his club and, bending down two pine-trees himself, fastened them to Sinis's own limbs. Then he released the trees, and the criminal met the same death that he had so often inflicted on innocent people. Henceforward the road to the Isthmus from the south was open to all travellers.

Theseus now turned eastward. Ahead of him on his right was the island of Salamis and on his left the two rounded citadels of Megara. Near here, on cliffs that towered above the sea, lived Sciron, another brigand of the most evil fame. First he would plunder travellers and then force them to wash his feet in a bronze bowl. While they were doing this, he would suddenly, from where he sat, kick them over the cliff into the sea. There their bodies were devoured by a large tortoise who for many years had swum around the base of the cliffs, fed continually on human flesh.

Theseus had heard of this cruel murderer, and when he met him in the narrow pathway over the rocks, he pretended to be willing to wash his feet. But, just as Sciron was preparing, with one blow of his foot, to hurl him into the sea, Theseus gripped his foot firmly, swung him round and, grasping him by the shoulder, threw him into the sea himself. Far below he saw the sea turn white as the body fell, and then he saw the back and head of the monstrous tortoise coming to the surface for his last meal of men's flesh.

There was yet another wicked enemy to strangers whom Theseus treated in the same way as he had treated others. This was the strong man Procrustes who wrestled with all travellers and, when he had overcome them, would make them lie down on his bed. If their bodies were too short for the bed, he would rack their arms and legs with weights or hammer them out until they were long enough to fit. If they were too tall to lie on it, he would chop pieces off their limbs until they fitted exactly. At last this cruel robber had met his match. Theseus, after wrestling for long with him, threw him to the ground. Then he bound him to his own bed and, though here his body was exactly the right length, he cut off his head.

Theseus was now close to Athens and had conquered all the human enemies whom he would meet on his way. What he met with next was a monstrous sow, which for long had terrorized the villages in the country districts near Athens itself. Some say that this sow had been the mother of the great boar that Meleager killed in Calydon. At all events she was an immense animal, strong and savage, and used to root up the crops with her snout, drag down the vines from their supports and kill and eat young children and defenceless old people. Theseus went out alone to hunt this sow. He avoided the animal's furious charges and each time she swept past him he planted a hunting spear in her back. Finally, with a blow of the club he had taken from Periphetes he killed the sow and enabled the country people to continue unmolested their work in the fields.

Soon afterwards from the top of a hill he saw below him the city of Athens which poets have called "violet crowned", because, as the sun sets, the ring of rocky hills that surround the city turns from shade to shade of violet and amethyst. He drew nearer and came to the great stone walls of the citadel, or Acropolis, where his father's palace stood. Having accomplished such brave deeds on his journey, he was confident that his father Aegeus would receive him kindly.

As it happened, however, he very nearly met his death at his father's hands. The enchantress Medea had fled to Athens after her cruel murder of her own children and of the royal house of Corinth. In Athens Aegeus had protected her, had made use of her magic powers and by her had had a child. Medea, by her enchantments, knew that Theseus was now on his way to Athens. She was jealous of the fame that he had won already and she wished her own son to have the throne of Athens after Aegeus's death. She therefore pretended that she had discovered by her magic arts that the stranger who would shortly arrive in Athens was a criminal who had come to murder the king. She instructed Aegeus to give him, as soon as he arrived and without getting into conversation with him, a cup of wine into which she had put deadly poisons. Aegeus believed her,

and, when Theseus arrived and stood before him, he himself handed to his son the poisoned cup. Theseus raised it to his lips and was about to drink when, at the last moment, Aegeus noticed at Theseus's side the ivory scabbard of the sword he had left long ago under the rock in Troizen. He dashed the cup from the young man's lips and folded him in his arms. Then he turned in anger upon Medea who had so nearly made him the murderer of his own son. But Medea, knowing that this time no excuses could save her, had mounted into her winged chariot and disappeared through the air. This was the last of her wicked deeds. Some say that she returned to her country of Colchis and became reconciled with her family, but nothing really certain is known about this.

Even now Theseus and his father were not entirely secure in the land of Athens. First there was the hero Pallas who, with his fifty sons, tried to seize the kingdom from Aegeus. They made a treacherous attack on Theseus, but he, fighting back at them with a small company of friends, killed every one of them.

Then, at the time when Theseus reached Athens, the whole plain to the north, the plain of Marathon, where later the great army of the Persians was destroyed, was ravaged by a great bull. The people of the district had turned in vain to their king for help. No man or body of men dared encounter this fierce tremendous animal. Theseus went out to Marathon alone. He captured the bull alive, bound it with ropes and brought it back to Athens. There, after a triumphant procession through the streets, he sacrificed it to Minerva, the goddess of the city. The joyful throngs of people acclaimed him gladly as their future king and as a hero who had driven from their country and its surroundings both robbers and wild beasts. No one in the world, they said, except Hercules, had done such deeds.

Theseus and the Minotaur

Athens was now safe and peaceful within the borders of her own land, but still every year she had to make a cruel sacrifice to a foreign power. At this time Minos, King of Crete, ruled the sea with his fleet of ships. Once he had made war on Athens because his son, a famous wrestler, had been murdered by the Athenians. He refused to make peace except on the condition that every year the Athenians should send him seven young men and seven girls. These, when they arrived in Crete, were to be put inside the famous labyrinth which the great artist Daedalus had built, and then they were to be devoured by the monstrous creature, half man, half bull, which was known as the Minotaur. The Athenians were forced to accept these conditions. Every year the youths and maidens were chosen by lot, and every year amongst the lamentations of the whole people, they set out for Crete in a ship which carried black sails as a sign of mourning.

When Theseus heard of this cruel custom he resolved to be himself one of the seven young men who were handed over to Minos. "Either I shall save my people," he said, "or I shall die with them. In any case I shall have done what I can."

His old father Aegeus was reluctant to let him go, but Theseus insisted on the plan which he had made. "Go then," said his father, "and may the gods preserve you! When the time comes I shall watch every day for your return. If you are successful and come back alive, change the sails of your ship to white, so that I may know at once what has happened."

Theseus promised to do as his father had asked him. Then he and the other thirteen victims, girls and young men, said farewell to their city, their friends, and their relations and embarked in a black ship with black sails which was to take them to Crete.

When they arrived at the great city of King Minos they looked in astonishment at the huge buildings decorated with paintings in all kinds of colours. There were paintings of bull-fights, at which the Cretans were particularly expert, of sea creatures, octopuses, dolphins and twining sea weeds. There were other paintings showing the life of the country—pictures of Cretan officers with their hired Negro troops, of priestesses, naked above the waist, with outstretched arms round which coiled sacred serpents. There were high halls and galleries, enormous buildings; and at the sea port thronged the ships of Egypt and of Asia doing trade with the kingdom of Minos.

Theseus and his companions were, according to the custom, entertained for one night at the palace of the king. On the next day they were to be sent into the intricate mazes of the labyrinth.

It was known that there was no escape from this place. The most that anyone could hope for was to die of hunger while wandering in the countless passages before meeting the monstrous Minotaur who would devour any human creature whom he met.

Theseus, as he sat at dinner and told King Minos of the exploits which he had already achieved, won not only the attention but also the love of the king's daughter Ariadne. She could not bear the thought that so beautiful and distinguished a young man should perish miserably on the next day and she determined to help him.

When, therefore, the fourteen young Athenians were led to the entrance of the labyrinth, Ariadne took Theseus aside and put into his hands a ball of wool. "Fasten one end of this wool," she said to him, "inside the doors, and, as you go, unwind the rest. Then, if you are successful in killing the monster, you will be able to find your way back again. I shall be waiting for you. In return for helping you I want you to take me back with you to Greece and make me your wife."

Theseus readily agreed to do as she said. As well as the ball of wool she had brought him a sword, and, hiding this underneath his cloak, he went forward into the labyrinth. The girls and the other young men waited for him inside the gates, while he picked his way along passages which turned and twisted and linked up with other passages, winding in and out, turning abruptly, or sweeping in long or short curves. As he went he unwound the ball of wool and listened carefully for any noise that might tell him of the whereabouts of the strange monster with whom he was to fight. For long he wandered in complete silence and then, as he approached a part of the labyrinth where the walls turned at right angles, he heard the noise of heavy breathing, a noise that might have been made by an animal or might almost have been made by a man. He put down the ball of wool, gripped his sword in his hand, and advanced cautiously to the corner. Looking round it he saw a monstrous shape. Standing, with his head lowered, was the figure of a giant, but, on the massive neck and shoulders was not a human head but the swinging dewlaps, blunt muzzle and huge horns of a bull. For a moment Theseus and the Minotaur gazed at each other. Then, after pawing the ground with his feet, the monster lowered his head and plunged forward. In the narrow passage Theseus had no room to step aside. With his left hand, he seized one of the creature's horns and violently threw the head back while he buried his sword in the thick muscles of its neck. With a roar of pain the Minotaur shook his head and fell backwards. Theseus clung to the beast's throat, avoiding the blows of the great horns, and, stabbing with his sword, soon drenched the floors and walls with blood. The struggle was soon over. Theseus left the great body on the ground and, picking up what was left of the ball of wool, he began to rewind it and so retrace his steps to the place where he had left his companions. Seeing him safe, with the blood upon his hands, they knew that he had been victorious and crowded round him to press his hand and congratulate him upon his victory.

But there was no time to lose. Ariadne was waiting for them and she hid them until nightfall. In the dark they reached their ship, hoisted the sails and escaped. Never more would Athens have to pay the abominable tribute to the King of Crete.

On their return voyage they stopped for the night at the island of Naxos. Here some god put into the hearts and minds of Theseus and his companions a strange and cruel forgetfulness. They rose at dawn and sailed away, leaving Ariadne asleep on the seashore. When she woke and saw the ship far away on the horizon and realized that she had been deserted, she wept and tore her hair, calling all the gods to witness how treacherously she had been treated by the man whose life she had saved. Alone and miserable she wandered on the rocky shore, frightened of wild beasts, but grieving most of all for the loss of her lover.

Here, in her terror, misery and loneliness, she was saved by the god Bacchus. Tigers and lynxes drew the chariot in which he rode. Behind him came, riding on a mule, his drunken old companion Silenus, with a band of fauns, satyrs and dancing worshippers waving their ivy wands, their loose hair wreathed in ivy or in myrtle. The sand and rocks of the deserted shore grew green with sprouting vines as the procession passed. Ariadne, too, felt the joy of the god's presence. Bacchus loved her and made her his wife. He took the crown that she wore upon her head and set it in the sky as a constellation among the stars.

Meanwhile Theseus sailed on to Athens. The joy and glory of his return was spoiled by another act of forgetfulness. His father Aegeus had told him that, if he returned safe, he was to change the black sails of the ship and hoist white sails as a sign of victory. This Theseus forgot to do, and when his old father, watching from the cliffs, saw a vessel with black sails coming from the south, believing that his son was dead, he threw himself down into the sea. So the day of Theseus's return was a day not only of triumph but of mourning.

Theseus, King of Athens

On the death of Aegeus Theseus became king of Athens and the surrounding country. His government, both in peace and war, was strong and just, and, though at the end of his life the Athenians showed themselves ungrateful to him, long after his death they gave him the honours due to gods and heroes.

During his reign he saved Athens from two great invasions. First the warlike nation of the Amazons swept over the northern passes and reached the walls of Athens itself. The Amazons were women who spent their lives in fighting. Their power extended over much of Asia, and now their great army entered Greece. These women fought on horseback with javelins and bows. They carried shields shaped like the crescent moon. Led by their queen Hippolyte they had already conquered many armies of men, and, at their approach, the country people deserted their fields and farms, flocking into the city of Athens to escape the ferocity of this host of women. Theseus led his army out against them and for a long time the battle swayed this way and that. The arrows of the Amazons darkened the sky; their horses wheeled and charged again and again upon the Athenian infantry. It was not until coming to close quarters, Theseus himself fought with the queen of the Amazons, dragged her from her horse and made her prisoner, that the ranks of the Amazons broke. Many of both sides lay dead upon the plain, but the Athenians were victorious. The Amazon army withdrew from Greece. Hippolyte, their queen, became the wife of Theseus and, before she died, gave birth to a son who was called Hippolytus, a strong and noble boy who devoted himself to hunting and to the worship of the goddess Diana.

The next invasion of the land of Athens ended without bloodshed and in a memorable friendship. Pirithous, king of the Lapiths who lived in the north near the country of the centaurs, had heard of the fame of Theseus and decided to see for himself whether he was as brave as he was said to be. So, with a large army, he invaded the country and reached the plain of Marathon where Theseus, at the head of his own army, marched out to meet him. On one side lay the sea and on the other the mountains. The two great hosts were drawn up in order of battle, and both Theseus and Pirithous stood out conspicuous in their armour in front of their men. The two kings looked closely at one another and each was so struck with the beauty and nobility of the other that they immediately laid down their arms and became ever afterwards the most inseparable of friends. Pirithous offered to pay for any damage that his army had done in Attica. Theseus promised him help and alliance for ever in the future. So instead of fighting together the two friends entered Athens in peace and spent many days in feasting and rejoicing.

Not long afterwards Pirithous married a wife who was called Hippodamia. To the wedding feast he invited not only his friend Theseus but all the heroes of Greece. He invited also the centaurs, half men, half horses, who lived on the borders of his territories. Also he invited the gods, but one of them he failed to invite. This was Mars, the god of war.

In anger at being passed over, Mars determined to make the wedding banquet a scene of blood and warfare. One of the centaurs was already drunk with wine and Mars put into his heart the desire to offer violence to the bride. In a drunken fury he attempted to carry Hippodamia away with him; but Theseus immediately killed the insulter of his friend's wife. This was the signal for a general fight. The centaurs sprang up, each on his four legs, and began to attack the Lapiths with arrows and with the short heavy clubs which they carried. The women fled shrieking from the palace and for long the battle raged. Theseus, Pirithous and Hercules were the chief champions on the one side. On the other was a mass of whirling clubs, clattering hooves and great hairy bodies that struggled and twisted in the battle. Finally the centaurs were defeated. With wild cries they fled from the hall and Pirithous with his Lapiths pursued them as they galloped away over the plain to their haunts in the mountains.

Whether because this terrible battle had shocked her too deeply or for some other reason, Hippodamia died soon afterwards. Theseus also had lost his wife and now the two friends determined to find themselves other wives to marry. This was a natural thing to do, but the way in which they did it was both unnatural and wrong.

First they decided to carry off by force the young girl Helen, who much later was to be the cause of the great war at Troy. They seized her from her home in Sparta, and since she was only ten years old, Theseus put her in the care of his mother Aethra until she should be old enough to marry him. But Helen's two great brothers, Castor and Pollux, soon heard what had happened and rode to Athens to rescue their sister. Theseus had never fought in an unjust war. He knew that what he had done was wrong, and he restored Helen safe and sound to her home.

But the next exploit of Theseus and Pirithous was even more wicked and even less successful. Pirithous actually dared to try to carry off Proserpine, the queen of the lower world and wife of Pluto. Theseus had promised to help his friend in everything and so he accompanied him down to the lower world. Successfully they passed the terrible watch-dog Cerberus and advanced into the pale kingdoms of the dead. But both Pluto and Proserpine had been forewarned of their wicked plan which was destined to come to nothing. As they wandered through the murky darkness of the outskirts of Hell, Theseus sat down to rest on a rock. As he did so he felt his limbs change and grow stiff. He tried to rise, but could not. He was fixed to the rock on which he sat. Then as he turned to cry out to his friend Pirithous, he saw that Pirithous was crying out too. Round him were standing the terrible band of Furies, with snakes in their hair, torches and long whips in their hands. Before these monsters the hero's courage failed and by them he was led away to eternal punishment. As he vanished from Theseus's sight, a voice could be heard saying: "From this warning learn wisdom and not to despise the gods."

So for many months in half darkness Theseus sat, immovably fixed to the rock, mourning both for his friend and for himself. In the end he was rescued by Hercules who, coming to Hades to fetch the dog Cerberus, persuaded Proserpine to forgive him for the part he had taken in the rash venture of Pirithous. So Theseus was restored to the upper air, but Pirithous never again left the kingdom of the dead.

Theseus himself was not fated to end his life happily. During the time of his imprisonment in Pluto's kingdom, a usurper, Menestheus, had seized the throne of Athens and driven out the children of Theseus. Partly by bribes and partly by terror he had made himself secure, and, when Theseus returned, his ungrateful people refused to recognize their true king. Theseus was forced to retire into exile in the little island of Scyros, and there he was treacherously murdered by the king of the island who, while pretending to show his guest the view from the top of a hill, pushed him over a steep precipice.

Many years later, when Athens was known as the great sea power which had conquered Persia, an Athenian admiral came to Scyros and found there in a huge coffin the bones of the great hero. In great state he brought the bones back to Athens, and there ever afterwards the people honoured the shrine and temple where the bones were laid.

ORPHEUS AND EURYDICE

Orpheus, son of one of the Muses, the famous poet and musician, married a wife who was called Eurydice. His marriage brought him no happiness, because while his bride was walking in the deep grass with two of her friends, she stepped upon a poisonous snake which bit her in the ankle. She fell to the ground and no skill of any doctor could save her life.

Her friends, the Dryads, wept for her and filled the mountains with their cries. Orpheus himself, sitting solitary on the seashore, from day-break to sunset mourned for his wife to the sad music of his lyre. He even dared to descend to the lower world where the insubstantial ghosts flit to and fro, the terrible kingdom of Proserpine. At the sound of the music of his lyre the ghosts came thronging in crowds like the flocks of birds that nightfall or a sudden winter shower drives down from the mountains to roost among the leaves of trees. There were mothers and fathers, the dead spirits of great heroes, boys and unmarried girls, young men who had died early and been placed on their funeral pyres before their parents' eyes. All these were penned in by the dark muddy banks of the slow rivers of Hell with their ugly reeds, the river Cocytus and the river Styx which folds in the ghosts with its nine sweeping circles. Not only these spirits, but the very prison house and torture chambers of the dead were lulled to rest by the music of Orpheus. The Furies themselves, with the snakes twined in their hair, stood still and for the first and only time their cheeks were wet with tears. Tantalus forgot to put his lips to the water that always escaped him; the vulture paused above the giant body of Tityus and no longer pecked at his liver; the wheel where Ixion was tortured stood still; the Belides put down their pitchers, and Sisyphus sat down on the rock that he was condemned for ever to push up hill.

Orpheus stood before Proserpine and her husband, the terrible King Pluto. Still striking music from his lyre he spoke to them: "Powers of the lower world, to whom all of us who are mortal must come in the end, let me speak to you sincerely and tell you the truth. I have not come here as a robber or to vex you in your kingdom. The reason I have come here is my wife. A serpent bit her and took away her life just as she was growing up. I tried to bear her loss, but I cannot. Love is too strong for me. In the world above Love is a well-known god: whether he is known here also I do not know, but I think that he must be and, if the old story is true, you also were joined together by Love. I pray you therefore, by the fearful silence of your vast kingdom, give me back Eurydice, give her back the life that was so quickly taken from her. In the end we shall all come to you. This is our final home, and you rule the longest over the race of men. Eurydice too, sooner or later, will come back to you. Now I ask you as a gift to allow me to enjoy her for a little time. If the Fates will not allow this, then I have decided not to return myself, and you may rejoice in the death of us both."

Proserpine and Pluto were touched by his words and by his music. They could not refuse his request and they called for Eurydice. She was among the ghosts who had only just arrived and she came still limping from the wound in her foot.

Orpheus then received his wife back, but only on the condition that he should go in front of her and not turn his eyes backwards until he had ascended the steep path from the lower world and had reached the upper air.

So, through thick dark mist, in the tremendous silence of Hades, they took the steep path, and they were already close to the borders of the upper world, when there swept over the mind of Orpheus, in his love and fear for Eurydice, a sudden madness, something which might, one would have thought, have been forgiven him, if only the powers below knew how to forgive. Now all his toil was in vain. He had broken the conditions which savage Pluto had made and three times came the crash of thunder from the lakes and rivers of Hell. Eurydice cried to him: "O Orpheus what is this madness which has betrayed us both? O see, the cruel fates are calling for me again, and sleep is falling over my swimming eyes. Farewell, O Orpheus. Still I stretch out to you my feeble hands, but I am yours no longer. I am being pulled away from you, and all round me is the vastness of night."

As she spoke she melted away suddenly from his sight and disappeared like smoke disappears into thin air. Eagerly he stretched out his arms to embrace her, but his arms encountered nothing that could be touched. He spoke to her, but there was no one to listen to him, nor would the guards of the lower world allow him to cross again the river that separated him from the dead. On that river Eurydice, already cold in death, was sailing back again to the abodes of the ghosts.

For seven months they say that Orpheus sang to his lyre in the rocky places, lamenting his wife twice lost to him. But however rocky the place, there was soon shade there; for the trees hurried to hear his music—oaks and ashes, firs, poplars, all the trees of the woods, with vines also, ivy and climbing plants. All beasts and birds came too to listen to him. There were tigers and cattle together, wolves and sheep, eagles and trembling doves. So Orpheus continued to sing, in pain for the loss of his wife, like the nightingale in the thick leaves of a poplar sings in pain for the loss of her brood which some rough ploughman has seen and taken from their nest before they can fly: meanwhile the mother bird mourns throughout the night and, sitting on a branch, starts again and again her sad song, and in all the country around one hears her piercing notes. So Orpheus sang, soothing the fierce hearts of tigers, and drawing trees after him.

In all this time he gave no thought to women, though many women loved him and wished to be married to him. At last, they say, a band of women, driven wild by their dancing in the mountains by night, and angry at being despised by him, swept down upon the divine singer and tore him limb from limb, scattering the fragments of his body far and wide throughout the fields of Thrace. As for his head, wrenched from the neck that was as white as marble, the river Hebrus carried it to the sea and across the sea to the island of Lesbos. And, as the head was rolled in the river's stream, the voice and cold tongue still cried: "Eurydice, my poor Eurydice!" and the name Eurydice was echoed from the banks.

The fragments of his body were collected together for burial and in the Thracian town where his tomb is, the nightingales still sing with greater beauty than in any other place. His spirit went below the earth and, on its last journey, recognized all the surroundings which it had visited before. Searching through the Elysian fields where the blessed spirits are, he found Eurydice and caught her in his arms. Now they wander there together; sometimes they walk side by side, sometimes he follows her, sometimes he goes in front and now can safely look back at her with no fear of ever losing her again.

THE LABOURS OF HERCULES

Hercules suffered much during his life, but after his death he became a god. His mother was Alcmena, his father was Jupiter, and he was the strongest of all the heroes who lived in his time.

All through his life he was pursued by the hatred and jealousy of Juno who tried to destroy him even in his cradle. She sent two great snakes to attack the sleeping baby, but Hercules awoke, grasped their necks in his hands and strangled them both.

Before he was eighteen he had done many famous deeds in the country of Thebes, and Creon, the king, gave him his daughter in marriage. But he could not long escape the anger of Juno, who afflicted him with a sudden madness, so that he did not know what he was doing and in a fit of frenzy killed both his wife and his children. When he came to his senses, in horror and shame at what he had done, he visited the great cliffs of Delphi, where the eagles circle all day and where Apollo's oracle is. There he asked how he could be purified of his sin and he was told by the oracle that he must go to Mycenae and for twelve years obey all the commands of the cowardly king Eurystheus, his kinsman. It seemed a hard and cruel sentence, but the oracle told him also, that at the end of many labours he would be received among the gods.

Hercules therefore departed to the rocky citadel of Mycenae that looks down upon the blue water of the bay of Argos. He was skilled in the use of every weapon, having been educated, like Jason was, by the wise centaur Chiron. He was tall and immensely powerful. When Eurystheus saw him he was both terrified of him and jealous of his great powers. He began to devise labours that would seem impossible, yet Hercules accomplished them all.

First he was ordered to destroy and to bring back to Mycenae the lion of Nemea which for long had ravaged all the countryside to the north. Hercules took his bow and arrows, and, in the forest of Nemea, cut himself a great club, so heavy that a man nowadays could hardly lift it. This club he carried ever afterwards as his chief weapon.

He found that his arrows had no effect on the tough skin of the lion, but, as the beast sprang at him, he half-stunned it with his club, then closing in with it, he seized it by the throat and killed it with his bare hands. They say that when he carried back on his shoulders to Mycenae the body of the huge beast, Eurystheus fled in terror and ordered Hercules never again to enter the gates of the city, but to wait outside until he was told to come in. Eurystheus also built for himself a special strong room of brass into which he would retire if he was ever again frightened by the power and valiance of Hercules. Hercules himself took the skin of the lion and made it into a cloak which he wore ever afterwards, sometimes with the lion's head covering his own head like a cap, sometimes with it slung backwards over his shoulders.

The next task given to Hercules by Eurystheus was to destroy a huge water snake, called the Hydra, which lived in the marshes of Argos, was filled with poison and had fifty venomous heads. Hercules, with his friend and companion, the young Iolaus, set out from Mycenae and came to the great cavern, sacred to Pan, which is a holy place in the hills near Argos. Below this cavern a river gushes out of the rock. Willows and plane-trees surround the source and the brilliant green of grass. It is the freshest and most delightful place. But, as the river flows downwards to the sea, it becomes wide and shallow, extending into pestilential marshes, the home of stinging flies and mosquitoes. In these marshes they found the Hydra, and Hercules, with his great club, began to crush the beast's heads, afterwards cutting them off with his sword. Yet the more he laboured, the more difficult his task became. From the stump of each head that he cut off two other heads, with forked and hissing tongues, immediately sprang. Faced with an endless and increasing effort, Hercules was at a loss what to do. It seemed to him that heat might prove more powerful than cold steel, and he commanded Iolaus to burn the root of each head with a red-hot iron immediately it was severed from the neck. This plan was successful. The heads no longer sprouted up again, and soon the dangerous and destructive animal lay dead, though still writhing in the black marsh water among the reeds. Hercules cut its body open and dipped his arrows in the blood. Henceforward these arrows would bring certain death, even if they only grazed the skin, so powerful was the Hydra's poison.

Eurystheus next ordered Hercules to capture and bring back alive a stag, sacred to Diana and famous for its great fleetness of foot, which lived in the waste mountains and forests, and never yet had been approached in the chase. For a whole year Hercules pursued this animal, resting for the hours of darkness and pressing on next day in its tracks. For many months he was wholly outdistanced; valleys and forests divided him from his prey. But at the end of the year the stag, weary of the long hunt, could run no longer. Hercules seized it in his strong hands, tied first its forelegs and then its hind legs together, put the body of the beast, with its drooping antlered head, over his neck, and proceeded to return to the palace of King Eurystheus. However, as he was on his way through the woods, he was suddenly aware of a bright light in front of him, and in the middle of the light he saw standing a tall woman or, as he immediately recognized, a goddess, grasping in her hands a bow and staring at him angrily with her shining eyes. He knew at once that this was the archer goddess Diana, she who had once turned Actaeon into a stag and who now was enraged at the loss of this other stag which was sacred to her. Hercules put his prey on the ground and knelt before the goddess. "It was through no desire of my own," he said, "that I have captured this noble animal. What I do is done at the command of my father Jupiter and of the oracle of your brother Apollo at Delphi." The goddess listened to his explanation, smiled kindly on him and allowed him to go on his way, when he had promised that, once the stag had been carried to Eurystheus, it would be set free again in the forests that it loved. So Hercules accomplished this third labour.

He was not, however, to be allowed to rest. Eurystheus now commanded him to go out to the mountains of Erymanthus and bring back the great wild boar that for long had terrorized all the neighbourhood. So Hercules set out once more and on his way he passed the country where the centaurs had settled after they had been driven down from the north in the battle that had taken place with the Lapiths at the wedding of Pirithous. In this battle they had already had experience of the hero's strength, but still their manners were rude and rough. When the centaur Pholus offered Hercules some of the best wine to drink, the other centaurs became jealous. Angry words led to blows, and soon Hercules was forced to defend himself with his club and with his arrows, the poison of which not only caused death, but also the most extreme pain. Soon he scattered his enemies in all directions, driving them over the plains and rocks. Some he dashed to the ground with his club; others, wounded by the poisoned arrows, lay writhing in agony, or kicking their hooves in the air. Some took refuge in the house of the famous centaur Chiron, who had been schoolmaster to Hercules and who, alone among the centaurs, was immortal. As he pursued his enemies to this good centaur's house, shooting arrows at them as he went, Hercules, by an unhappy accident, wounded Chiron himself. Whether it was because of grief that his old pupil had so injured him, or whether it was because of the great pain of the wound, Chiron prayed to Jupiter that his immortality should be taken away from him. Jupiter granted his prayer. The good centaur died, but he was set in Heaven in a constellation of stars which is still called either Sagittarius or else The Centaur.

Hercules mourned the sad death of his old master. Then he went on to Erymanthus. It was winter and he chased the great boar up to the deep snow in the passes of the mountains. The animal's short legs soon grew weary of ploughing through the stiff snow and Hercules caught it up when it was exhausted and panting in a snowdrift. He bound it firmly and slung the great body over his back. They say that when he brought it to Mycenae, Eurystheus was so frightened at the sight of the huge tusks and flashing eyes that he hid for two days in the brass hiding place that he had had built for him.

The next task that Hercules was ordered to do would have seemed to anyone impossible. There was a king of Elis called Augeas, very rich in herds of goats and cattle. His stables, they say, held three thousand oxen and for ten years these stables had never been cleaned. The dung and muck stood higher than a house, hardened and caked together. The smell was such that even the herdsmen, who were used to it, could scarcely bare to go near. Hercules was now ordered to clean these stables, and, going to Elis, he first asked the king to promise him the tenth part of his herds if he was successful in his task. The king readily agreed, and Hercules made the great river Alpheus change his course and come foaming and roaring through the filthy stables. In less than a day all the dirt was cleared and rolled away to the sea. The river then went back to its former course and, for the first time in ten years, the stone floors and walls of the enormous stables shone white and clean.

Hercules then asked for his reward, but King Augeas, claiming that he had performed the task not with his own hands, but by a trick, refused to give it to him. He even banished his own son who took the side of Hercules and reproached his father for not keeping his promise. Hercules then made war on the kingdom of Elis, drove King Augeas out and put his son on the throne. Then, with his rich reward, he returned to Mycenae, ready to undertake whatever new task was given him by Eurystheus.

Again he was ordered to destroy creatures that were harmful to men. This time they were great birds, like cranes or storks, but much more powerful, which devoured human flesh and lived around the black waters of the Stymphalian lake. In the reeds and rocky crags they lived in huge numbers and Hercules was at a loss how to draw them from their hiding places. It was the goddess

Minerva who helped him by giving him a great rattle of brass. The noise of this rattle drove the great birds into the air in throngs. Hercules pursued them with his arrows, which rang upon their horny beaks and legs but stuck firm in the bodies that tumbled one after the other into the lake. The whole brood of these monsters was entirely destroyed and now only ducks and harmless water-fowl nest along the reedy shores.

Hercules had now accomplished six of his labours. Six more remained. After the killing of the Stymphalian birds he was commanded to go to Crete and bring back from there alive a huge bull which was laying the whole island waste. Bare-handed and alone he grappled with this bull, and, once again, when he brought the animal back into the streets of Mycenae, Eurystheus fled in terror at the sight both of the hero and of the great beast which he had captured.

From the southern sea Hercules was sent to the north to Thrace, over which ruled King Diomedes, a strong and warlike prince who savagely fed his famous mares on human flesh. Hercules conquered the king in battle and gave his body to the very mares which had so often fed upon the bodies of the king's enemies. He brought the mares back to King Eurystheus, who again was terrified at the sight of such fierce and spirited animals. He ordered them to be taken to the heights of Mount Olympus and there be consecrated to Jupiter. But Jupiter had no love for these unnatural creatures, and, on the rocky hill-sides, they were devoured by lions, wolves, and bears.

Next Hercules was commanded to go to the country of the Amazons, the fierce warrior women, and bring back the girdle of their queen Hippolyte. Seas and mountains had to be crossed, battles to be fought; but Hercules in the end accomplished the long journey and the dangerous task. Later, as is well known, Hippolyte became the wife of Theseus of Athens and bore him an ill-fated son, Hippolytus.

Hercules had now travelled in the south, the north and the east. His tenth labour was to be in the far west, beyond the country of Spain, in an island called Erythia. Here lived the giant Geryon, a great monster with three bodies and three heads. With his herdsman, and his two-headed dog, called Orthrus, he looked after huge flocks of oxen, and, at the command of Eurystheus, Hercules came into his land to lift the cattle and to destroy the giant. On his way, at the very entrance to the Atlantic he set up two great marks, ever afterwards to be known by sailors and called the Pillars of Hercules. Later, as he wandered through rocks and over desert land, he turned his anger against the Sun itself, shooting his arrows at the great god Phoebus Apollo. But Phoebus pitied him in his thirst and weariness. He sent him a golden boat, and in this boat Hercules crossed over to the island of Erythia. Here he easily destroyed both watchdog and herdsman, but fought for long with the great three-bodied giant before he slew him, body after body. Then he began to drive the cattle over rivers and mountains and deserts from Spain to Greece. As he was passing through Italy he came near the cave where Cacus, a son of Vulcan, who breathed fire out of his mouth, lived solitary and cruel, since he killed all strangers and nailed their heads, dripping with blood, to the posts at the entrance of his rocky dwelling. While Hercules was resting, with the herds all round him, Cacus came out of his cave and stole eight of the best animals of the whole herd. He dragged them backwards by their tails, so that Hercules should not be able to track them down.

When Hercules awoke from his rest, he searched far and wide for the missing animals, but, since they had been driven into the deep recesses of Cacus's cave, he was unable to find them. In the end he began to go on his way with the rest of the herd, and, as the stolen animals heard the lowing of the other cattle, they too began to low and bellow in their rocky prison. Hercules stopped still, and soon out of the cave came the fire-breathing giant, prepared to defend the fruits of his robbery and anxious to hang the head of Hercules among his other disgusting trophies. This, however, was not to be. The huge limbs and terrible breath of Cacus were of no avail against the hero's strength and fortitude. Soon, with a tremendous blow of his club, he stretched out Cacus dead on the ground. Then he drove the great herd on over mountains and plains, through forests and rivers to Mycenae.

Hercules' next labour again took him to the far west. He was commanded by Eurystheus to fetch him some of the golden apples of the Hesperides. These apples grew in a garden west even of the land of Atlas. Here the sun shines continually, but always cool well-watered trees of every kind give shade. All flowers and fruits that grow on earth grow here, and fruit and flowers are always on the boughs together. In the centre of the garden is the orchard where golden apples gleam among the shining green leaves and the flushed blossom. Three nymphs, the Hesperides, look after this orchard, which was given by Jupiter to Juno as a wedding present. It is guarded also by a great dragon that never sleeps, and coils its huge folds around the trees. No one except the gods knows exactly where this beautiful and remote garden is, and it was to this unknown place that Hercules was sent.

He was helped by Minerva and by the nymphs of the broad river Po in Italy. These nymphs told Hercules where to find Nereus, the ancient god of the sea, who knew the past, the present and the future. "Wait for him," they said, "until you find him asleep on the rocky shore, surrounded by his fifty daughters. Seize hold of him tightly and do not let go until he answers your question. He will, in trying to escape you, put on all kinds of shapes. He will turn to fire, to water, to a wild beast or to a serpent. You must not lose your courage, but hold him all the tighter, and, in the end, he will come back to his own shape and will tell you what you want to know."

Hercules followed their advice. As he watched along the sea god's shore he saw, lying on the sand, half in and half out of the sea, with seaweed trailing round his limbs, the old god himself. Around him were his daughters, the Nereids, some riding on the backs of dolphins, some dancing on the shore, some swimming and diving in the deeper water. As Hercules approached, they cried out shrilly at the sight of a man. Those on land leaped back into the sea; those in the sea swam further from the shore. But their cries did not awake their father till Hercules was close to him and able to grip him firmly in his strong hands. Immediately the old god felt the hands upon him, his body seemed to disappear into a running stream of water; but Hercules felt the body that he could not see, and did not relax his grasp. Next it seemed that his hands were buried in a great pillar of fire; but the fire did not scorch the skin and Hercules could still feel the aged limbs through the fire. Then it was a great lion with wide-open jaws that appeared to be lying and raging on the sands; then a bear, then a dragon. Still Hercules clung firmly to his prisoner, and in the end he saw again the bearded face and seaweed-dripping limbs of old Nereus. The god knew for what purpose Hercules had seized him, and he told him the way to the garden of the Hesperides.

It was a long and difficult journey, but at the end of it Hercules was rewarded. The guardian nymphs (since this was the will of Jupiter) allowed him to pick from the pliant boughs two or three of the golden fruit. The great dragon bowed its head to the ground at their command and left Hercules unmolested. He brought back the apples to Eurystheus, but soon they began to lose that beautiful sheen of gold that had been theirs in the western garden. So Minerva carried them back again to the place from which they came, and then once more they glowed with their own gold among the other golden apples that hung upon the trees.

Now had come the time for the twelfth and last of the labours that Hercules did for his master Eurystheus. This labour would seem to anyone by far the hardest; for the hero was commanded to descend into the lower world, and bring back with him from the kingdom of Proserpine the terrible three-headed watch-dog Cerberus.

Hercules took the dark path which before him had been trodden only by Orpheus and Theseus and Pirithous. Orpheus had returned. Theseus and Pirithous, for their wicked attempt, were still imprisoned.

Hercules passed the Furies, undaunted by the frightful eyes beneath the writhing serpents of their hair. He passed the great criminals, Sisyphus, Tantalus and the rest. He passed by his friend, the unhappy Theseus, who was sitting immovably fixed to a rock, and he came at last into the terrible presence of black Pluto himself, who sat on his dark throne with his young wife Proserpine beside him. To the King and Queen of the Dead Hercules explained the reason of his coming. "Go," said Pluto, "and, so long as you use no weapon, but only your bare hands, you may take my watch-dog Cerberus to the upper air."

Hercules thanked the dreadful king for giving him the permission which he had asked. Then he made one more request which was that Theseus, who had sinned only by keeping his promise to his friend, might be allowed to return again to life. This, too, was granted him. Theseus rose to his feet again and accompanied the hero to the entrance of hell, where the huge dog Cerberus, with his three heads and his three deep baying voices, glared savagely at the intruders. Even this tremendous animal proved no match for Hercules, who with his vice-like grip stifled the breath in two of the shaggy throats, then lifted the beast upon his shoulders and began to ascend again, Theseus following close behind, the path that leads to the world of men. They say that when he carried Cerberus to Mycenae, Eurystheus fled in terror to another city and was now actually glad that Hercules had completed what might seem to have been twelve impossible labours. Cerberus was restored to his place in Hell and never again visited the upper world. Nor did Hercules ever go down to the place of the dead, since, after further trials, he was destined to live among the gods above.

THE DEATH OF HERCULES

Many more great deeds, too many to tell, were done by Hercules before the end of his life amongst men. But he was unfortunate in his love for women.

His first wife, Megara, he had killed in a fit of madness. Then, when he had finished his labours, he wished to marry Iole, daughter of the famous archer, King Eurytus, who had made it known that he would give his daughter in marriage to the man who could defeat him and his three sons in a shooting match. This Hercules did; but King Eurytus, either because he was angry at losing his reputation for archery, or because he remembered the fate of Megara and feared for his own daughter, refused to keep his promise. Hercules departed in anger, vowing revenge. Later, indeed, he had his revenge, but, in having it, he brought upon himself his own fate.

Since he could not have Iole as his wife, he became the suitor of Deianira, daughter of the King of Calydon and sister to Meleager. Many other heroes wished to marry this beautiful girl, but among them all stood out Hercules himself and the great river-god Achel-

ous, whose stream runs through the country of Calydon. Each of these two claimed the right to marry Deianira, Hercules because he was the son of Jupiter and had accomplished the twelve labours of which all the world was speaking, Achelous because he was a god and because mortals should give way to gods. "As for Hercules," he said, "he is a foreigner, whereas my river flows through Calydon. As for his father Jupiter, all we know is that Juno hates him and drives him mad. I do not believe that Jupiter is his father at all."

So Achelous spoke, and, while he was speaking, Hercules kept staring at him with fierce eyes beneath his lowering brows. Finally, unable to control his anger, he said: "My hand is better than my tongue. You may conquer me in words, but not in fair fight."

So threatening, he approached Achelous, who after his boastful speeches, was ashamed not to resist him. He threw aside his green clothes, and the two made ready to wrestle, rubbing sand over their bodies, so that the grip of each on each might be firmer. Then they rushed together and Hercules caught now at the river-god's neck, now at his waist, now at his knees. But Achelous, with his great weight, stood firm like a huge breakwater against which wave after roaring wave beats in vain. After a time they drew apart, and then rushed together again, each planted firmly in his tracks, determined not to give in. Foot was locked with foot: the straining breasts heaved against each other: fingers were knitted together in the struggle, and forehead pressed against forehead.

Three times, with enormous effort, but in vain, did Hercules try to thrust away from him the weight of the breast that pressed on his. Finally he broke away from the hold, knocked Achelous sideways with a blow from his fist and sprang upon his back. To the river god it seemed that he was carrying a mountain. His arms were pouring with sweat as he tried to loosen the fierce grip of his antagonist. Hercules gave him no chance to recover his strength, but, bearing down upon his neck, forced him, gasping for breath, to touch the ground with his knees.

Never before had the god been overthrown, and, now knowing that he could never conquer Hercules by strength, he attempted to conquer him by magic tricks. He changed his body and slipped out of Hercules' grasp in the form of a long snake, which wound itself into great coils, reared up and darted out its forked tongue in savage hissing. Hercules merely laughed. "Achelous," he said, "I used to kill snakes when I was in my cradle. And as for you, with your one head, think of the Hydra of Lerna, with its hundred ever-growing heads. I killed that monster, and what do you think will become of you, who are not really a snake at all?"

So he spoke, and fastened his tremendous grip on the neck of the false serpent, till, half-throttled, the river-god knew that in this shape also he was conquered. There was one more thing that he could do. He turned himself into a bull, and fought in that shape. But Hercules flung his arms round the bull's neck and dragged it down as the bull tried to run. He pressed the hard horns right down to the earth and overthrew the great body in the deep sand. Not content with this he tore off one of the horns from the forehead. This horn the nymphs took and filled with fruit and sweet-smelling flowers, making it a holy horn. Now it is carried by the glad goddess Abundance. But Achelous retired to his own stream. In his real shape he used to have two small horns on his head. Now he had lost one of them, and attempted to disguise the loss by covering the empty space with leaves of willow and with reeds.

Hercules now had won Deianira for his wife. But while he was on his way home with her, he came to the swift stream of the river Evenus, which, swollen by winter storms, was higher than usual, full of whirling eddies and hard indeed to pass. While Hercules stood on the bank, with no fear for himself, but frightened for his young wife, the centaur Nessus came up to him. Nessus knew the fords well and was himself strong of limb. "Let me," he said, "carry your wife across the river, Hercules. You, with your great strength, can swim across."

Hercules agreed. He threw his club and his bow over to the other side, and then, just as he was, with his lion skin and his quiver, he plunged into the roaring water, breasted it strongly and reached the further bank. There, as he was picking up his bow, he heard his wife's voice crying out, and, looking round, saw that the treacherous centaur was trying to carry her away. "Nessus you thief," he cried out, "you who have dared to touch what belongs to me, have no faith in your four horse's legs. If not my feet, then my arrows will overtake you." The thing was no sooner said than done. He shot an arrow at the fleeing centaur. It struck him in the back and the point came out through his breast. Nessus tore the arrow out of the wound and there followed a stream of blood all infected with the deadly poison of the Hydra. The blood soaked through the tunic which he wore, and Nessus, on the point of death saying to himself, "I shall not die unavenged," gave the tunic to Deianira, telling her that, if ever her husband should cease to love her, this tunic would prove a powerful charm to bring back his love.

After this many years went by, and the fame of the deeds of Hercules had filled the earth. In the end he made war on King Eurytus, who once had refused him Iole. He conquered him in battle and took his family prisoner. On his way home he came to Mount Oeta, and there he prepared to sacrifice to his father Jupiter. First, however, he sent his servant Lichas to Deianira, asking her to give him clean clothes for the sacrifice. Meanwhile, however, Rumour, which exaggerates everything, had been busy. Deianira had been told that Hercules had once again fallen deeply in love with Iole, whom he was bringing home with him as a captive. Deianira believed this story and, in her love for Hercules, was terrified by it. First she burst into tears of agony and self-pity. Then she said to herself: "Why should I cry? This other woman would be glad to think of me crying. I must think of some plan worthy of the sister of Meleager."

Many ideas occurred to her, but in the end what seemed best was to send to Hercules the blood-soaked tunic which Nessus had given her so long ago, and which, she thought, would make her husband love her again. So she gave the tunic to Lichas, who little knew what he was carrying. She herself also sent kind messages, and had no knowledge that she was destroying both her husband and herself. Hercules, all unsuspecting, took the gift and put on his body the poison of the Hydra.

Then, as the flames began to leap up on the altars, as he was praying, with the incense curling in smoke from the flames, suddenly from the heat of his body the violence of the poison was aroused and began to spread like fire over his limbs. So long as he could do so, he kept back his groans, forcing down the pain with his strong and resolute mind. But when the pain was past endurance, he threw the altar down and filled the forests of Oeta with his cries. He tried to tear the deadly tunic from his body, but it stuck to his flesh and, where he tore it away, he tore away also his own skin, laying bare veins and huge muscles and strong bones. His very blood boiled and hissed with the poison, like when red-hot iron is put into cold water. Flames spread into every corner of his body, and, in his agony, he raised his hands to heaven and cried out: "O Juno, now you may feed your cruel heart with my sufferings. Are they not enough to be pitied even by an enemy? Will you not take away my life? It was born for toil. Now let it go."

He spoke and again was overcome by pain. Like a bull, with the shaft of a weapon sticking in his neck, roars and tosses its head, though the giver of the wound has fled, so Hercules raged along the ridges of Oeta, struggling to rip off his garments, tearing up great trees, and stretching out his arms to his father's heaven.

Suddenly he noticed the trembling Lichas, who was hiding himself in the hollow of a rock. On this his suffering all turned to the madness of anger. "Was it you, Lichas," he said, "who brought this gift that is killing me?"

The young man trembled and grew pale. He began to make excuses for his ignorance, but, while he was still speaking, Hercules seized hold of him, whirled him three or four times round his head and hurled him out over the sea, like a bolt sent from a catapult. While still in mid-air the boy's body began to grow hard. Fear had dried up his blood, and, just as rain in a cold wind is said to change first to snow and then to hard hail, so, hurled by those strong arms through the air, the body of Lichas changed to rock and as rock fell into the Euboean sea. To this day there rises where he fell a rock of human shape, and, as though it was still able to feel, the sailors refuse to step upon it, and they call it Lichas.

Deianira too had had no knowledge of what she had done when she sent the fatal garment to Hercules. But soon messengers came to her with the news of what was happening, how her husband was being torn to pieces by the poison and was dead or dying. In bitter remorse and anguish Deianira put an end to her own life, calling the gods to witness that what she had desired was not her husband's death but his love.

And now Hercules himself cut down the trees on high Oeta, and with their trunks make a great funeral pyre. He was aided by his friend Philoctetes, who lit the pyre and to whom, as a reward, Hercules gave the famous bow which later was to go to Troy. Now, at the point of death, with burnt and withered flesh, Hercules grew calm again. On top of the pyre he spread the skin of the Nemean lion. He rested his head on his club as on a pillow, and lay down among the flames with peaceful face, as if, after cups of fine wine and crowned with garlands, he were lying on a couch at a banquet.

The gods from heaven looked down and saw that the defender of the earth was dying. Even Juno at last pitied him, and to all the

gods and goddesses Jupiter spoke: "Fear not. Hercules has conquered everything, and he will conquer those flames. Part of him is
immortal, and, as an immortal, he will live with the gods for ever."

So indeed it happened. As a snake changes its old skin, so Hercules, as the flames consumed his body, seemed to put on a new body,
stronger, more heroic, more beautiful and more stately even than
before. Thunder pealed, and through the hollow clouds Jupiter
sent his four-horsed chariot which bore him to Heaven, where he
was welcomed among the shining stars and in the assembly of the
gods.

CEPHALUS AND PROCRIS

Cephalus, Prince of Thessaly, married Procris, the daughter of
Erectheus, King of Athens, and came to live in his wife's country.
Both their love and their beauty were equal, and they were rightly
called happy. But, two months after the marriage, when Cephalus
was hunting deer on the slopes of flowery Hymettus, Aurora, the
golden goddess of the Dawn, having just put the darkness to flight,
saw the young man and was at once fascinated by his beauty. She
snatched him away from earth and took him up to heaven, wishing
that he might live with her for ever. Yet in her golden house, full
of rosy light, Cephalus thought and talked only of Procris and of
the joys of his life with her. The goddess grew angry with him and
said, "Stop complaining, you ungrateful man! You can have your
Procris. But, if I have any gift of seeing the future, you will end by
wishing you had not had her."

So, in anger, she sent Cephalus back to earth. At first he longed
only to see his wife, but, as he drew near to Athens, and thought of
the goddess's warning, he began to wonder whether Procris had
been faithful to him in his absence. She was beautiful and she was

young. He knew the goodness of her character, but he had been absent a long time; he had discovered that even goddesses are faithless and then also people who are in love are apt to fear everything. He decided to disguise himself and so try to discover whether his wife was true to him. Aurora helped him in this and made his appearance different from what it had been.

So he entered the city of Athens and, unrecognized, came to his own house. Here he found everything in order, and when, with much difficulty, he had reached the presence of Procris, the sight of her sadness and of her beauty almost made him give up his plan. She was weeping in longing for her lost husband, and Cephalus too longed to tell her who he was and to kiss her, as he ought to have done. However, he went on in the way that he had planned and over and over again offered her great gifts if she would love him. Over and over again she replied: "There is only one man whom I love. Wherever he is, I keep myself for him alone."

Anyone of any sense would have been satisfied with such proofs of faithfulness, but Cephalus continued to offer her great fortunes and enormous gifts. In the end she seemed to hesitate, and then, throwing off his disguise, and appearing in his true form, he cried out: "False wife, it is I, your husband, who was tempting you. I myself am the evidence of your unfaithfulness."

Procris said not a word. Silently and with bowed head she fled from the treachery of her house and of her husband. Hating him and the whole race of men, she wandered in the woods and mountains of Euboea, hunting beasts in the company of Diana and the nymphs.

But, as soon as she had gone, Cephalus became on fire with love for her. He regretted his cruel trick, asked her pardon and confessed that he also, in the same position, would have acted in the same way. Then Procris came back to him and for many years they lived together in perfect happiness, each equally loving the other.

Procris, when she returned to her husband, gave him two gifts which she herself had received from Diana. One was a wonderful hound, called Hurricane, which ran faster than any hound in the world: one was a javelin which always went straight to its mark and then, covered with blood, returned to the hand that had hurled it. Each of these gifts has a story. The story of the javelin is a sad one; the story of the hound is strange.

A monster came into the land of Thebes, killing the cattle and driving the country people into the towns away from their crops. Cephalus, together with the young men of Thebes and of Athens, set out to hunt the beast. They spread their hunting nets, but the fierce animal easily leapt over the top of them. They unleashed their hounds and set them on the track, but the hounds were quickly outdistanced. Then all the hunters called on Cephalus to let Hurricane go from the leash. All the time the hound had been straining forward and struggling to get its neck loose from the strap. Now, no sooner was he let go than he seemed to disappear from sight. His footprints were there in the hot sand, but the dog had sped off faster than an arrow or a sling-stone. The hunters climbed to the top of a hill and saw far away in the plain the hound and the animal that it was pursuing close together. At each moment it seemed that the hound would fasten its teeth in the animal's flanks, but then the animal would turn and twist, and the teeth would snap on empty air. Still the hound followed step for step; still the animal barely escaped.

Cephalus took his javelin. For a moment, while he was fitting his fingers into the loop, he turned his head aside, and when he looked back to the plain, he saw a strange sight. Two marble statues stood there, the one appearing to escape, the other to be seizing upon its prey. Some god must have willed that it should be so, that neither of the two should be conquered by the other.

But it was the javelin that brought to Cephalus his great sorrow and ended the happy years in which he and Procris loved each other fully and so much that she would not have taken Jupiter himself instead of her husband, nor could he have been taken from her, not even by the goddess Venus.

Every day in the morning Cephalus used to go hunting in the woods. He went by himself, with no companions and no hounds. His javelin, which never missed its mark, was enough. When he had had enough of hunting, he would go back to the cool shade and the gentle breeze that blows along the cold valleys. The name of the breeze was "Aura", and Cephalus, tired of the heat and the chase, got into the habit of talking to the breeze as though it was a real person. "Come, Aura," he used to say, "come, you sweet thing! Come and refresh me! Come and relieve the heat in which I burn." Or else he would say: "You, Aura, are my chief joy. You comfort and refresh me. You make me love the woods and lonely places. How I love to feel your breath upon my cheek!"

Someone heard Cephalus speaking like this and thought that he must be speaking to some nymph whose name was "Aura", and must certainly be in love with her. The rash informer, so quick at leaping to the wrong conclusions, went to Procris and whispered to her what he had heard. Love will believe anything, and Procris, as Cephalus found out later, fainted away in pain when she heard the story. When she came to herself she lamented her own fate and her husband's unfaithfulness, anxious over something which did not exist, a mere name without a body, just as if it had been a real person and a rival for her love. Still, in all her misery, she often hoped that she was deceived in what she thought, and said to herself that she would not believe it, unless she saw it with her own eyes.

Next day, when dawn rose, Cephalus left his house and went to the woods to hunt. He killed the beasts which he pursued, then, as he often did, he lay down on the grass and said: "Come to me, Aura! Come and soothe me after my exercise!" As he was speaking he thought he heard from somewhere near at hand a moaning sound. But he went on: "Come, dearest!" and then, hearing distinctly something rustling in the leaves and thinking that it was some beast, he hurled his javelin into the thicket.

It was Procris that was hiding there. With a deep wound in her breast she cried out: "Alas! Alas!" At the sound of his faithful wife's voice Cephalus, half out of his mind, rushed to the place from which the voice had come. He found her dying, with the blood pouring over her torn dress, trying to drag out from the wound the very javelin which she had given him as a present. Gently he lifted up the body that was dearer to him than his own; cutting a piece from her dress he bound up the wound and tried to stop the flow of blood, begging her not to leave him with the guilt of having killed her. But now her strength began to fail her. Still, though she was at the point of death, she forced herself to say: "Cephalus, I beg and pray you by our marriage, by all the gods, by all that I have done for you, by our love together, the love which I still feel for you now I am dying, and which caused my death, do not let Aura come and take my place in our bed!"

Then at last Cephalus realized the mistake that she had made. He began to tell her the truth, but the truth could not bring back her life. The little strength that remained to her fled away; she fell back in his arms; so long as she could look at anything, she looked into her husband's face and on his lips breathed out her life. It seemed to him that, before she died, her face changed and her expression became a happy one.

ARACHNE

Arachne was not famous for her birth or for her city, but only for her skill. Her father was a dyer of wool, her mother also was of no great family. She lived in a small village whose name is scarcely known. Yet her skill in weaving made her famous through all the great cities of Lydia. To see her wonderful work the nymphs of Tmolus would leave their vineyards, the nymphs of Pactolus would leave the golden waters of their river. It was a delight not only to see the cloth that she had woven, but to watch her at work, there was such beauty in the way she did it, whether she was winding the rough skeins into balls of wool, or smoothing it with her fingers, or drawing out the fleecy shiny wool into threads, or giving a twist to the spindle with her quick thumb, or putting in embroidery with her needle. You would think that she had learnt the art from Minerva herself, the goddess of weaving.

Arachne, however, when people said this, would be offended at the idea of having had even so great a teacher as Minerva. "Let her come," she used to say, "and weave against me. If she won, she could do what she liked with me."

Minerva heard her words and put on the form of an old woman. She put false grey hair on her head, made her steps weak and tottering, and took a staff in her hand. Then she said to Arachne: "There are some advantages in old age. Long years bring experience. Do not, then, refuse my advice. Seek all the fame you like among men for your skill, but allow the goddess to take first place, and ask her forgiveness, you foolish girl, for the words which you have spoken. She will forgive you, if you ask her."

Arachne dropped the threads from her hand and looked angrily at the old woman. She hardly kept her hands off her, and her face showed the anger that she felt. Then she spoke to the goddess in disguise: "Stupid old thing, what is wrong with you is that you have lived too long. Go and give advice to your daughters, if you have any. I am quite able to look after myself. As for what you say, why does not the goddess come here herself? Why does she avoid a contest with me?"

"She has come," Minerva replied, and she put off the old woman's disguise, revealing herself in her true form. The nymphs bowed down to worship her, and the women also who were there. Arachne alone showed no fear. Nevertheless she started, and a sudden blush came to her unwilling face and then faded away again, as the sky grows crimson at the moment of sunrise and then again grows pale. She persisted in what she had said already, and, stupidly longing for the desired victory, rushed headlong to her fate.

Minerva no longer refused the contest and gave no further advice. At once they both set up their looms and stretched out on them the delicate warp. The web was fastened to the beam; reeds separated the threads and through the threads went the sharp shuttles which their quick fingers sped. Quickly they worked, with their clothes tucked up round their breasts, their skilled hands moving backwards and forwards like lightning, not feeling the work since they were both so good at it. In their weaving they used all the colours that are made by the merchants of Tyre—purple of the oyster and every other dye, each shading into each, so that the eye could scarcely tell the difference between the finer shades, though the extreme colours were clear enough. So, after a storm of rain, when a rainbow spans the sky, between each colour there is a great difference, but still between each an insensible shading. And in their work they wove in stiff threads of gold, telling ancient stories by pictures.

Minerva, in her weaving, showed the ancient citadel of Athens and the story of the old quarrel between her and Neptune, god of the sea, over the naming of this famous land. There you could see the twelve gods as witnesses, and there Neptune striking with his huge trident the barren rock from which leapt a stream of sea-water. And there was Minerva herself, with shield and spear and helmet. As she struck the rock, there sprang up a green olive-tree, and the victory was hers. Athens was her city, named from her other name, Athene.

As for Arachne, the pictures which she wove were of the deceitful loves of the gods. There was Europa, carried away by a bull over the sea. You would have thought it a real bull and real waves of water. Then she wove Jupiter coming to Danaë in a golden shower, to Aegina as a flame, to Mnemosyne, mother of the Muses, in the disguise of a shepherd. There was Neptune too, disguised as a dolphin, a horse or a ram. Every scene was different, and each scene had the surroundings that it ought to have. Round the edge of the web ran a narrow border filled with designs of flowers and sprays of ivy intertwined.

Neither Minerva nor Envy itself could find any fault with Arachne's work. Furious at the success of the mortal girl, Minerva tore to pieces the gorgeous web with its stories of the crimes of the gods. With the hard box-wood spindle that she held she struck Arachne on the head over and over again.

Arachne could not bear such treatment. In her injured pride she put a noose round her neck and hung herself. As she hung from the rope, Minerva, in pity, lifted her body and said: "You may keep your life, you rude and arrogant girl, but you and all your descendants will still hang."

Then, as she went out, she sprinkled over her some magic juices, and immediately her hair felt the poison it fell off; so did her nose and ears; her head became minute and all her body shrunk; her slender fingers were joined on to her body as legs; everything else was stomach, and now, turned into a spider, she still spins thread out of her own stomach and everywhere still exercises her old craft of weaving.

NIOBE

Niobe was the daughter of the great king Tantalus of Lydia. She married Amphion, the great singer and musician, to the sound of whose music the walls of Thebes had risen miraculously from the ground.

Before her marriage she had known Arachne, but she was not warned by Arachne's fate to give way to the gods and to speak reverently of them.

She had many reasons for being proud—the high birth of her husband and herself, their wealth, their royal power. But, proud as she was of all this, she was even prouder of her children. Indeed she might have been called the most happy of all mothers, if she had not thought herself so.

Once in Thebes the prophetess Manto, daughter of the old blind seer Tiresias, went through the streets, crying out: "Women of Thebes, go all together to Latona's temple. Bind your hair in wreaths of laurel and offer up prayers and incense to Latona and her two children, Apollo and Diana. The goddess is speaking to you through my mouth."

The women obeyed the prophetess, and went to the temple to pray, wearing their laurel wreaths; but they were interrupted on their way by Niobe who came proudly walking, surrounded by a crowd of her friends, bright in her gold robes, and beautiful so far as anger allowed her to look beautiful, as she tossed back her fine head with the hair falling on her neck and shoulders. She stopped, and, looking haughtily around her, said: "What is the meaning of this madness? Will you give more honour to the gods, whom you have only heard of, than to those whom you have seen with your own eyes? Why should Latona have an altar and be worshipped, while I, just as divine as she is, have no incense burnt to me? My father was Tantalus, the only mortal who has ever shared the meals of the gods. My mother is a sister of the Pleiades. One of my grandfathers is Atlas, who holds heaven on his shoulders; the other is Jupiter himself. The people of Asia fear me. I am Queen of Thebes, and the walls which rose to the music of my husband's lyre together with all the people are under the rule of my husband and myself. In my house, wherever I turn my eyes, I see enormous riches. I am as beautiful as a goddess, and then, on top of all this, I have seven sons and seven daughters. Soon I shall have sons- and daughters-in-law.

"You see what reasons I have to be happy. How then can you prefer to me this Latona, whoever she may be? When she was about to give birth, there was no corner of the earth that would receive her. Only the little island of Delos, which floated on the surface of the sea, a wanderer like she was on land, took pity on her and allowed her to rest. Then she bore two children. I have seven times as many. I am happy. Who can deny it? And I shall remain happy. That also cannot be questioned. I have so much that I am safe. Even if Fortune took much from me, much more would be left. Even if I lost some of my children, I should still have many more than Latona's two. Indeed to have only two children is to be practically childless. Now leave this temple! You have sacrificed enough. Take off the wreaths from your hair!"

The Theban women obeyed her and left the sacrifice half finished. Still in their hearts they silently gave worship to the goddess.

Latona had heard the words of Niobe. In her heavenly place she spoke to her children, Apollo and Diana: "See how I, your mother, who am so proud of having given birth to you both, see how I am treated. People doubt whether I am a goddess at all, and, unless you help me, I shall no longer have altars at which I am worshipped. And this is not all. Niobe has added insult to injury. She has called me childless (let that fate be hers!) and has preferred her children to you."

At this Apollo interrupted her and said: "There is no need to say more. It would only delay their punishment." His sister Diana said the same. Swiftly they glided through the air, and with clouds enfolding them, alighted on the citadel of Cadmus's city, Thebes.

In front of the city there was a wide open plain, levelled out and hardened by the constant beat of horses' hooves and the rolling wheels of chariots. Here some of Amphion's seven sons were riding their strong horses, sitting on saddles that glowed bright with Tyrian purple and gripping in their hands reins that gleamed with gold. One of them, Ismenus, his mother's first born, was pulling hard on the foam-flecked bit as he made his horse turn a corner of the track, when suddenly he gave a cry and, with an arrow fixed in his heart, he dropped the reins and slowly slipped to the ground dead over the horse's right shoulder. Another brother, hearing through the empty air the sound of arrows rattling in a quiver, began to urge his horse forward at full speed. But, just as it was breaking into a gallop, the arrow that none can escape stuck quivering in his neck, with the iron point showing through at the other side. He pitched forward over the horse's mane and stained the ground with his warm blood. Two other brothers had finished their riding and were now enjoying a wrestling bout together. As they strained, breast to breast, each looking for a hold, one arrow pierced them both. Together they groaned, together their limbs relaxed as they fell to the ground, together they turned about them their dying eyes and breathed their last. Two more of Niobe's sons ran to lift up the dead bodies, but, while they were bending over them, they too felt the arrows in their backs and fell forward over the bodies which they had come to raise up. Now only the youngest brother was left. He stretched out his arms to Heaven and cried out: "O all you gods together, spare me, I pray you." He did not know that it was not necessary to pray to *all* the gods. Apollo pitied him, but it was too late. The shaft had already left the bow. The young man fell, pierced with only a light wound, but pierced to the heart.

News of the disaster came fast to the city, and Amphion, driven out of his mind by the loss of his fine sons, thrust a dagger into his heart, ending his sorrow and his life together.

Niobe, amazed that this could have happened and angry that the gods could have such power, came out of the city—a very different Niobe from the one who had turned the women away from Latona's altar and had strode through the streets, proud and envied by her friends. Now even her enemies might pity her. She threw herself down upon the cold bodies, crying and wildly kissing them. Then she lifted up her arms to Heaven and cried out: "Cruel Latona, feed your fierce heart on my sufferings! It is as if I myself had died seven times. Be happy in your hateful victory! And yet it is not a victory. In all my misery I still have more children than you in your happiness. Even after all these deaths, I am still the winner."

As she spoke there came the ringing sound of a taut bow-string, a sound that terrified everyone except Niobe herself. Suffering had made her bold.

In front of their brothers' bodies their sisters were standing, in black robes and with loose hair. One of these was just pulling from the wound the arrow that stuck there, when she sank forward, dead, over the body that she was tending. A second sister, while she was trying to console her mother in her grief, suddenly stopped speaking, doubled-up by an unseen wound. Others died as they turned to run away, and one was killed standing speechless and motionless in fear. Now six had perished, and only the youngest one remained. Her mother threw her arms about her, covering and hiding her in her dress. "Oh leave me just one," she cried, "my youngest one. Out of many I only ask now for one, and that one the smallest."

Even while she spoke, the child for whose life she was begging fell dead. Deprived of everything, the poor mother sat down among the lifeless bodies of her sons, her daughters, her husband. Sorrow made her stiff as stone. The breeze did not stir the hair around her forehead; her face was white and bloodless; her eyes stood fixed like stones in her sad cheeks; there was nothing of her that seemed alive; her very tongue froze to the roof of her mouth; the blood ceased to run in her veins; her neck could no longer bend, nor could she move her arms and her feet. All her flesh and all the inside of her body became hard rock. Still her tears flowed. Soon came a great rushing wind which whirled her away and carried her to her own country, setting her down on the top of a mountain. Here she still weeps and to this day the tears well out from the marble.

ACIS AND GALATEA

On the rocky coast of Sicily once lived the giant Cyclops, called Polyphemus. He was the son of Neptune, but he despised both gods and men. In the middle of his forehead was set one great eye, an eye which, later on, he was destined to lose at the hands of the Greek hero Ulysses on his return from Troy. His mind was rough and churlish as was his great hairy body. Indeed it was no pleasure to look at him or to be near him.

Once, as he wandered along the shore, supporting his heavy steps on a huge staff as tall as the mast of a ship, and feeding his flocks of sheep, he caught sight of the sea nymph Galatea, and immediately, so far as anything so uncouth could feel love, he fell in love with her. She, however, loved the young shepherd Acis, and he returned her love, keeping himself for her alone.

As for the Cyclops, Galatea hated him and his wooing almost as much as she loved her Acis. Yet this did not make the Cyclops give up his attempts to win her heart. He forgot his flocks and his caves, with their stores of cheeses and of milk. Now he began to think of his appearance, and of how he could become charming. He combed his shaggy hair with a rake, and cut off his stiff beard with a sickle. Then he would look at his rough face in a pool of water, and try to make the expression more pleasing.

There was a high promontory which, shaped like a wedge, jutted out into the sea, with water on either side of it. Here the savage Cyclops climbed up and sat down. His woolly sheep followed him at random, since he paid no attention to them. In front of his feet he threw down his great staff, and took out his pipe, which was made of a hundred reeds. The mountains all around felt the sound of his piping, and Galatea herself, who, in the shelter of a rock a long way away was resting in the arms of Acis, heard clearly the words that the Cyclops sang.

"O Galatea," he sang, "you who are whiter than the leaves of the snowy privet, more like a flower than all the flowery meadows,

standing straight and tall as the elder-tree, brighter than crystal, gay and playful as a young kid, smoother than shells polished by the rolling waves, more lovely than the sun in winter or the shade in summer, more glorious than apples, more to be admired than the tall plane-tree, shining more brightly than ice, sweeter than the ripe grape, softer than swan's down or curdled milk, O, and if only you would not run away from me, more beautiful than a fresh green garden! And yet, Galatea, you are more headstrong than an untamed heifer, harder than old oak wood, falser than water, tougher than willow twigs, less to be moved than these rocks, more violent than a river torrent, vainer than the peacock when it is praised, fiercer than fire, sharper than thorns, more surly than a she-bear with young, deafer than sea-water, more relentless than a snake that is trodden on, and (this particularly I would like you not to be) more fleet of foot not only than a stag before the hounds but even than the winds and the flying breezes.

"If only you knew me well you would wish that you had not fled from me. I have a whole mountainside to live in, deep caves where the sun's heat never comes in summer, nor does the cold in winter. In my orchard the boughs are weighed down with apples. On my vines grow grapes as yellow as gold, and purple grapes as well. Both kinds are meant for you. You with your own hands will be able to pick in the shady woods the wild strawberries, cherries in the autumn, and plums, not only the juicy black kind, but also the big yellow ones that look like wax. If you marry me, you can have chestnuts as well, and all the trees will be your servants. Then there are my flocks, so many that I do not bother to count them, my goats and my kids, and always plenty of snow-white milk.

"And if you want a pet to play with, I should not give you anything ordinary and common like a fawn, or a hare or a kid, a pair of doves or a nest of birds taken from a rock. No, I have got two bear cubs for you to play with, so like each other that you could not tell them apart. When I found them I said: 'I'll keep these for the girl I love.'

"O come now, Galatea! Raise your bright head from the blue sea, and do not despise what I offer you! I have a good idea of myself now, since I recently looked at my face in the mirror of a clear pool. I liked what I saw. Look how big I am! A great mass of hair juts out over my forehead and falls over my shoulders like a forest. You must not think it ugly to be covered all over the body, like I am, with thick shaggy hair. Trees are ugly without their leaves, and sheep without their wool. Men, too, ought to be covered in bristling hair like mine. It is true that I have only one eye in the midde of my forehead, but this eye is as big as a cart-wheel.

"O Galatea, I fear none of the gods, but I fear you and your anger. It would be easier to bear your refusal of me, if you refused everyone else. How is it that you can love Acis and prefer him to me? I wish I could get near him. He'd soon find out what strength there is in me. I'd tear his heart out of his body, I'd pull him to pieces, limb from limb, and scatter the pieces over the fields and over the waters of your sea. For I am on fire with love, and all the more on fire because I am rejected. It seems as though I have a volcano in my heart, and you, Galatea, do not mind at all."

So the Cyclops sang and roared over the sea. Then he got to his feet to wander restlessly about, just as a bull, furious when the cow is taken from him, cannot stand still but paces through the woods and well-known pastures.

Suddenly he saw Galatea and Acis hiding under the rock in each other's arms. "I see you," he shouted out, "and I will make sure that this meeting of yours will be your last."

His huge terrible cries made the whole of Etna ring and re-echo with the sound. Galatea, in terror, sprang back into the sea and dived beneath the waves. Acis turned to run, but the Cyclops ran after him, tore a great piece from a mountainside and hurled it at the young man. Only the corner of the huge mass reached him, but it was enough to bury him entirely beneath earth and rock.

The gods had pity on Acis. Through the earth beneath which he was buried first crimson blood began to ooze up; then, after a little time, the red colour began to fade away; now the colour was like muddy river water, swollen by a storm; then the great mass of rock cracked open, and a tall green reed shot up through the crack. Next, through the opening came a stream of bright leaping water, a new fresh river, and, standing waist high in the stream, appeared the god of the river, a beautiful youth, with small fresh-grown horns all wreathed with shining reeds upon his forehead. This was Acis, just as he had been except for the horns and except that he was bigger. The river joined its waters with the sea and was called after its own god.

GLAUCUS AND SCYLLA

Glaucus, a god of the sea, was once a mortal man. He lived in the island of Euboea, and even then, in his mortal life, he was devoted to the sea, and spent all his time upon it, sometimes dragging in his nets full of fish, sometimes sitting on the rocks with rod and line, looking out over the blue water to the mountains and the islands.

There is a part of the shore where green grass runs down to the water. Here no horned cattle have ever grazed, nor have peaceful sheep cropped the grass, nor hairy goats. No busy bees have ever crossed the meadow in search of honey, nor have human hands plucked the flowers for garlands. It is a deserted place, and Glaucus was the first ever to sit down on the soft turf, where he spread out his lines and wet nets to dry, and began to count the fish that he had caught, laying them all out upon the grass in rows.

While he was doing so, he was amazed to see that the fish, as soon as they were laid on the grass, began to stir and to wriggle; then they began to move about on land as though they were on water, and soon they all moved down again to the sea and swam away.

Glaucus stood for a long time in amazement, wondering what could be the reason for this strange happening. Was it one of the gods who had given this power to the fish? Or was it the effect of some magic in the grass? He decided to see whether the grass would have any effect on him and, taking up a handful of grass and flowers together, began to eat it. Hardly had he begun to taste the strange juices when he felt his heart trembling and longing for an entirely different way of life. "Farewell, Earth!" he cried out. "I shall never come back to you again." And he plunged into the sea.

The gods of the sea welcomed him and made him one of them. They purged away from him everything that was mortal, first by repeating over him nine times a magic charm, then by washing his body in the streams of a hundred rivers. As the rivers poured their waters over his head, Glaucus lost consciousness. When his senses came back to him, he found that both his body and his mind had changed. Now he had a long streaming beard, dark green hair that floated beside him in the waves, huge shoulders, sea-blue arms and curved legs that ended in the fins of fishes. Blowing on a horn made of a deep-sea shell, he swam and dived with the Nereids and other gods and goddesses of the ocean.

There was a mortal girl, Scylla, who, in her pride, had refused all offers of marriage, and who used to come and talk with the nymphs of the sea. Glaucus fell in love with her and told her his story, wishing to show her that, though he was a god, he was also able to understand mortals. She, however, fled from him, as she had fled from everybody else, and Glaucus, angry and bitter at being refused, went for help to the wonderful palace and island of the goddess Circe.

With his huge arms and sinuous legs and tail he swam past Sicily and Italy and came to the grassy hills and woods where Circe had her palace. In the woods were bears and lions, panthers, tigers, beasts of all kinds—all once men, but now turned into these shapes by Circe's enchantments. Circe welcomed him and he said to her: "O goddess, have pity upon a god. You alone, if you think me worthy of your help, can help me in my love. I myself know the power of magic herbs, since it was by them that I became a god. Now I am in love with a mortal. Her name is Scylla and she lives on the coast of Italy, opposite Sicily. I beg you to use some charm or some magic herb to help me. I do not want you to cure me of my love, but to make her love me with at least a little of the feeling that I have for her."

Circe, however, was a goddess whose heart was very easily moved to the love either of gods or of men. When she saw Glaucus, she desired to have him for herself and said to him: "It would be much better to leave someone who does not want you and to follow someone who does. You who might be wooed yourself ought not to waste your time in wooing. And to give you confidence in your own charm I tell you that I myself, the daughter of the sun, a goddess, would like to be your love."

To this Glaucus replied: "I can tell you that, so long as Scylla is alive, leaves will grow in the sea and seaweed on the tops of the mountains, before my love changes."

Circe was angry. She could not hurt him, and perhaps since she loved him, she did not want to. All her anger turned against the woman who had been preferred to her. At once she mixed together the juices of terrible herbs and, as she did so, she muttered charms that are used by Hecate, the goddess of witches. Then she put on a blue cloak and went out through the wild beasts that licked her hands and fawned upon her as she passed. She walked over the waves of the sea as though it was dry land, just skimming the surface with dry feet, and she came to the channel where Italy looks across at Sicily.

There was a little rock pool shaped like a crescent moon, a place where Scylla loved to come and rest. Here she used to refresh herself in the heat of midday, and in this pool, before Scylla arrived, Circe put the terrible poisons which she had brought, again murmuring over them her charmed words.

Then Scylla came and had gone into the pool as far as her waist when, looking downwards, she saw all round the lower part of her body the shapes of barking monsters. When first she saw them she could not believe that they were actually parts of her body, but fled away terrified at the sight of the fierce dog's heads. As she fled, however, she drew with her what she was running away from. Putting down her hand to feel the flesh of her thighs, her legs and her feet, all she felt was the gaping heads of dogs, fearful as Cerberus himself. Instead of feet she stood on the hairy necks and savage faces of wild beasts.

Glaucus, who loved her, wept for her and fled far away from Circe who had used her charms so cruelly. As for Scylla, she remained fixed to the rock in that place. Opposite her was the fig-tree and great whirlpool of Charybdis. Later, when she had a chance, she tried to revenge herself on Circe by destroying the sailors of Ulysses, who had been Circe's friend.

BELLEROPHON

Bellerophon was son of the King of Corinth and grew up to be a young man of remarkable strength and beauty, brave also, and ready to undertake any difficult adventure.

Soon after he grew to manhood he unluckily and by accident killed one of his relations and, to avoid the guilt of blood, he left his native land and went to live in Argos.

Here Proetus was king and here Bellerophon received a generous welcome. The king admired the young man's courage and beauty; he was glad to have his services in peace and war, and raised him to a position of honour in his court. Bellerophon might have lived for long in Argos, had it not been that the king's wife Antea fell in love with him. She approached him with endearing words, begging him to take her from her husband. Bellerophon, grateful to the king for his hospitality and for his many kindnesses, indignantly refused to listen to the shameful suggestions of Antea. Then her love turned to hatred. She went to Proetus and said: "If you have any respect for your wife, I demand that this young man be put to death. He is on fire with love for me, and has already attempted by force to take me away from you."

Proetus believed the false words of his wife, but still he did not wish himself to have the guilt and unpopularity of putting the young man to death. He therefore sent him to visit his father-in-law Iobates, King of Lycia in Asia Minor, and before he left he gave him a sealed message in which was written: "If you love me and value my friendship, ask no questions but immediately put the bearer of this message to death."

Bellerophon took the message with no suspicion that he was carrying his own death-warrant, and set out on his voyage across the sea to Lycia. When he arrived King Iobates, knowing him to be the favourite of the King of Argos, welcomed him warmly and feasted him in the rich halls of his palace. They were merry and friendly together at the feast, but when it was over Bellerophon gave the King the message which he had brought, and the King read it in sorrow and amazement, unwilling to believe that so gallant a young man could have injured his protector, unwilling too to offend against the sacred laws of hospitality by killing a stranger whom he had entertained in his own halls. Nevertheless he could not refuse to obey the clear instructions of the King of Argos. A plan occurred to him by which it seemed certain that the young man would meet his death, while the king himself would not incur the guilt of having directly brought it about. Bellerophon had already offered to help the king in any way in which his services could be used. Now the king ordered him to find and to destroy the Chimera, an invincible monster that lived in rocky caves and ravaged all the country around. The Chimera had a lion's head, the body of a great shaggy she-goat, and a dragon's tail. Out of its mouth it breathed such blasts of fire and smoke that no one could approach it. It moved with incredible speed, hunting down men and cattle, so that for miles around its rocky lair the country was a wilderness.

Bellerophon knew the difficulties and dangers of his task, but he gladly and willingly undertook it. His courage, however, would not have proved enough if he had not been helped by the goddess Minerva. She told him that he could never conquer the Chimera without the help of Pegasus, the winged horse who had sprung to life from the blood of Medusa, whom Perseus slew, and who now lived on Mount Helicon with the Muses, never yet having felt the weight of a man upon his back. So Bellerophon set out once more on a long journey. He found the horse, a wonderful and swift animal, snow-white and smooth as silk not only over all his skin but also where the gleaming feathery wings lay along his shoulders. For a whole day Bellerophon tried to throw a bridle round the animal's neck, but Pegasus would never allow him to come close enough to do so. Whenever Bellerophon approached, the horse would either gallop away out of reach or would rise on wings in the air, alighting further off in the cool meadows where he grazed. In the evening, worn out and despairing, Bellerophon lay down to sleep. He dreamed that Minerva had come to him and given him a golden bridle. On waking up he found that this was actually what had happened. At his side was a beautiful bridle of gold and, with this in his hand, he immediately set out again to look for Pegasus. When the horse saw the bridle, he bowed his head and came gently forward, willingly allowing Bellerophon to bridle and to mount him. Then he sprang into the air and sped like a shooting star through the clouds to the country where the Chimera lived; for the horse was a divine horse, knowing exactly for what reason he was wanted.

Flying over the deep gullies and rocky caves in the mountains, Bellerophon saw beneath him the red glow of fire and smoke ascending into the air. He checked the course of Pegasus and flew nearer to the earth, and soon appeared the vast body of the monster as it came raging out of its lair. Pegasus hovered over it like a hawk hovers above its prey, and first Bellerophon shot his arrows into the great goat-like body below him, until the ground was drenched in blood. Then he swooped down through the clouds of smoke, thrusting his sword over and over again into the animal's neck and flanks. It was not long before the Chimera lay dead and sprawling on the ground. Then Bellerophon cut off its head and said good-bye to the noble horse who had helped him, since Minerva had told him that once his task was accomplished, he must let the animal go. Pegasus was never again mounted by any mortal man. He sped away like lightning. Some say that he went back to the grassy pastures of Helicon and that where his hoof struck the ground there issued forth the fountain of Hippocrene. Others say that it was at this time that Jupiter set the winged horse among the stars.

Bellerophon himself returned to King Iobates carrying with him the head of the Chimera. The king was glad that the monster had been destroyed and he admired the courage of the young man who had destroyed it. Still he felt bound to carry out the instructions of the King of Argos and secure Bellerophon's death. Next he sent him to fight against the Solymi, a tribe of fierce mountaineers who lived upon the borders of Lycia and who had conquered the king's armies whenever they had been sent against them. Bellerophon, with a small force, marched into the mountains, killed or made prisoners of the whole tribe, and returned without a wound.

Next he was sent against the warrior nation of the Amazons, the fierce women who had conquered so many armies of men in battle. These also Bellerophon defeated, and now the king determined on a last plan by which he could do the will of the King of Argos. He picked out of his forces the best and strongest of his fighting men, and told them to lay an ambush for Bellerophon as he was on his

way back from his conquest of the Amazons. Again the gods pre-
s˄rved him. With his own hand he killed every one of his attackers,
and when he reached the king's court Iobates exclaimed: "There
can be no doubt that the young man is innocent. Otherwise the
gods would not have saved his life so often."

He gave Bellerophon his daughter to be his wife, sharing with
him his riches and his throne. And when Iobates died, Bellerophon
became King of Lycia.

MIDAS

Old Silenus, the fat companion of the god Bacchus, was nearly
always drunk. Once in the country of Phrygia, when he was lying
on the ground drowsy with wine, some countrymen found him.
They bound him in wreaths of flowers and took him to their king,
who was called Midas.

Midas reverenced both Bacchus and his followers. He was glad
to see old Silenus and entertained him hospitably. For ten days and
nights he feasted him and on the eleventh day joyfully brought
him back to Bacchus.

So pleased was Bacchus to find his companion safe and sound
that he said to Midas: "Choose anything you like for a gift, and it
shall be given to you."

Midas made bad use of the opportunity which the god had given
him. "What I should like," he said, "is that everything which I
touch should be turned to gold."

Bacchus granted his prayer, but wished that he had made a better choice, since what he had asked for would only bring him sorrow. But Midas went away full of joy and at once decided to try
the effects of his new power. Hardly daring to believe in it, he
broke off a twig from a small oak-tree. Immediately the twig turned

to gold. He picked up a stone from the ground, and the stone sparkled and shone with precious metal. He touched a clod of earth, and the clod became a great nugget of gold. He let his hand stray over the ears of growing corn, and the harvest was a harvest of gold. He picked an apple from a tree and, when he held it in his hand, it was like one of the apples of the Hesperides. If he touched the pillars in his palace, the pillars gleamed and shone. When he washed his hands, the running water that he poured over them turned to a golden shower. As he thought of turning everything to gold, it seemed to him that he was happy beyond his wildest dreams.

Then, as he was still rejoicing in his new power, his servants brought out a table covered with fine meats and bread. But when he put out his hand to take the bread, it immediately became hard and stiff. When he put a piece of meat in his mouth and started to bite it, he found that his teeth were biting on hard metal. He mixed water with his wine to drink, but, when he raised the glass to his lips, it was molten metal that flowed into his mouth.

This was far from being what he had expected. He was rich indeed, but also most miserable. Now he longed to escape from his wealth, and hated the very thing for which he had prayed. All the food in the world could not relieve his hunger. His throat was parched with thirst. He was tortured by the hateful gold. Lifting up to the sky his shining arms and hands, he prayed: "O Father Bacchus, forgive me my mistake! Have pity on me, and take away this gift that seemed so very different from what it really is!"

The gods are kind. Midas had confessed his fault and Bacchus made him as he had been before. "And," he said, "so that you may not remain with your skin all covered in the gold which you stupidly desired, go to the river Pactolus that flows past the great city of Sardis. Follow the stream through the mountains till you come to its source. There, where the foaming river comes gushing from the rocks, bathe your head and body. This, at the same time, will wash away your sin."

Midas did as the god had told him. The golden touch passed from his body into the water. Even to this day the river rolls over golden sands and carries gold dust to the sea.

Now Midas had had enough of wealth. He wandered through the fields and forests, worshipping the goat-god Pan, who lives in the caves of the mountains. His mind, however, was still dull and foolish, and soon once more did him harm.

Near the city of Sardis stands the great mountain Tmolus, and here one day Pan was singing his songs to the beautiful nymphs and playing to them on his pipe made of reeds joined together with wax. As he sang he dared to say that his own music was better than Apollo's, and challenged the god of music himself to a contest with Tmolus as a judge.

Apollo came, and Tmolus, god of the mountain, took his seat, shaking the trees away from the sides of his head. Round his dark hair was a wreath of oak, and acorns hung about his hollow temples. He looked at Pan, the god of shepherds, and said: "See, the judge has not been slow. He is ready to listen."

Then Pan made his music on his country pipes. It was rough music, but it charmed Midas, who happened to be among the listeners. When Pan had finished, Tmolus turned his face towards Apollo and, as he turned, the forests turned with him.

On his golden hair the god wore a wreath of laurel from Mount Parnassus. His long cloak, sweeping the ground, was dyed red with Tyrian dyes. In his left hand he held his lyre, bright with ivory and precious stones. In his right hand he held the plectrum to pluck the strings. Even from the way he stood you could tell that he was a musician. Then he plucked the strings, and soon Tmolus, charmed utterly by that sweet and noble music, told Pan that his pipes were no match for the lyre of Apollo.

All agreed with the judgment of the mountain god—all except Midas, who kept disputing it and calling it unjust. Apollo then decided that he was unworthy to have human ears. He made them grow long, filled them with rough grey hair, and made them able to move from the base. In all other ways Midas was human: only as a punishment for his bad taste, he had the ears of an ass.

Naturally he was ashamed of them and covered them up in a purple turban which he wore upon his head. But the servant who used to cut his hair discovered his secret. He dared not tell others what he had discovered, but he could not bear to keep the secret to himself. So he went out and dug a hole in the ground. Kneeling down he whispered into the hole: "King Midas has asses' ears." Then he carefully put back the earth and went away, relieved that he had spoken the words, even though no one had heard them. But a crop of whispering reeds sprang up in the place, and, when they were full-grown and swayed by the winds of the autumn, they repeated the words that were buried at their roots. "Midas has asses' ears," they said to every breeze, and the breezes carried on the news.

ATALANTA'S RACE

The huntress Atalanta, whom Meleager, before he died, had loved, could run faster even than the fastest runners amongst men. Nor was her beauty inferior to her swiftness of foot; both were beyond praise.

When Atalanta asked the oracle about whom she ought to marry, the god replied: "Do not take a husband, Atalanta. If you do, it will bring disaster on you. Yet you will not escape, and though you will continue to live, you will not be yourself."

Terrified by these words, Atalanta lived in the dark woods unmarried. There were many men who wished to marry her, but to them, in their eagerness, she said: "No one can have me for his wife unless first he beats me in a race. If you will, you may run with me. If any of you wins, he shall have me as a prize. But those who are defeated will have death for their reward. These are the conditions for the race."

Cruel indeed she was, but her beauty had such power that numbers of young men were impatient to race with her on these terms.

There was a young man called Hippomenes, who had come to watch the contest. At first he had said to himself: "What man in his senses would run such a risk to get a wife?" and he had condemned the young men for being too madly in love. But when he saw her face and her body all stripped for the race—a face and a body like Venus's own—he was lost in astonishment and, stretching out his hands, he said: "I had no right to blame the young men. I did not know what the prize was for which they were running."

As he spoke his own heart caught on fire with love for her and, in jealous fear, he hoped that none of the young men would be able to beat her in the race. Then he said to himself: "But why should not I try my fortune? When one takes a risk, the gods help one."

By now the race had started, and the girl sped past him on feet that seemed to have wings. Though she went fast as an arrow, he admired her beauty still more. Indeed she looked particularly beautiful when running. In the breeze her hair streamed back over her ivory shoulders; the ribbons with their bright borders fluttered at her knees; the white of her young body flushed rose-red, as when a purple awning is drawn over white marble and makes the stone glow with its own colour. While Hippomenes fixed his eyes on her, she reached the winning post and was crowned with the victor's garland. The young men, with groans, suffered the penalty of death according to the agreement which they had made.

Their fate, however, had no effect on Hippomenes. He came forward and, fixing his eyes on Atalanta, said: "Why do you win an easy glory by conquering these slow movers? Now run with me. If I win, it will be no disgrace to you. I am a king's son and Neptune is my great grandfather. And, if you defeat me, it will be an honour to be able to say that you defeated Hippomenes."

As he spoke, Atalanta looked at him with a softer expression in her eyes. She wondered whether she really wanted to conquer or to be conquered. She thought to herself: "What god, envious of beautiful young men, wants to destroy this one and makes him seek marriage with me at the risk of his dear life? In my opinion, I am not worth it. It is not his beauty that touches me (though I might easily be touched by that); it is because he is still only a boy. And then there is his courage, and the fact that he is willing to risk so much for me. Why should he die, simply because he wants to live with me? I wish he would go, while he still may, and realize that it is fatal to want to marry me. Indeed he deserves to live. If only I were happier, if only the fates had not forbidden me to marry, he would be the man that I would choose."

Meanwhile Atalanta's father and the whole people demanded that the race should take place. Hippomenes prayed to Venus and said: "O goddess, you put this love into my heart. Now be near me in my trial and aid me!"

A gentle breeze carried his prayer to the goddess and she was moved by it. Little time, however, remained in which she could help him. But it happened that she had just returned from her sacred island of Cyprus, where in one of her temple gardens grows a golden apple tree. The leaves are gold; the branches and the fruit rattle with metal as the wind stirs them. Venus had in her hand three golden apples which she had just picked from this tree. Now she came down to earth, making herself visible only to Hippomenes, and showed him how to use the apples.

Then the trumpets sounded and the two runners darted forward from the starting post, skimming over the sandy course with feet so light that it would seem they might have run over the sea or over the waving heads of standing corn. The crowd shouted their applause. "Now, Hippomenes," they cried, "run as you have never run before! You are winning." It would be difficult to say whether Hippomenes or Atalanta herself was most pleased with this encouragement. For some time Atalanta, though she might have passed the young man, did not do so. She ran by his side, looking into his face. Then, half unwillingly, she left him behind. He with parched throat and straining lungs followed after; still the winning post was far in the distance; and now he took one of the golden apples which Venus had given him and threw it in her way. The girl looked with wonder at the shining fruit and, longing to have it, stopped running so that she could pick it up. Hippomenes passed her and again the spectators shouted out their applause. Soon, however, Atalanta made up the ground that she had lost and again left Hippomenes behind. He threw the second apple, once more took the lead and once more was overtaken. Now they were in sight of the winning post, and Hippomenes, with a prayer to Venus, threw the last apple rather sideways, so that it went some distance from the course. Atalanta seemed to hesitate whether she should go after it or not, but Venus made her go, and, when she had picked up the apple, she made it heavier, handicapping the girl not only by the time she had lost but by the weight of what she was carrying. This time she could not catch up to Hippomenes. He passed the winning post first and claimed her as his bride.

Then, indeed, Hippomenes should have offered thanks to Venus, but he forgot entirely the goddess who had helped him, neither giving thanks nor making sacrifice.

Venus was angry and determined to make an example of them both. On their way to the home of Hippomenes they came to a holy temple, sacred to the mother of the gods, great Cybele. No mortal was allowed to pass the night in this temple, so hallowed was the spot; but Venus put it into the hearts of Hippomenes and Atalanta, who were tired from their journey, to rest there all night and treat the temple of the goddess as though it were a common inn. So in the most holy of the temple's shrines, where wooden images of the ancient gods turned away their eyes in horror at the profanation, they rested together. But the terrible goddess, her head crowned with a crown of towers, appeared to them. She covered their necks, which had been so smooth, with tawny manes of hair; their fingers became sharp claws, and their arms turned to legs. Most of their weight went to their chests, and behind them they swept the sandy ground with long tails. Instead of the palace they had hoped for, they lived in the savage woods, a lion and a lioness, terrible to others but, when Cybele needed them, tame enough to draw her chariot, champing the iron bits between their gnashing jaws.

CEYX AND HALCYONE

Ceyx was the son of Lucifer, the morning star. Halcyone, his wife, was the daughter of Aeolus, god of the winds. The gods who were their parents could not save them from disaster; but in the end they were happy.

Once Ceyx, disturbed by many strange events which had taken place in his kingdom, decided to go on a voyage across the sea to

consult a famous oracle. He told his faithful wife Halcyone what
he intended to do, and when he told her, her face became as pale
as box-wood, tears ran down her cheeks and she felt cold to the
marrow of her bones. "What have I done, dearest husband," she
said, "to make you change? Why have you stopped caring for me
above everything? Can you go away with an easy mind and leave
your Halcyone behind you? If your journey was by land, though I
should be sad, I should not be frightened. But the sea and the
stern face of the waters terrify me. Only the other day I saw some
broken planks tossed up on the shore; and I have often read men's
names on empty tombs. Do not be rash just because my father
keeps the winds in their prison. Once the winds are let out and
reach the open sea, nothing can be done to stop them. I have seen
them when I was a little girl in my father's house, and I know what
they are like. But if nothing that I can say can make you change
your mind, if you are so fixed on going, then, dear husband, take
me with you too. Then at least we shall face the storms together
and I shall have nothing to fear except what I can see and feel."

Ceyx, who loved his wife as much as she loved him, was moved by
her words and her tears. But he did not want to put off his journey,
nor did he wish her to share the dangers of it. Many arguments he
used in trying to comfort her timid heart, but still he did not con-
vince her. The only thing that consoled her at all was when he
said: "I know this separation will seem long to both of us, but I
swear to you by the fire of my father's star, that, unless the fates
prevent me, I will return before two moons have passed."

This promise of return made her rather happier, and Ceyx immediately ordered his ship to be made ready for the sea. When she saw
it, Halcyone, as though she could read the future, began to tremble
and the tears came again to her eyes. When she had kissed her
husband and said good-bye, she fainted. Ceyx himself tried to think
of some excuse for delaying, but already the rowers, sitting in order
at their benches, were pulling back the oars to their strong breasts,
churning the sea white beneath their regular strokes. Then Halcyone opened her eyes, still wet with tears. She saw her husband
standing on the high stern and waving his hand to her. She waved
back to him, and, as the ship went further from the land and she
could no longer see his face, she still followed the fast-moving ship
with her eyes. When the ship had disappeared, she fixed her gaze
on the sails that bellied out at the top of the mast. Then she went

to her room and threw herself down upon her bed. Her room and her bed made her cry again, since they reminded her that a part of herself had gone away.

Meanwhile the ship had left the harbour and a fresh breeze began to sing in the ropes. The captain shipped the oars, and spread all sail. So all day she ran over the sea, but at nightfall, when the land on either side was far away, the waves began to whiten and the wind began to blow more strongly. "Quick!" shouted the captain, "lower the yard, and reef the sails." The wind blowing in his face took away the sound of his words, still, of their own accord, the sailors began to draw in the oars, to close the oar-holes and to reef the sails. Some bailed out water, others hurriedly made their different preparations to face the storm. And now every moment the storm increased in force. The fierce winds came rushing from every direction, lashing up the angry waves. The captain himself stood in terror, admitting that he did not know what orders to give, since the weight and mass of wind and water were too powerful for his skill. All was in an uproar—men shouting, squalls hissing through the rigging, the waves roaring and thunder crashing out through the upper air. Waves, running mountain-high, seemed to be combing the lowering clouds with the spray that they swept with them. In their troughs you could see the yellow sand, churned up from the bottom of the sea.

As for the ship, sometimes it was lifted high up in the air so that the terrified sailors could look down into the gulfs beneath; sometimes it was plunged downwards as though to the depths of hell, and from the depth they looked up to heaven towering above them. Waves battered and thudded on the ship's sides, like iron battering rams on the wall of a besieged city. Soon the wedges that tightened the hull began to work loose. More and more of the sea came in, and meanwhile sheets of rain fell from the bursting clouds. It seemed as though the whole of heaven was pouring itself into the sea, while the swelling sea was itself mounting into the sky. No stars were to be seen. Everything was black night, except when the fitful lightning flashed along the clouds and made the waves gleam red.

As when soldiers are storming a city's wall and, when one or two have found a foothold, the task becomes easier for the others, so when one wave had leaped over the ship's side, others followed and soon the ship was half full of water. Skill and courage had failed.

Some of the sailors were weeping, others stood dumb with terror; some prayed for at least burial ashore, others thought of their brothers, their wives or their children whom they had left behind.

Ceyx thought of Halcyone and only her name was upon his lips. He longed only for her, but he was glad that she was not with him. He would have liked to turn his eyes for the last time towards his own country and towards his home, but he had no idea in which direction they lay.

A whirlwind snapped off the mast; the rudder too was smashed. Then one last wave, as though proud in victory, curled itself up above the others, and with a roaring crash fell headlong on the ship, crushing the deck and sending it to the very bottom of the sea. Most of the men were dragged down with her and died, sucked in by the whirlpool where she sank. Some still clung to bits of wreckage, and amongst them was Ceyx, whose hands were used to holding a sceptre.

As he struggled to keep himself afloat, he called in vain on his father Lucifer, and on his father-in-law, the king of the winds. But chiefly, as he swam, the name of Halcyone was on his lips. It was she whom he most remembered, and he prayed that the waves might carry his body back to her so that her dear hands might prepare him for burial. So long as he had strength to swim, and so long as the waves allowed him to open his mouth, he spoke her name and murmured it to the waters that were closing over him. A black and curving wave broke over his head, plunging him down beneath the whitening rush of foam. At dawn Lucifer, the morning star, was dim and hard to see. He could not leave his place in heaven, but he wrapped up his light in thick clouds.

Halcyone meanwhile, knowing nothing of what had happened, was counting up the nights that would have to pass before her husband returned; she was busy weaving clothes for him to wear when he came back, and imagining an arrival which would never take place. She was careful to burn incense to all the gods, and especially to Juno, constantly praying for her husband, who no longer existed. She prayed that he might be safe, that he might come back, and that he should never love anyone more than her. This last was the only one of the prayers that could be granted.

Juno could not bear to listen to prayers that concerned one who was already dead. She spoke to her messenger Iris, the goddess of the rainbow. "Iris," she said, "my faithful servant, go to the drowsy court of Sleep, and order him to send to Halcyone a dream in the shape of dead Ceyx to tell her the truth of what has happened."

Iris then put on her thousand-coloured veil, and, marking the sky as she went in the great curve of a rainbow, came to the hidden cloudy dwelling of the King of Sleep.

Near the land of the Cimmerians, in a hollow mountain, there is a deep long cave, the home and secret hiding place of heavy Sleep. Neither rising, nor setting, nor at midday can the sun dart his rays into this place. A cloud of mist and dark twilight shadows are like a breath coming up from the ground. Here no crested cock watches for the dawn and crows, no dogs bark to break the silence, nor geese, still more to be relied upon than dogs. There is no sound of wild beasts, or cattle, or branches moving in the breeze or noisy talk of men. It is the home of utter silence, though from the end of the cave there flows the stream of Lethe, river of forgetfulness, whose sliding waves, gently stirring the pebbles over which they run, invite to sleep. In front of the cave's entrance there grows a mass of poppies, and there are all the numberless herbs whose drowsy juices Night gathers and spreads over the darkening earth. The house has no door, lest there should be hinges to creak; nor does any servant keep watch on the threshold. But in the middle of the cave there is a couch of ebony raised above the floor. The couch is as soft as down, black in colour and covered with dark coverlets, and on it lies the god Sleep, with his limbs stretched out in weariness. Around him lie the shapes of empty dreams, able to imitate every form of life, innumerable as are the grains of corn in harvest, the leaves of the forest, or the sand lying on the shore.

When Iris had entered this cave and brushed away with her hands the dreams that clustered round her, the sacred place was lit up with the shining of her garments. The god could hardly lift his heavy eyelids and again and again slipped back into sleep as he tried to raise his chin from his breast. Finally he roused himself, propped himself on an elbow and asked her (for he recognized her) why she had come.

"Sweet Sleep," she said, "you who bring peace to everything, most mild of all the gods, you who ease the heart and are the refuge from care, you who calm our tired bodies and make them fit for work again—I ask you to shape a dream in the form of King Ceyx and send it to his wife Halcyone, to tell her the story of his shipwreck. This is what Juno commands."

Iris then went away, for she already felt stealing over her the drowsiness of sleep. She went back on the curve of the rainbow by which she had come.

The god chose out one of his sons, Morpheus, to do the task which had been given him. He told him what he must do, then once more let his body relax in idleness upon the high couch.

Morpheus on his soft and noiseless wings flew through the darkness to the city where Halcyone was queen. Then he put off his wings and took on the shape of Ceyx, but with a pale worn face like that of a dead man. So he stood naked by the bed of the unhappy Halcyone. His beard and hair seemed wet and heavy with sea-water. He leant over her bed, and his tears seemed to fall upon her face. "Do you recognize your Ceyx, my poor wife?" he said. "Or has death altered my face? Look at me and you will find not your husband, but his ghost. All your prayers, Halcyone, were of no help to me. I am dead. Do not hope any more. It is no use. The stormy wind caught my ship in the Aegean Sea and wrecked it. The waves filled my mouth, as I called uselessly your name. Now you must get up and weep for me. Put on a black dress and do not let me go unmourned to the shadowy world of the dead."

He spoke, and both his voice and the very gestures of the hands were exactly like those of Ceyx himself. Halcyone groaned in her sleep and stretched out her arms, trying to clasp them about his body; but it was only the empty air that she held. She cried out: "Stay! Stay! Where are you going? Let me go with you!" And then the sound of her own voice woke her up.

First she looked round to see if the vision was still there. Her servants had heard her voice and had brought in a lamp. When she could see no sign of him anywhere, she shrieked and tore her hair. Her nurse asked her what was the reason for her grief, and she said: "Halcyone has ceased to exist. She died when Ceyx died. Do not try to console me. He is shipwrecked and dead. I saw him just now and knew him and stretched out my hands to him as he went away, trying to keep him back. True, he had not got the bright look in his eyes which I know. He was pale and naked and his hair was all wet. He stood just here" (and she looked at the floor to see if he had left any footprints behind). "This was just what I feared when I asked him not to leave me. Oh, how I wish that he had taken me with him! Then we should never have been separated in life, nor should we have been divided in death. Now my heart would be more cruel than the sea if it urged me to overcome my grief and to go on living. I shall not struggle with my grief, nor shall I leave you, my poor husband. Now at least I shall come and be your companion. If our ashes cannot rest in the same urn, our names will be written on the same tomb. If my bones cannot mingle with yours, at least the letters in which our names are inscribed will touch each other."

She could speak no more. Instead of words groans came from her despairing heart.

It was morning and she went out of her palace down to the shore, seeking again in her sorrow the place from which she had watched him sail away. While she lingered there and said to herself: "This was where he loosed his cable. This was where he gave me his parting kiss," and was bringing back to her mind everything that had happened, staring over the sea, she saw in the distance something which looked like a dead body, though at first she could not be sure what it was. The waves carried it nearer in, and, though it was still some distance away, it was clearly the body of a dead man. She did not know whose body it was, but, because it was a drowned man, she wept and cried out. "Ah, poor man, whoever you are! And poor wife, if you have a wife!"

The waves brought the body nearer and nearer. The more she looked at it, the more did she strain her eyes and the more did her heart beat. Now it was close to the shore: she could see it clearly. It was the body of her husband. "It is he," she cried, and, tearing her hair and her dress, she stretched out to him her trembling hands and said: "O Ceyx, dearest husband, is this the way that you come back to me?"

Near to the sea there was a breakwater that stood in the way of the first force of the waves. She ran to this breakwater and leaped out from it towards the sea. But she did not fall. As she leaped into the air she flew, and, with wings that had grown in an instant, skimmed over the surface of the waves in the shape of a bird. As she flew there came from her long pointed beak notes that seemed full of sorrow and complaint. But when she reached the silent bloodless body, she folded her new wings around the limbs that she had loved and, with her rough beak, tried to set kisses on his cold lips. It seemed to the people who were watching that Ceyx felt her touch, or perhaps it was the movement of the waves that had raised his head for a moment. But no, it was her touch that he had felt. Finally the gods had pity on them and they were both changed to birds. Their fates were inseparable; still, as birds, they are married; they mate together and bring up their young. And there are seven quiet days in the winter months when Halcyone broods upon her nest that floats over the sea. At this season the waves of the sea are calm and still; for Aeolus guards the winds closely and forbids them to go out, making all the waters safe for his own grandchildren.

OEDIPUS

After Apollo and Diana had entirely destroyed the race of Amphion, Thebes was without a king, and the people summoned Laius, a descendant of Cadmus, to come to the throne which, indeed, was his by right.

Laius had been warned by an oracle that, if he had a son, this son was fated to kill his own father. When, therefore, his wife Jocasta bore a son, Laius, in fear of the oracle, decided to put the child to death. Soon after the baby was born, a spike was thrust through his feet and he was given to a goat-herd, who was told to leave the child on the cold steep slopes of Mount Cithaeron, where he would be devoured by wild beasts. The goat-herd reported to the king that he had carried out his orders and the king's mind was set at rest. In fact, however, the man had not had the heart to destroy the small child and had given it to one of the servants of Polybus, King of Corinth, whom he had met on the mountain. This servant took the child to Corinth and there he was brought up and adopted by Polybus and his wife Merope, who were childless. They gave him the name of Oedipus, or "Swollen feet", because of the marks left on his feet by the spike with which they had been pierced.

So in Corinth Oedipus grew to manhood, believing himself to be the son of Polybus and Merope. He was distinguished in every way, and it was through jealousy of him that once at a feast a drunken young man mocked at him for not being the true son of his parents. Oedipus, in great anxiety, went to Merope and asked her for the truth. She attempted to set his mind at rest, but still he was not satisfied. He left Corinth alone and on foot, and went to ask the advice of Apollo's oracle at Delphi. What he heard terrified him. "Unhappy man," replied the oracle, "keep far away from your father! If you meet him, you will kill him. Then you will marry your mother, and have children who will be fated to crime and misfortune."

Now Oedipus believed that it was because of some knowledge of this dreadful fate that Polybus and Merope had given indefinite answers to his questions. He was determined not to do them any harm and vowed that never again would he set foot in what he believed to be his native city of Corinth.

So, still startled by the oracle's reply, he left Delphi, turning away from the sea and the way to Corinth, and travelling inland over the lower slopes of Mount Parnassus. On his left were the high mountains where eagles circled overhead; below him, on the right, was a long river valley where olive trees grew in such numbers that they themselves seemed a great flood of grey-green and silver flowing to the sea.

In the mountains there is a place where three roads meet, and here, as Oedipus was travelling on foot, he was overtaken by an old man in a chariot, with servants running at the side of the chariot. One of these servants struck Oedipus on the back with his staff, telling him rudely to make way for his betters. This was treatment that the young man, who had been brought up as a king's son, could not tolerate. He struck the servant down and killed him. He was then attacked by the old man in the chariot, and by the other servants, and, defending his own life, he killed them all except for one who escaped and made his way back to Thebes with the news that King Laius had been killed. Since the man did not like to admit that he and the rest had been destroyed by one man single-handed, he pretended that they had been attacked by a large band of robbers.

Oedipus, with no idea that he had killed his own father, went on his way in the direction of Thebes. He went past Helicon and came

in sight of Mount Cithaeron, where, as an infant, he had been left
to die. From the country people he learned not only that the King
of Thebes had been killed, but that the whole land was terrorized
by the Sphynx, a monster with lion's body and the head of a
woman. The Sphynx guarded the approaches to the plain of
Thebes. It had a riddle to which it demanded the answer from all
whom it met. Already in the rocky plain were many piles of the
bones of those who had failed to give the right answer, and now it
had been proclaimed that if any man could answer the riddle and
free the country of the Sphynx, he should have Queen Jocasta for
his wife and himself become King of Thebes.

Oedipus resolved to make the attempt. Going out to a rock
which towered above the plain, he found the Sphynx sitting on top
of it, with great claws clutching the sandy ground. He demanded
to know the riddle and the Sphynx said: "What is it that in the
morning walks on four legs, in the midday walks on two, and in the
evening on three?"

"Is it Man," replied Oedipus. "In the morning of his childhood
he crawls on hands and knees; in the midday of his youth he walks
on his two legs; in the evening of his old age he needs a stick to
support himself, and so goes on three legs."

The Sphynx, finding that at last her riddle was answered, threw
herself down, as was fated, from the rock and died. Oedipus received his reward. He was made King of Thebes and took Jocasta,
little knowing that she was his own mother, to be his wife. So the
oracle was fulfilled, though none of those who had fulfilled it knew
what the truth was.

Oedipus for many years ruled Thebes well and wisely. He was
happy with Jocasta, who bore him four children—two twin sons
Eteocles and Polynices, and two daughters Antigone and
Ismene. It was not until these children had grown up that the
truth was revealed and the happiness of Oedipus turned into the
greatest misery.

Thebes, since the death of the Sphynx, had been prosperous and
successful; but in the end a plague fell upon the land. The cattle
died in the fields; blight fell upon the crops; then the people began
to die, and the air was full of ravens and of vultures, ill-omened
birds that came to feast upon the dead bodies of animals and of
men. The people called in vain upon the gods to help. They looked

also to their king, who had saved them before from the persecution of the Sphynx.

Oedipus sent Creon, the brother of Jocasta, to the oracle at Delphi to ask the god how Thebes might be free of the plague. The reply came back that the plague had been sent because of the murder of Laius and because not even yet had the murderer made atonement for the bloodshed.

Oedipus immediately and with his usual energy began to make inquiries into the murder which he had himself unknowingly committed so long ago. He examined those who had heard the story at the time, and he sent for the old prophet Tiresias, whose wisdom was greater than that of mortals. The gods had taken away his sight, but had given him knowledge of the future and the past.

When the old man was summoned before the king, he had no wish to speak. "Let me go home again," he said, "and do not ask me these questions. It would be better, far better, for you to remain in ignorance. Take my advice, which is meant kindly to you."

But Oedipus, anxious for his people, and determined to show himself once more their deliverer, pressed on with his inquiries. As the old prophet still refused to speak, he began to grow angry, and to insult him. "Either," he said, "you are an old cheat who knows nothing, or else you have been bribed by the murderer to conceal his name, or else perhaps you are the murderer yourself. Either speak, or suffer every punishment that I can think out for you."

Then Tiresias spoke: "You yourself, Oedipus, are the man who murdered Laius. You murdered him in the place where three roads meet on the way from Delphi. It is because of you that the plague has fallen on this city. And there is worse news still that waits for you."

Oedipus remembered the old man in the chariot whom he had killed so long ago. He was horrified at the thought that he might have killed his wife's husband and began to question her as to his appearance and the number of his servants. As she answered him, he became convinced that the prophet had spoken the truth.

But Jocasta attempted to persuade him that Tiresias should not be believed. "Even Apollo's oracle," she said, "sometimes tells lies. For example Laius was told that he would be killed by his own son, but the only son we ever had was killed and eaten by the wild beasts on Mount Cithaeron."

Oedipus was interested by this story and demanded proof of it. The goat-herd, now a very old man, who had taken the baby to Mount Cithaeron, was summoned. Oedipus questioned him closely and now, thinking that he had nothing to fear, the goat-herd admitted that he had not killed the child, as he had been told to do. Instead he had given the poor weak thing to a servant of the King of Corinth.

As he spoke, and as Oedipus, in increasing excitement, went on questioning him, Jocasta suddenly realized the truth. Oedipus had been brought up by the King of Corinth, he still had on his feet the marks of the iron that had pierced them; it was indeed he who had killed Laius, and he who, fulfilling the oracle, had married his own mother. She cried out once. "I am an unhappy woman," she said, and then, looking for the last time on Oedipus, she went into the house. Then she tied her girdle to a beam, made a running knot in it, and hanged herself.

Meanwhile Oedipus was sifting the evidence of the goat-herd. His keen intelligence saw how all the story fitted together, but only gradually could his mind grasp the truth—that, though he had never known it or suspected it, the words of the oracle had for long been proved in fact, that he had killed his father and become the husband of his mother. As he became fully conscious of his own position, he heard a cry from indoors. There he found Jocasta dead, hanging from the palace roof. In misery, despair and shame, he took the pins from the buckle of her girdle and with them pierced his eyes. Then, with the blood streaming down his face, and with all the world dark to him, he came back to his people, resolved finally to leave them and to go abroad in exile, so that he might atone for the guilt which he had never imagined as being his.

His daughters, Antigone and Ismene, went with him, and for long, guiding the steps of their blind father, they wandered in the hills and valleys of Cithaeron and the mountains of Attica. In the end they came to Colonus, a little town near Theseus's kingdom of Athens. It is a town where fine horses are bred and where all the summer the tawny nightingale sings among the berries of the ivy that cloaks the trees. Here at last Oedipus found peace. Theseus gave him sanctuary, partly for his own sake, partly because an oracle had revealed that the land where Oedipus died would be famous and prosperous. Yet if Oedipus died at all, he died in a way that was miraculous. Theseus alone saw, or might have seen, the manner of his departing from life. For suddenly, in the sunshine and among the singing of the birds, the blind king began to feel the power of the gods upon him. He left his two daughters in the grove of Colonus and commanded Theseus to lead him forward over the rolling ground to the place where he had to be. Then, taking leave of Theseus also, he went on alone, with firm, though slow, steps, as though he still had the use of his eyes. From the clear sky came the roar of thunder and Theseus, in fear and reverence for the gods, hid his eyes. When he looked up again, Oedipus had gone, taken perhaps to Heaven or lost in some invisible fold in the ground.

In leafy, well-watered Colonus, and in Athens itself he received for ever the honours due to a hero, and to one whom, in the end, the gods loved.

THE SEVEN AGAINST THEBES

When the blind Oedipus left Thebes the kingdom was divided between his two twin sons, Eteocles and Polynices. It was arranged that each brother should rule for a year, and, since Eteocles had been born first, he held the kingship for the first year. It was not long before it became clear that the hatred and jealousy which existed between the brothers would lead to trouble, if not disaster, for the city. Before the end of his first year of rule Eteocles drove Polynices from Thebes, intending to keep the royal power entirely in his hands.

Polynices, determined on his revenge, went to the court of Adrastus, King of Argos. Adrastus welcomed him, gave him his daughter in marriage and, with all his power, supported his claim to the throne of Thebes. First he sent to Eteocles the savage warrior Tydeus, an exile from Calydon who lived at the court of Argos, and was renowned both for his skill in battle and for his savagery. Tydeus, in the name of the King of Argos, demanded that Polynices should be restored to his country and to his royal rights; Eteocles, however, replied that the wolf would make friends with the lamb sooner than he would forget his anger against his brother. He defied the King of Argos to do his worst, and sent out fifty men to ambush Tydeus on his return. Tydeus killed every one of them, and returned to Argos eager for war and for revenge.

Immediately King Adrastus planned an expedition against Thebes. There were seven captains of the army—Adrastus himself, his brothers Hippomedon and Parthenopaeus, his nephew Capaneus, Tydeus, Amphiaraus, and the claimant of the throne, Polynices. One of these seven, Amphiaraus, was not only a famous warrior but also a prophet. With his skill in prophecy he knew that of the seven captains in the Argive army, only one would return alive from the war. He therefore went into hiding, telling no one except his wife Eriphyle where his hiding place was. Adrastus was now unwilling to make the expedition, since he had the greatest faith both in the generalship and in the wisdom of Amphiaraus. It was known that the prophet was entirely devoted to his wife. Polynices therefore determined to secure the help of Eriphyle.

At first she refused to tell where her husband was in hiding or to attempt to persuade him to join in a war which he knew would be fatal to nearly all the captains. But her vanity and her love for fine things proved stronger than her feelings for her husband. Polynices had brought with him from Thebes the famous necklace that Vulcan, the god of fire, had once made for Venus's daughter Harmonia, when she married Cadmus. Now he offered this necklace to Eriphyle as a bribe, and she, when she saw the flashing jewels and the varied lights that shone from each marvellously set stone, could resist no longer. She revealed where her husband was and herself joined King Adrastus and Polynices in persuading him to go to the war. Amphiaraus went, but he went unwillingly. He was angry, too, that his wife's vanity had been more powerful with her than her affection for himself, and he made his son Alcmaeon swear that, if he did not return, he would avenge his father's death by killing his mother.

So the great army, under its seven leaders, moved northwards and camped on the slopes of Mount Cithaeron in view of the walls and the seven gates of Thebes. Eteocles with his army awaited the attack inside their walls. Before the coming battle he consulted the old prophet Tiresias and Tiresias said to him: "Great indeed is the army that is coming against you. There will be death upon death. As for Thebes herself, she can be saved only by the sacrifice of the youngest child of Cadmus's blood."

Creon, brother of Jocasta and uncle of Eteocles, heard the words of the prophet with fear and horror. He knew that his own son, Menoeceus, was the youngest of the descendants of Cadmus, and he planned to have the boy sent out of the city into safety. But the young boy had himself heard the prophecy of Tiresias. "I am too young to fight," he said, "but still I can be of more good to my country than even the bravest fighting man." Then he ran to the wall and hurled himself down to his death among the army that was besieging his city.

Thebes itself was certainly saved. Each of the seven generals of the Argive army led his force against one of the gates, but, after bitter fighting, each one was repulsed. Then Eteocles and the Thebans sallied out and fighting raged throughout the plain. Champions on both sides fell. The dusty ground was covered with the still or writhing bodies of men and horses. So great indeed was the slaughter that Eteocles sent a message to the invading army and proposed that the whole issue of the war should be decided by single combat between himself and Polynices.

Polynices welcomed the proposal, and the two brothers stood out alone between the armies for their last fight. So fiercely they fought that each seemed possessed by some god who fanned their unnatural anger into something more than human. The armies on each side stood applauding their own champions, but so even was the fight that none could say which of the two seemed likely to be the victor. At one moment it seemed that the force and fury of Polynices must be irresistible; at the next moment it appeared that Eteocles was on the point of beating down his enemy. Swords carved the flesh from arms and shoulders; blood streamed to the ground, and still the brothers fought grimly, neither giving way a foot. Even when loss of blood made their blows weaker, their anger was as strong as ever, and in the end each sank to the ground in death, each having won the victory and each having been defeated.

Instead of this double death being a signal for peace, it merely roused the two armies to greater ferocity. All day they fought and, as the prophet Amphiaraus had foretold, six out of the seven generals of the Argives lost their lives. Tydeus slew the Theban general who was opposing him, but was himself mortally wounded. Before he died he had brought to him his enemy's body which, in his rage, he horribly maltreated. They say that the goddess Minerva was on her way to help him and to make him immortal, but that, seeing his cruel savagery, she turned away from him and left him to his death. Amphiaraus himself died, and before he died called upon the gods to witness the treachery of his wife. His son, as he had promised, avenged his father's death, and took back from his mother the fatal necklace. Later he was pursued by furies, nor did the necklace bring him any good fortune.

Of all the leaders of the force of Argos, only King Adrastus returned. Thebes remained unconquered, but the victory had been bought at the price of the blood of its best and strongest soldiers. Creon, uncle of the two sons of Oedipus, became king. His aim was to restore the strength of his city and bring back peace and good government after the war; yet his first act was to bring more trouble to the family of Oedipus and to himself.

ANTIGONE

Creon became King of Thebes at a time when the city had lost half its army and at least half of its best warriors in civil war. The war was over. Eteocles, the king, was dead; dead also was his brother Polynices, who had come with the army of the Argives to fight for his own right to the kingdom.

Creon, as the new king, decided first of all to show his people how unforgivable it was to make war upon one's own country. To Eteocles, who had reigned in Thebes, he gave a splendid burial; but he ordered that, upon pain of death, no one was to prepare for funeral or even sprinkle earth upon the body of Polynices. It was to lie as it had fallen in the plain for birds and beasts to devour. To make certain that his orders should be carried out Creon set a patrol of men to watch the body night and day.

Antigone and Ismene, sisters of Polynices, heard the king's orders with alarm and shame. They had loved both their brothers, and hated the thought that one of them should lie unburied, unable to join the world of the ghosts, multilated and torn by the teeth of dogs and jackals and by the beaks and talons of birds. Ismene, in spite of her feelings, did not dare oppose the king; but Antigone stole out of the city by night, and, after searching among the piled-up bodies of those who had died in the great battle, found the body of her brother. She lightly covered it with dust, and said for it the prayers that ought to be said for the dead.

Next day it was reported to Creon that someone (the guards did not know whom) had disobeyed the king's orders and scattered earth over the body of Polynices. Creon swore an oath that if the guilty person should be found, even though that person was a member of his own family, he or she should die for it. He threatened the guards also with death if they failed to find the criminal, and told them immediately to uncover the body and leave it to the birds and beasts of prey.

That day a hot wind blew from the south. Clouds of dust covered the plain, and Antigone again stole out of the city to complete her work of burying her brother. This time, however, the guards kept better watch. They seized her and brought her before King Creon.

Creon was moved by no other feelings than the feelings of one whose orders have been disobeyed. "Did you know," he asked Antigone, "the law that I made and the penalty that I laid down for those who broke the law?"

"I knew it," Antigone replied, "but there are other laws, made not by men but by the gods. There is a law of pity and of mercy. That law is to be obeyed first. After I have obeyed that, I will, if I may, obey the laws that are made by men."

"If you love your brother," said Creon, "more than the established laws of your country and your king, then you must bear the penalty of the laws, loving your brother in the world of the dead."

"You may kill me with your laws," Antigone replied, "but to me death is, in all these sufferings, less of an evil than would be treachery to my brother or cowardice when the time came to help him."

Her confident and calm words stirred Creon to even greater anger. Now her sister Ismene, who had at first been too frightened to help Antigone in her defiance of the law, came forward and asked to be allowed to share in Antigone's punishment; but Antigone would not permit her to claim a share with her in the deed or in its results. Nor would Creon listen to any appeal for mercy. Not wishing to have the blood of his niece upon his own hands, he gave orders that she should be put into an underground chamber, walled up from the light and then left to die.

So Antigone was carried away to a slow and lingering death, willing to suffer it, since she had obeyed the promptings of her heart. She had been about to marry Haemon, the king's son, but, instead of the palace that she would have entered as a bride, she was now going to the house of death.

Haemon himself came to beg his father to be merciful. He spoke mildly, but let it clearly be understood that neither he nor the rest of the people of Thebes approved of so savage a sentence. It was true that Antigone had broken the law; but it was also true that she had acted as a sister ought to act when her brother was unburied. And, Haemon said, though most people did not dare oppose the king in his anger, nevertheless most people in their hearts felt as *he* did.

Haemon's love for Antigone and even his goodwill towards his father only increased the fury of the king. With harsh words he drove his son from him.

Next came the blind prophet Tiresias to warn King Creon that the gods were angry with him both for his merciless punishment of Antigone and for leaving the body of Polynices to be desecrated by the wild beasts and birds. Creon might have remembered how often in the past the words of Tiresias had been fulfilled, but now, in his obstinate rage, he merely insulted the prophet. "You have been bribed," he said, "either by Haemon or by some traitor to try and save the life of a criminal by dishonest threats that have nothing to do with gods at all."

Tiresias turned his sightless eyes on the king. "This very day," he said, "before the sun sets, you will pay twice, yes, with two dead bodies, for the sin which you could easily have avoided. As for me, I shall keep far away from one who, in his own pride, rejects the gods and is sure to suffer."

Tiresias went away, and now Creon for the first time began to feel that it was possible that his punishments had been too hard. For the first time, but too late, he was willing to listen to the advice of his council, who begged him to be merciful, to release Antigone and to give burial to the body of Polynices.

With no very good grace Creon consented to do as he had been advised. He gave orders for the burial of Polynices and went himself to release Antigone from the prison in which she had been walled away from the light. Joyfully his son Haemon went ahead of the rest with pick axes and bars for breaking down the wall. But when they broke the stones of the wall they found that Antigone had made a noose out of the veil which she was wearing and had hanged herself. Haemon could not bear to outlive her. He drew his sword and plunged it into his heart before the eyes of his father. Then he fell forward dead on the body of the girl whom he had wished to be his wife.

As for Creon he had scarcely time to lament for his son when news reached him of another disaster. His wife had heard of Haemon's death and she too had taken her own life. So the words of Tiresias were fulfilled.

TEREUS, PROCNE AND PHILOMELA

Tereus was a great warrior king of Thrace. Once he came from the north and helped King Pandion of Athens against his enemies. Though he was a barbarian, he was strong and wealthy, so that Pandion was glad of his alliance and allowed him to marry his daughter Procne. But neither Juno, the goddess of marriage, nor any god or goddess blessed this wedding. Nor did they bless the birth of the child Itys who was born to Tereus and Procne. Instead the screech-owl sat upon their roofs and cried. This was the omen both for the wedding and for the birth. All Thrace, however, rejoiced at the alliance which Tereus had made, and, at the birth of Itys there were feasts held throughout the country.

Now four years passed and Procne said to her husband: "If you love me at all, either send me to visit my sister in Athens or else let her come to see me here. You can promise my father that after a short stay she will come back."

So Tereus launched his fleet and, with sail and oar, came to Piraeus, the port of Athens. As soon as he had met his father-in-law they clasped their right hands together and began their talk by wishing each other well. Tereus was telling how his wife desired to see her sister and would promise that she should return quickly, when Philomela, the sister of whom he spoke, entered the room. Her clothes were rich, but her own beauty was richer still. She was like a nymph of the woods or streams, except that she was better dressed and had more refined manners.

As soon as he saw her Tereus fell in love with her. In his wicked heart he desired her love rather than her sister's, and now he repeated Procne's message over and over again. As he spoke there were tears in his eyes, so that old Pandion and Philomela gave him credit not for his wickedness, but for a kind heart. Philomela herself, little knowing what was to come of it, put her arms round her father's neck, begging him for her sake as well as her sister's to allow her to go back to Thrace with Tereus. Her father gave her her own way, and the poor girl thanked him. What she thought would bring such pleasure to her and her sister would in fact bring ruin upon them both.

In the evening a royal feast was prepared. Wine was drunk from cups of gold. They rested, and next day Pandion took the hand of Tereus and, with tears in his eyes, said to him: "My son, it is natural for your wife to want to see her sister and for her sister to want to see her. Now I put Philomela in your care. Look after her well, and in a short time send her back to me to be the comfort of my declining years. However short a time she is away, to me the time will seem long."

Tereus made promises that he never intended to keep. Now he felt wickedly secure of his prize, and as the ship cut its way through the blue sea to Thrace, he gazed at Philomela in the same way as a hungry eagle gazes upon a hare that he has caught in his hooked claws and dropped helpless into his high nest.

As soon as the boat reached the shores of Thrace, Tereus dragged Philomela off to a hut in the deep woods. There he shut her up, pale and trembling, frightened of everything and tearfully asking him where her sister was. And now he admitted his wicked purpose and forced her, alone and helpless, to be his wife against her will. When she reproached him for his treachery to her, to her father and to her sister, and threatened to tell everyone of his wickedness, both anger and fear drove him on to further cruelty. He bound her hands and with his sword cut out her tongue, so that she could never reveal to anyone what had happened to her.

Then, setting guards around the hut, he went to his palace where Procne was waiting for him, anxious to see both her sister and her husband. Tereus groaned aloud and told a false story of how Philomela had died on the journey. His pretended tears convinced his wife. She took her golden robe from her shoulders, and dressed herself in black. Also she built a monument to her sister's memory and made sacrifices to her spirit. True enough that her sister deserved to be mourned for, but not in this way.

A year went by. What could Philomela do? Guards and a stout wall of stone prevented her escape. Her speechless mouth could tell her tale to no one. Yet sorrow can sharpen the wits, and cleverness often comes to one's help in misfortune. On her loom she hung a Thracian web, and, weaving in purple on a white background, she told in pictures the story of how she had been wronged. Then, when the weaving was finished, she took the web from the loom and gave it to an old woman who was her own servant, begging her in gestures to take it to the queen. The old woman, not knowing what she was carrying, took it to Procne who unrolled the cloth, and read and understood the message that it contained. She did not utter a word, and it was strange that she was able to keep silent. Grief and anger made her speechless. Nor was there time for tears. She would mix right and wrong together, seeking revenge before anything else.

It was the time when the women of Thrace hold their feast to Bacchus on the mountains by night. There they dance and revel madly. No man at this time dares to stand in their way. And now Procne, dressed as a worshipper of Bacchus and surrounded by a crowd of women, rushed through the woods, pretending to be pos-

sessed by the god. She came to the hut where Philomela was imprisoned, swept aside the guards and then, hiding her sister's face and
disguising her with wreathes of ivy, she took her back to her palace.
Then she folded her in her arms, looking with pity on the sad and
speechless figure that she had believed dead. They might for long
have wept together, but Procne's anger was too great for this.
"There is no room here for tears," she said. "A sword would be
better, or something stronger than a sword. I am ready for anything—to burn the palace with my husband in it, or to cut him
limb from limb, letting his wicked life-blood flow away through a
thousand wounds. I only hesitate to find what will give him most
pain."

While she was speaking her son Itys came to her. Then she realized what to do and prepared a grim and terrible crime. Drawing a
knife she killed the boy with one blow. Philomela cut his throat
and together the two sisters cut the body to pieces. Then they
roasted part of it and boiled other parts in brass kettles on the
fire.

This was the flesh which Procne invited her husband to eat. She
pretended that it was a sacred feast at which only a husband was
allowed to be present, and she made all the slaves and attendants
go away. The savage king sat alone on his high throne. Then, when
he had filled himself with the flesh of his own son, he said "Bring
Itys to me!"

Procne could not conceal her cruel joy. She longed to be the first
to tell him the dreadful news. "If you want Itys," she said, "look
for him inside your own body."

Then Philomela, with loose hair and hands stained with the
blood, leaped forward. She could say nothing of what was in her
heart, but she hurled the boy's head straight into his father's face.

Tereus sprang to his feet, overturning the table and crying aloud
in his agony. Then he drew his sword and rushed at the two sisters.

They fled from him, and as they fled, they seemed to be flying on
wings. And indeed they were. In the shape of birds one, Philomela,
flew to the woods, the other, Procne, flew up to the roof. Now
Philomela is a nightingale and still in song mourns for her cruel
fate. Procne is a swallow and bears still in the feathers of her breast
the marks of blood. Tereus himself, as he sped in pursuit, was

changed to a hoopoe. On his head there is a stiff crest, and instead of his huge sword he has a long and curving beak.

CUPID AND PSYCHE

Psyche was the youngest daughter of a king and queen. She had two elder sisters both of whom were remarkably beautiful. Their beauty, however, might be described in words. But the beauty of Psyche herself was past all description, as was the majesty of her bearing and her sweet and gracious disposition. So from all over the world people came to the country where she lived merely to look at her. They looked at her with wonder and adoration, believing her to be either the goddess Venus herself, who was born from the foam of the sea, or else a new Venus, no less divine than the goddess of beauty and of love.

Thus the temples and ceremonies of Venus were neglected. People no longer offered sacrifices and prayed to her. Instead they thronged to visit Psyche, worshipping her as soon as she left her home in the morning, and laying garlands before her feet.

The true Venus was greatly angered by the neglect shown to her by men. "It is I," she said to herself, "to whom, on Mount Ida, Paris gave the prize of beauty. And am I to share my honours with a mere mortal girl? She will soon be sorry for being more beautiful than is allowed."

Then Venus called for her winged son, Cupid, the god of love, who with his arrows can conquer the gods themselves, who ranges over the earth like a bee, the brilliant and mischievous youth. "Now, my dear son," she said to him, "you must revenge the injury that is done to your mother. Mortals are worshipping this girl Psyche instead of me. I want you to make her fall in love with some wretched creature, poor and abject, the ugliest in the world. You with your bow and arrows can do this."

She took him then to the city where Psyche lived and pointed her out to him. Then she herself, after kissing her son, went to the shore near by, planted her rosy feet on the sea-water, making it calm, and took her way over the sea to her sacred island of Cyprus. Around her played the dolphins and sea gods rose from the waves to make music for her on their horns of shell; nymphs of the sea came to shade her from the sun with their veils of silk or to hold before her eyes her golden mirror.

Meanwhile Psyche received no advantages from the adoration which was given everywhere to her extraordinary beauty. She was praised and worshipped, but no king or noble or even any common person came to woo her to be his wife. All wondered at her, but only as one might wonder at a picture or exquisite statue. Her two sisters, though less beautiful than she, had married kings. Psyche sat alone at home, hating the beauty which delighted everyone except herself.

In the end her father, suspecting that the gods must be envious of his youngest daughter, sent messengers to the oracle of Apollo to inquire what he should do. The reply of the oracle was: "Let Psyche be dressed in black, as for a funeral, and let her be placed on the top of the mountain that rises above your city. Her husband is no mortal being. He is like a dragon that flies in the night. The gods of heaven and earth, even the darkness of Styx, fear his powers."

Psyche's father and mother, who had been so proud of their daughter's beauty, now wept and lamented the sad fate that was in store for her. What the oracle commanded seemed more like death than a wedding. As they prepared to carry out the will of the oracle not only they, but all the people, wept continuously in mourning for the unhappy event. But Psyche said: "You should have wept before, in the time when everyone worshipped me and gave me the name of Venus on earth. Now you see what has come of my beauty. I am overtaken by the jealousy of the gods. Come now, lead me to the dreadful place. I myself long for this marriage I have been promised. At least it will end my unhappiness."

Then, in a great procession, most unlike a wedding procession, they took her to the wild rocky summit of the mountain. There were no glad songs or bright lights. Tears put out the torches. The people went back to their houses with bowed heads, and Psyche's wretched parents shut themselves for days in their palace, mourning for her fate.

Meanwhile Psyche was left alone, trembling and weeping, on the high rock. But there came a mild gentle breeze which softly lifted her from the ground and carried her, with her clothes lightly fluttering, gradually past the precipices and forests till it brought her to a deep and sheltered valley where she was laid down on a bed of grassy turf among the most beautiful and sweet-smelling flowers. This soft bed and the fragrance of the flowers calmed Psyche's restless and astonished mind. Soon she rose to her feet and saw in front of her a fine and pleasant wood with, in the middle of it, a running river as bright as crystal. And there among the trees stood a palace so beautiful that you would think it to be a mansion for one of the gods. The roof was made of citron and ivory. It was supported by pillars of gold. The pavements were of precious stones arranged by some great artist in the form of splendid pictures of animals, birds and flowers. The walls were built of great blocks of gold, and each door and porchway seemed to give out its own light.

The wonder of the place so enchanted Psyche that she boldly went inside and here again she found everything magnificent and looked lovingly at everything. There were fine store rooms full of rich dresses and of all kinds of wealth. What greatly surprised her was that in all the palace nothing was barred or bolted, nor was there anyone there to guard all these immense riches. While she stood still, half in amazement and half in delight at what she saw, she heard a voice, though no body was to be seen. "Why do you wonder, my lady, at all this wealth? It is all yours to command. We, whose voices you hear, are your servants and are ready to do everything you desire. Go therefore to your room and rest on your bed. Then tell us what kind of bath you wish to have prepared for you. Then, when you have refreshed your body, a royal dinner will be served."

Psyche, wondering still more, went to her room and rested. After a perfumed bath, she found the table all set for her convenience. Invisible hands brought her rare wines and delicious dishes of food. After dinner another unseen servant came and sang; yet another played on the harp. Then it seemed that she was in the middle of a great choir of voices singing most perfectly to the sound of all kinds of instruments. Yet singers and instruments were alike invisible.

As night approached the concert of music ended and Psyche went to bed. Now she became frightened at the thought of the terrible husband promised her by the oracle; but again invisible voices assured her that her husband was one to be loved and not feared. When it was dark he came and lay down beside her. Though she never saw his face, she heard his voice and felt his body. In the morning he left before dawn, after telling her of his love and promising to return to her each night. So, though she was lonely in the day, she passed each day in great pleasure, being most pleased with the beautiful singing voices that surrounded her; and each night she spent with her husband whom she loved more and more.

Meanwhile her father and mother did nothing but weep and lament for their daughter whom they thought must certainly be lost for ever, either devoured by wild beasts or by the terrible dragon. The news of her fate spread far and wide, and Psyche's two sisters came to visit their parents and to mourn with them. That night Psyche's husband spoke to her. He said: "My sweet love and dear wife, a cruel fortune is bringing you into terrible danger, and I wish you to be greatly careful. Your sisters, thinking that you are dead, will come to the mountain in order to mourn for you. If you hear their voices, do not answer them, for, if you do, you will bring me great sorrow and bring yourself absolute ruin."

Psyche listened to him and promised that she would do as he said; but, when he went away next day, she passed all her time in weeping, and began to think that her fine house was really no better than a prison, if she was allowed to see no one and not even able to console her dear sisters who were mourning for her. She ate nothing that day and took no pleasure in her music. Red-eyed with crying, she went to bed early. Her husband also returned earlier than usual and at once he said to her: "Is this the way you keep your promise, my sweet wife? Crying all day and not even now comforted in your husband's arms? Do what you want to do. You may remember my words too late, if you bring on yourself your own ruin."

Then Psyche begged him more and more urgently to give her what she wanted, that she might see her sisters and speak with them. In the end he was won over by her entreaties and told her that she should give her sisters all the gold and jewels that she wished; but he earnestly entreated her never to be led by her sisters' advice into a longing to see his own face. If she did so, he said, she would lose the good life she had now, and would never feel his arms about her again.

Psyche was now full of gratitude and love for him. "I would die a hundred times," she said, "rather than be separated from you, my sweet husband. Whoever you are, I love you and keep you in my heart as though you were my own life. I could not love you more if you were the god Cupid himself. Now I beg you to let your servant the West Wind bring my sisters down to me here to-morrow, as he brought me." Then she kissed him and called him her sweet soul, her husband and her darling. He, such was the power of her love, agreed to do as she desired.

Next day her sisters came to the rock where Psyche had been seen last, and there they cried and lamented for her, so that the rocks rang with their cries. The sound came to Psyche's ears and she called back to them, "I whom you weep for am here, alive and happy." Then she called to the West Wind who gently carried her two sisters down to the valley where she lived. For long there was nothing but embracing and tears of joy. Then Psyche showed her sisters her gorgeous house with its stores of treasure. She ordered the unseen musicians to sing; she feasted them with fine food and wine, and they (shameful creatures as they were) became filled with envy of her and determined in some way to ruin her happiness. Often they asked her about her husband, and Psyche, remembering the warning that she had had, pretended that she knew him by sight. He was a handsome young man, she said, with the down just growing on his chin, and his chief pleasure in the day was to go hunting in the mountains. Then, since she feared that she might make some mistake in her speech, she gave them all the gold and jewels that they could carry and ordered the West Wind to take them back to the mountain.

No sooner were they alone together than they each began bitterly and enviously to complain of Psyche's good fortune. "She is the youngest one of us three," said the older sister. "Why should she have a palace and stores of wealth? Why should she have those miraculous servants and be able to give orders to the West Wind? Indeed her husband may end by making her into a goddess. Even now she has every happiness. As for me, my husband is old enough to be my father. He is as bald as a coot and he keeps all his riches under lock and key."

The second sister was just as jealous as the first. "My husband," she said, "is always ill and I have to waste my time nursing him as though I were a doctor's assistant. I certainly cannot bear to see my younger sister so happy. Let us therefore tell no one of what we have seen; and let us try to think out some way in which we can do her harm."

So these unnatural sisters hid the gold and jewels which Psyche had given them. Instead of consoling their parents with the news of her safety and happiness, they pretended that they had searched the mountains for her in vain and that they were, with their sad faces, still mourning for her loss. Afterwards they went back to their own homes, and there began to think out plans by which they could somehow injure the sister whom they pretended to love.

Meanwhile Psyche's husband again spoke to her in the night. "My sweet wife," he said to her, "those wicked sisters of yours are threatening you with great evil. I think that they will come to see you again. Now I beg you either not to talk with them at all (which would be the best thing) or at least not to talk to them about me. If you obey me, we shall still be happy. Already you have in your body a child of yours and mine. If you conceal my secret, the child, when it is born, will be a god; if you do not, then it will be a mortal."

Psyche was very glad to know that she would have a divine child and was more pleased with her husband than ever. But her sisters hastened on with their wicked plots and, as they had arranged, came once more to the country where Psyche was. Once again her husband warned her: "Now is the last and final day," he said. "Now I beg you, sweet Psyche, to have pity on yourself, on me and on our unborn child. Do not even see these wicked women who do not deserve to be called your sisters."

But Psyche said, "Dear husband, you know that you can trust me. Did I not keep silent before? Let me at least see my sisters, since I cannot see you. Not that I blame you for this, and indeed darkness is like day to me when I hold you, who are my light, within my arms."

With such words she persuaded him once more to order the West Wind to carry her sisters to her. Before dawn he left her, and early in the day her sisters were brought to the soft and fragrant valley and to her palace. They were gladly welcomed as before by Psyche, who told them proudly that before many months she would become a mother. This made the sisters more jealous than ever, but they hid their feelings beneath smiling faces and began to ask her once more about her husband. Psyche, forgetting that before she had told them that he was a young man, now said that he was a great merchant from a nearby province, and that among his brown hair he had a few hairs of grey. Instantly the two sisters, when Psyche had left them for a moment alone, began to say that she must be lying. "Perhaps," said one of them, "she has never seen her husband. If so, then he must be one of the gods and she will have a child who will be more than mortal. How can we bear this, that our youngest sister should have everything? Let us at once think out some lies by which we may destroy her."

So they spoke together, and when Psyche returned to them she found that they were both weeping. Not knowing that their tears were all pretended, she asked them in surprise what had happened. "Poor Psyche," they said, "you who do not know the face of your husband, it is terrible for us to tell you the truth, but we must do so to save your life and the life of the child who will be born to you. The real shape of your husband is not what you think at all. No, it is a great and savage snake that comes to you every night. Remember the oracle that said you would be married to a fierce dragon. The country people have often seen him, swimming through the rivers as he returns at evening. They say that he will wait a little longer and then eat both you and your child. We have done our sad duty in telling you of this. If you are wise, you will take our loving advice and escape from your danger while you still may."

Poor Psyche in her simplicity believed in the false story and in her sisters' love. "It is true," she said, "that I have never seen my husband's face, and he tells me that something dreadful will happen to me if I try to see it. Oh, what am I to do?"

Then her sisters began to work still more upon her fears. "We will help you in this, as in everything," they said. "What you must do is to take a knife as sharp as a razor and hide it under your pillow. You must have hidden also in your bedroom a lamp with oil ready for burning. When he comes to bed and his limbs are all relaxed in sleep, you must get up quietly, on your bare feet, light the lamp, and, holding the knife firmly, cut off the head of that poisonous serpent just where it joins the neck. If you do this, we will come back to you next day. We will take all the riches out of his house and marry you to some real man who is not a monster."

Then these wicked women left her, and Psyche, trembling and shrinking from the thought of it, still prepared to do what her sisters had advised. Night came, and her husband, after he had kissed her and taken her in his arms, soon fell asleep. Psyche, made bold by her fear, yet still scarcely able to believe that what her sisters had told her was true, slipped from the bed, grasped the knife firmly in her right hand and took the lamp, hardly daring to wonder what she would see when the lamp was lit. What she saw was no monster, but the sweetest of all things, Cupid himself, at whose sight even the lamp burned more brightly. His hair was gold and seemed itself to shine; his neck was whiter than milk; the tender down on the feathers of his wings trembled with the light movement of his breathing and of the air. For long Psyche gazed in love and wonder at the beauty of his divine face, his smooth and soft body. In shame at what she had thought of doing she turned the knife against herself, but the knife shrunk from such a dreadful act and slipped from her hands. At the foot of the bed were Cupid's bow and arrows, small weapons for so great a god. Psyche took them up and, as she tried the sharpness of an arrow on her finger, she pricked herself. Then of her own accord she fell in love with Love and she bent over the bed, kissing him in joy and thankfulness as he slept.

As she was doing so a drop of burning oil fell on the white shoulder of the sleeping god. He woke and saw that she had broken her promise and her faith. Without uttering a word he fled away from her kisses and her embraces; but she clung to him, following him out of the great palace and crying to him.

Then he alighted on the top of a cypress-tree and spoke angrily to her: "Oh foolish Psyche, think how I disobeyed the orders of my mother, who told me that you should be married to some base and worthless man, and instead of this I came myself to be your husband. Did I seem a monster to you that you should try to cut off my head with its eyes that love you so much? Did I not warn you often of this? Your sisters will suffer for what they have done. You too will suffer from not having me with you."

He fled away through the air and Psyche, as long as she could see him, kept her eyes fixed on him as he went, weeping and crying for him. When he had gone beyond her sight, in her despair she threw herself into the running river; but the gentle stream would not take her life; instead it set her on the bank, where again she lamented what she had lost.

The sun rose in the sky and Psyche, weary and wretched, turned away from the palace where she had lived, and wandered through forests and rocky ways aimlessly, except that her aim was to find somehow, if it might be possible, her husband again. In her wandering she came to the city where the husband of her eldest sister was king. She could not forgive her sister's treachery, and now she pretended to be more simple than she really was. To her sister's questions she replied, "I took your advice, my dear sister, but, when I raised the lamp, I saw no monster but Cupid himself. Because of my disobedience he has left me, and he said that instead of me he would have you as his wife."

No sooner had Psyche spoken these words than her sister, without offering Psyche herself any help in her distress, hurried away from her home and came to the mountain as she had done before. There was no West Wind blowing, but in spite of this the greedy and deceitful creature threw herself down, crying out: "Now Cupid, I come to you. Take me to yourself as a more worthy wife." Instead of the gentle passage through the air which she had expected, her body was torn and broken on the rocks. Wild beasts and birds tore it limb from limb and devoured it. The other sister suffered the same fate, for Psyche in her wanderings came also to her city and told her the same story that she had told to the elder of the two. Her greed and folly were the same, and she had the punishment that she deserved.

So Psyche went through country after country looking for her husband Cupid. He, however, was resting in his mother's house, ill and suffering from the wound in the shoulder which had been made by the burning oil. Nor did his mother Venus yet know anything of what had happened. But a talkative white gull came to her as she was bathing on the sea-shore and told her of how Cupid was wounded and how he had lived in marriage with her enemy Psyche. At this news the anger of Venus grew greater than ever it had been. "Will he," she said, "not only disobey his own mother, but actually fall in love with this wicked girl whose beauty was said to be equal to mine? I shall lock him in the house and make him suffer for it. As for the girl, I shall find her and make her wish she had never set eyes upon my son."

Then she mounted her glorious chariot of gold, thick set with precious stones. Four white doves drew the chariot lightly through the air; sparrows chirped merrily around it, and there followed flocks of all kinds of singing birds, who, being in the choir of Venus, had no fear of hawks, eagles or other fierce birds of prey. So, as the clouds yielded before her, Venus went on her way to heaven and there she complained to all the gods and goddesses of her son Cupid and of his love for Psyche. The others, and especially Juno and Ceres, tried to soothe her anger, partly because they were afraid of Cupid themselves; but Venus refused to be comforted, and ordered her servants to search for Psyche throughout the world.

Meanwhile Psyche, tired out with her wandering and with the weight of her child that had not yet been born, visited the temples of all the gods, asking them for their help. Juno and Ceres indeed would have wished to help her, but they did not dare to offend Venus. Though all pitied her, none would give her rest and sanctuary, so that in the end Psyche decided, in her despair, that she would go to the house of Venus herself. "Perhaps," she thought, "my mother-in-law will forgive me and have pity on me. Perhaps I shall see my husband. Then at least I shall die happy. And in any case my life is now unbearable."

Venus, when she saw the girl for whom she had been so long searching, laughed cruelly at her. "So you have at last decided to come and call on me, have you?" she said. "I suppose you are thinking that, just because you are going to have a baby, I shall be glad to be called a grandmother! You wicked immoral girl, I shall soon show you what I think of you."

Then she leapt on Psyche, tearing her clothes and pulling her hair and knocking her head upon the ground. Afterwards, with her fierce cruel anger satisfied, she put in front of her a great pile of wheat, barley, millet, poppy-seed, pease, lentils and beans. She said, "You are so ugly that no one could want you for your face. Possibly you might find a husband by being a good housewife. Let me see what you can do. I order you to separate all these different grains, each from each, before I come back from dinner." Then Venus, putting garlands on her bright gold hair, went away to a great ban-

quiet and Psyche sat in front of the heap of grain, weeping to herself since she knew that her task was impossible.

But a little ant took pity on her. He went out and spoke to all the other ants, saying, "My friends, let us help this poor girl who is the wife of Cupid and in great danger of her life." So the ants came and with their quick careful labour soon neatly separated the grains each in its own pile.

At midnight Venus returned, all fragrant with perfumes and well warmed with wine. When she saw how the work was done, she said: "This is not your doing, you vile wicked thing. It must be the work of him who loves you." Then she threw Psyche a crust of brown bread and she saw that Cupid was locked in the most secure room of the house. So these two, who loved each other, spent separate and sad hours in the same house.

In the morning Venus came to Psyche and said, "You see that river over there, with reeds and bushes along the banks. By the river is a flock of sheep which have fleeces gleaming with gold. Go and bring me back some of their wool."

Psyche rose from the hard floor and went out. Her real wish now was to throw herself in the river and die; but when she reached the river a tall green reed, by divine inspiration, spoke to her and said: "Poor innocent Psyche, do not stain my holy water by your death. But do not go near those terrible wild sheep until after the middle of the day. Till noon they are fierce and will kill anyone who comes near them. Afterwards they will rest in the shade and you may easily go up to them and take the wool which you will find hanging on the briars."

Warned by this gentle reed, Psyche did as she was advised and in the afternoon came back to Venus with her apron full of the wool from the golden fleeces. Venus still frowned at her in anger. "This again," she said, "is no work of your own. Now I will prove whether you have the courage that you pretend to have. Do you see that overhanging rock at the top of the great mountain over there? From that rock gushes out a stream of black and freezing water that feeds the rivers of Hell, Styx and Cocytus. Go to the very summit and bring me a bottle of water from the middle of the source of the stream."

Psyche climbed the mountain, but when she drew near the summit she thought indeed that it would be better to hurl herself down on the rocks than to proceed any further with her task. The black stream ran in great foaming cataracts, or slid over slippery stone. Even the force of water and the rugged steep slopes were enough to make her journey impossible. Then on each side of the stream she saw great dragons creeping over the hollow rocks and stretching out their long necks. Their sleepless eyes never ceased to watch the sacred water, and the water itself foamed and bubbled with voices all saying, "Go away! Go away! Fly or you will die."

Psyche therefore stood still, weeping at the hopelessness of what lay before her. But Jupiter's royal eagle saw her and wished to do good to the wife of Cupid. He flew past her face and said to her, "Poor simple girl, do you think that you can even approach these terrible waters that are feared even by the gods? Give me your bottle." Then, taking her bottle in his beak, he flew past the darting tongues and flashing teeth of the dragons, plunged the bottle in the stream and brought it back filled with the water of Styx. Psyche took it back to Venus who again looked angrily at her and spoke harshly. "You must be," she said, "some sort of a witch or enchantress to carry out my orders so quickly. Well, there is one more thing that I want you to do. Take this box and go down to hell, to the dwellings of the dead. There you are to ask Proserpine, the Queen of Hell, to send me a little of her beauty, just enough to last for a day. Tell her that I have lost some of mine in looking after my son who is wounded. But you must return quickly, as I have to go to the theatre of the gods."

Now poor Psyche felt that all pretence was over and that she was surely doomed to die. She knew of no way of going to the House of the Dead except by killing herself, and so she climbed a high tower, resolved to throw herself down from the top. But the tower spoke to her and said: "Do not yield, Psyche, to this last and final danger. If you kill yourself, you will indeed visit the world of the dead, but you will never come back to this world. Listen to my words and do as I say. Not far from here is Taenarum where you will find a great hole in the ground. Go down the path bravely and it will lead you to the very palace of Pluto. But you must not go empty-handed. In your hands you must carry two cakes of barley and honey mixed. In your mouth you must have two halfpennies. When you have gone some way on your journey you will see a lame donkey carrying wood and a lame man driving him. The man will ask you to help him pick up some of the sticks that have fallen, but

you must go on without a word, and do no such thing. Then you
will come to the river of the dead where the foul old man Charon
with his leaking boat ferries the souls between the banks. He will
do nothing unless he is paid, and you must let him take from your
mouth one of your two halfpennies. When you are on the black
and deathly river you will see an old man swimming there who will
beg and pray you to help him into the boat. You must not listen to
him, since this is not allowed. When you have crossed the river you
will pass by some old women weaving. They will ask you to help
them, but you must not listen to them. These are all traps which
Venus will set for you so as to make you drop one of the cakes from
your hands. Yet without these cakes you can never make the journey
or return again; for you will come to the great three-headed watch-
dog Cerberus, whose barking rings for ever through this desolate
plain. He will never let you pass till you have given him one of your
cakes to eat. Once you have passed him you will come into the
presence of Proserpine and she will offer you a fine chair on which
to sit and fine food to eat. But you must sit upon the ground and
ask only for brown bread. Then tell her why you have come and
receive what she gives you. On your return give the other cake to
Cerberus and your other halfpenny to grim Charon. Then you can
come back to the upper air by the same way as you went down.
Above all, do not look inside the box that Proserpine will give you.
There is no need for you to have any curiosity about the treasure
of heavenly beauty."

So the tower advised Psyche, and she took the two halfpennies
and the two cakes and then made her way to Taenarum. She descended the dreadful path to Hell, passed by the lame donkey in
silence, paid her halfpenny to Charon, gave no attention either to
the man swimming in the river or to the women weaving, gave one
of her cakes to the terrible watchdog and came finally into the
presence of Proserpine. Here she refused the fine food that was set
before her and sat humbly on the ground, asking only for a crust of
bread. Then she gave Venus's message and received the secret gift
in the closed box. On her way back she gave the cake to Cerberus
and her last halfpenny to Charon. So she reached the upper air in
safety, but then she said to herself, "What a fool I am to be carrying in this box the divine beauty and not to take a little of it for
myself. If I take some I may please my husband in the end."

She opened the box but could see no beauty in it at all. Instead a deadly sleep came over her like a cloud and she fell fainting to the ground, lying where she fell like a dead body.

But Cupid was now cured of his wound, and, in longing for his wife, had climbed out of an upper window. He flew straight to her and, when he had wiped away the deadly sleep from her face and put it back in the box, he woke her by gently pricking her hand with one of his arrows. "Poor creature," he said, "again you were nearly ruined by your excess of curiosity. Now go back to my mother and leave me to arrange the rest." Then he flew into the air and Psyche brought the box to Venus.

Cupid meanwhile flew up to heaven and begged Jupiter, the father of the gods, to help him in his faithful love. Jupiter called all the gods and goddesses to council and said to them, "It is not good that Cupid should be always loose and wandering about the earth. He has chosen a wife and it is right that he should enjoy her company and her love. In order that the marriage shall not be an unequal one I shall make Psyche immortal, and she and Cupid will live together in happiness for ever. This is my will and, since Psyche will be a real goddess, even Venus must be glad of the marriage."

Then he sent Mercury to bring Psyche up to heaven and, when she had come there, he said, "Take this cup of immortality, Psyche, and drink it to the end, so that you may live for ever and that Cupid may never leave you again, but be your everlasting husband."

Then the great feast and wedding banquet was prepared. Cupid and Psyche sat in the places of honour and by them were Jupiter and Juno and all the gods in order. Bacchus filled their glasses with nectar, the wine of the gods. Vulcan prepared the supper. The Hours and Graces adorned the house with roses and other sweet-smelling flowers. Apollo and the Muses sung together and Venus danced with divine grace to the music. So Psyche was married to Cupid and in time she bore a child whom we call Pleasure.

GREEKS &
TROJANS

BOOK ONE

The Greeks and the Trojans

THE CITY OF TROY

Not far from the sea coast in the north of Asia Minor once stood the city of Troy. Here was fought the great war between the Greeks and the Trojans, a war in which Achilles and Hector and so many other heroes lost their lives but won eternal fame. The gods also took part in the war, some on the side of the Trojans and some on the side of the Greeks. For ten years the struggle was undecided and the rivers of Troy, the Scamander and the Simois, ran red with blood. In the end the city was destroyed but of the Greeks many who had escaped the battle died on their homeward voyage, or wandered for long years in stormy seas along inhospitable coasts, or at their return found murder and treachery waiting for them in their own homes. It is said that the war was for a woman's sake, the sake of Helen, the wife of Menelaus. Yet the rivalry of the gods, the folly and ambition of men played their part also.

The great walls of Troy were built by the gods. Once Apollo was banished from heaven by Zeus, the King of the Gods. There are many stories of Apollo's doings on earth, but what concerns us here is that he, with Poseidon, the god of the sea, built the high walls of Troy for the Trojan King Laomedon. This treacherous and ungrateful king, in spite of the kindness he had received, refused, when the work was done, to pay the reward which he had promised. Then Apollo sent a pestilence among the people of Laomedon, and Poseidon sent from the sea a great monster which ravaged the crops and easily destroyed the warriors who were sent against it. In the distress of his people Laomedon consulted the oracle and was told that the gods' anger could not be appeased except by the sacrifice each year of a Trojan maiden to the monster. So each year a maiden was chosen by lot and then, in spite of her tears and the tears of her parents and her friends, was taken to the sea shore and left there to be devoured by the great beast that came out of the sea.

For five years the city paid this terrible penalty for the treachery of its king, and in the sixth year the daughter of the king himself, Hesione, was chosen to be sacrificed. Now indeed Laomedon and his wife wished that greater respect had been paid to the gods, and that the promise had been fulfilled. Yet the gods were merciful, and in their misery help was at hand.

At this time the great hero Herakles with a band of his companions was returning from his expedition against the Queen of the Amazons, whose girdle he had taken from her by the orders of his cowardly master, King Eurystheus. As his ship put in to Troy he saw on the beach the sad procession which was accompanying Hesione to her doom, and he asked the reason for the black clothes and the wailing and the lamentation. King Laomedon told him of the danger in which his daughter stood and Herakles undertook to fight with the monster on the condition that, if he was successful, the king would give him a number of his fine horses, swift as the wind, great spirited animals that raced over the plains of Troy. Laomedon gladly and willingly agreed, and Herakles threw aside his lion skin cloak, gripped his club in his strong hands and made ready for battle.

Soon, at a great distance from the shore, one could see the blue water churned white as the beast approached. Its great head towered above the waves and through its rows of enormous teeth it belched out the foam. Herakles stood firm and indeed stepped forward to the shore, meeting the monstrous animal in the shallow water. With one blow of his club he stunned it; then, thrusting his sword into its heart he stained all the water scarlet with its blood.

Hesione was saved and now one would have thought that Laomedon, in gratitude for his daughter's safety and warned already by the previous punishment for his treachery, would ungrudgingly have given the hero his reward. It seems however that many people are unable to learn from experience. Once again Laomedon refused to carry out his part of the bargain. Herakles then, with his companions, attacked the city of Troy, took it by storm, killed King Laomedon and took the whole of his family prisoner. He gave Hesione to his follower Telamon who by her had a son, Teucer, who later was to fight with the Greeks against his mother's country in the great Trojan War. As for the other descendants of King Laomedon, only one was allowed to remain. This was the young boy Priam who was to become the last and the greatest of the Trojan kings. Herakles, before he sailed away, accepted a ransom for this boy and placed him on his father's throne.

So for many years, under the rule of King Priam and his Queen Hecuba, Troy grew ever richer, stronger and more prosperous. Priam made alliances with the neighbouring princes; he strengthened the vast fortifications of his city; ships that passed along the coast paid tribute to his officers; his kingdom became one of the mightiest in the world.

Priam and Hecuba had nineteen children who, when they grew up, became famous princes and princesses. Among them none was more famous than Hector both for his strength and skill in war and for his goodness of heart and loyalty to his friends. In these qualities he had no rival unless it was Priam's nephew Aeneas, whom Aphrodite loved, since he was her son. For she, the goddess of love, had fallen in love herself with the young Prince Anchises of the Trojan royal house. Anchises was feeding his sheep along the slopes of Mount Ida, the mountain that towers above the city of Troy, when the goddess, charmed by his beauty, visited him and by him became the mother of Aeneas, the hero who long afterwards and after many adventures was to found the great race of the Romans.

With such princes and warriors, with so many allies, such wealth and such magnificence, it might have seemed that the city of Troy was securely fixed in power and happiness and that it would last for ever, standing proudly in the plain below Mount Ida, with the holy rivers Simois and Scamander crossing the plain, tall and mighty with its towers, its huge walls and its tremendous gates. But this was not the will of the gods.

THE JUDGEMENT OF PARIS

It is said that before Priam's son, Paris, was born, his mother Hecuba dreamed that she would give birth not to a baby but to a flaming torch. Terrified by her dreams she consulted the prophets and soothsayers of Troy. Their answers were all the same—that the child whom she would bear would be the destruction of his city and of his family.

It seemed to Priam and to Hecuba better that the infant should perish than that he should bring such a doom on themselves, their people and their other children. Yet they had not the heart to kill the child: instead they gave him, soon after his birth, to a shepherd and told him to leave the baby on the rocky heights of Mount Ida, where the wild beasts and birds would soon find him and devour him.

Yet this was not what happened. Whether it was this shepherd himself that spared the boy and brought him up, or whether it was other shepherds or herdsmen on the mountain who had mercy on the small exposed body, Paris was certainly saved, although for long his parents did not know it. He grew up among the country people whose living was on Mount Ida, and as he grew up he stood out among the rest of the young boys because of his strength and his beauty. He was skilful in the use of his weapons and would spend long hours hunting wild boars in the thickets or lions on the bare slopes of the mountain. Particularly was he skilled in archery, and at every competition he would take the first prize. As he grew stronger, so he grew more beautiful. He married one of the mountain nymphs, Oenone, who was as beautiful as himself, who had a perfect knowledge of all healing herbs and who loved him most tenderly. So on this mountain with a divine creature for his wife, famous among the humble folk who surrounded him, Paris might have lived his whole life through in happiness. Yet it seems that he was not contented with what he had, and he was drawn into disaster by a conflict among the gods themselves.

For at this time there took place the famous wedding between the sea goddess Thetis and the great Greek hero Peleus. Of Thetis it had been foretold that she was destined to bear a son even mightier than his father. Zeus himself had desired her for his wife, but he feared a son who might one day take his power from him and so it was to a mortal that Thetis was married. The prophecy indeed came true since the son of Peleus and Thetis was Achilles himself, the greatest warrior and fastest runner of his time, one against whom not even Hector could stand in battle.

To the wedding all the gods and goddesses were invited except one. This was Eris, the goddess of strife and discord, and she determined to be revenged for being overlooked. This was the method she chose. She stole up to the great banqueting hall where the wedding feast was being held and she threw into the middle of the assembled guests a golden apple on which were inscribed the words: "A prize for the most beautiful." Quarrelling immediately broke out among the goddesses, since each one considered herself to be more beautiful than the next. In the end, however, the inferior goddesses had to withdraw their claims. Three remained, none of whom would give way to the others. These goddesses were Hera, the wife of Zeus, Athene, the goddess of wisdom, and Aphrodite, the goddess of love. Not even the gods themselves dared to judge between these powerful and embittered goddesses. Instead they elected to leave the decision in the hands of a mortal, and the mortal they chose for the task was Paris, who watched the sheepfolds on Mount Ida.

Quickly the goddesses prepared themselves for the contest in beauty. They came to the plain of Troy, and first they bathed themselves in the river Scamander, which the gods call "Xanthus" or "the yellow river." After they had perfumed themselves and dressed their hair, they came together, all naked, to Mount Ida, to the wooded glen in the mountain where Paris was watching his sheep. And as the goddesses trod over the grassy ground, in clear sunlight or in the dappled shade of trees, the air, even where the sun shone, seemed to grow brighter; birds sang more cheerfully among the leafty thickets; wild beasts, boars and lions looked reverently from their lairs as the divine shapes of beauty passed them by. All nature was glad. Only the nymph, Oenone, in a kind of foreboding trembled at what she saw and hid her face behind her hands as the tears flooded to her eyes.

Paris himself, with his mortal eyes, could scarcely bear the vision of such loveliness and of such power. But the goddesses reassured him. Though they seemed unwilling to speak to each other, they spoke readily to him. They told him to look at them well and then to make his decision which one of the three was most beautiful. Then as Paris, abashed by the difficulty of making the choice, still hesitated, each began to attempt to influence his choice by offering him rewards. First Hera spoke and promised him that, if he gave the prize to her, she would give him power over men and over cities; his armies should conquer wherever they went; his name should be famous throughout the world; nothing, she told him, can give a man more satisfaction than absolute power which brings with it also all kinds of experience and enjoyment.

Paris, as he looked at the goddess's fine brow and great resolute eyes, felt that she spoke the truth and was on the point of giving her the apple. But Athene, fixing him with her grey eyes, calm and fearless, spoke scornfully and said: "Power without Wisdom will always lead to certain disaster. But Wisdom will bring you not only its own delights but power as well, should you desire to have it. What I offer you is the most precious thing of all—Knowledge of men and of all arts, knowledge of yourself, the power to choose rightly between opinions and between actions. It is this wisdom which, more than all else, men learn to wish that they had or that they could acquire."

With such dignity and certainty did Athene speak that once more Paris hesitated. How could he disobey a goddess in whose clear eyes he read such assurance?

But now the laughter-loving Aphrodite turned to him and smiled as she shook back from her head the loose tresses of her golden hair. "Paris," she said, "the life of mortals is a short one and there are few pleasures that are certain. But in love certainly there can be pleasure with no pain attached. What I offer you is love, the love of the most beautiful woman whom the world holds. Helen is her name and she is half divine since Zeus himself was her father. All the heroes of the Greeks came to be her suitors and now she lives in Sparta with her husband Menelaus. Give the prize to me and Helen shall be yours."

As he listened to the goddess's urgent voice and looked into her smiling eyes, Paris felt as though his bones were melting within him. Of power and of wisdom he could not think at all; nor did he even remember his own wife, the nymph Oenone, who at that very moment among the trees of Ida was weeping in a hidden glade. All his desire was to possess Helen for his own. He took the golden apple in his hand and gave it to Aphrodite, who laughed as she received the prize, while the other two goddesses, stern and angry, turned both from her and from Paris who had rejected them.

This judgement was the beginning of endless sufferings, of death, wounds, treachery and destruction both for the Trojans and for the Greeks. But at the time neither Paris himself nor any of those thousands whom his actions would bring to ruin had any knowledge of what the future would bring. It is said indeed that Oenone, who had the gift of prophecy, told Paris that, if he went to Greece, the result of his action would be certain disaster for himself and for his people, that he would die in battle and ask in vain for the help of her healing arts. But Paris gave no consideration either to Oenone's love for him or to her warnings. He left her behind him on Mount Ida and came into the city of Troy, certain that in some way or other the promise of Aphrodite would be fulfilled.

In the great city his beauty and his prowess made him remarkable even among the princes and warriors who were his brothers. Some of these he defeated in an athletic contest, and then they say that Cassandra, his sister and a prophetess, by closely questioning him about his age and his upbringing was able to show that he was indeed the boy whom Priam and Hecuba had believed to have died upon the mountains. Seeing him now in the beauty of his youth, his old parents forgot the warning of the oracles and felt nothing but joy in recovering so fine a son. Every honour was given to Paris and in the end King Priam gave him a fleet of ships and allowed him to sail into Greek waters. The purpose of the voyage was supposed to be in order to bring back Hesione, the sister of Priam, whom Herakles and his men had taken away. But this was not the purpose of Paris. Instead he sailed to southern Greece and came to

Sparta, the city where Menelaus was King and Helen Queen.

But now the story must be interrupted to tell of Menelaus and Agamemnon, his great brother, who ruled over the city of Mycenae which is called "golden."

THE HOUSE OF ATREUS

When close to Greece Paris's ships must have gone through the blue waters of the sea that is called the Myrtoan Sea. This sea took its name from Myrtilus, a charioteer, who had once been basely murdered by Pelops, the grandfather of Agamemnon and Menelaus. As we shall see, very many misfortunes came upon this family, which in every generation offended the gods by their pride and men by their unjust dealings. Of them all Menelaus alone lived a blameless life and he in the end was rewarded by the gods with a place in the Islands of the Blessed.

The founder of the family was Tantalus, the wealthy king of Lydia, who was admitted to the banquets of the gods. But in his wicked pride he wished to discover whether the gods could be deceived and he thought out a cruel and a barbarous plan. He killed his own son, Pelops, cut the body up, cooked it and served it to the gods as meat. The goddess Demeter was present at the feast and she at this time was mourning for her daughter Persephone, whom Pluto, god of the lower world, had carried away. In her grief she was distraught and, without noticing what she did, she ate a portion of the boy's shoulder. The other gods and goddesses, in no way deceived, had risen from the table in anger and disgust. Tantalus himself had partaken of their own food and so was immortal; yet his immortality could not save him from eternal punishment. Now in the deepest prison of Hell, where the great criminals suffer continually for their sins, Tantalus remains tortured by hunger and by thirst. Branches loaded with fruit sway before his eyes; but when he reaches out a hand to relieve his hunger, the fruit moves always out of his reach. He stands by a pool of shining water; but when he bends down to take even a little in his hands to cool his burning thirst, instead of the pool he sees ashes or desert sand.

When the gods had punished the guilty, they proceeded to restore the innocent. They gave Pelops back his life and instead of the shoulder which had been devoured they gave him a shoulder of ivory. This shoulder had miraculous powers and by its touch alone could cure wounds that otherwise would have been mortal.

So Pelops grew up in Lydia, a country that is near the boundaries of Troy. Yet it was fated for him to found his kingdom elsewhere. Long before the time of Priam a Trojan King conquered Lydia, and Pelops with his followers came to southern Greece. Here at the court of King Oenomaus of Pisa he saw the King's daughter Hippodamia and he immediately fell in love with her. His wealth and his person made him one whom any father might wish to have as a son-in-law. But King Oenomaus wished to keep his daughter to himself and would give her to no man who could not first beat him in a chariot race. The penalty for losing the race was death, and already thirteen young men, suitors of Hippodamia, had perished by her father's hand. His horses were as swift as the wind and, as he swept past his defeated rivals, he would plunge into their bodies his heavy spear and leave them dead upon the level plain.

Pelops knew the danger that stood between him and the bride whom he desired. He accepted the contest, but previously he bribed Myrtilus, the King's charioteer, to loosen the linchpins of his master's chariot, so that at the first bend of the course the chariot would be dashed in pieces. He knew that if he could survive so long, the victory would be his.

It was the habit of King Oenomaus to give a short start to those who raced with him, and, as Pelops, with his chariot in front, sped towards the bend of the long course he prayed to the gods that he might reach it in time. Behind him he could hear the thundering hooves of his opponent's horses, and as he reached the bend he seemed to feel their breath upon his back. In a second or two, he knew, the heavy javelin would be through his body. But he turned the bend, and hardly had he turned it when he heard from behind him cries and the noise of the breaking up of the cruel king's chariot. The wheels had sprung from the axle. Oenomaus, the reins tangled round his waist, was being dragged over the stony ground by wild horses that he could no longer control. So this fierce king was killed. Pelops took Hippodamia as his bride and in the place where the race had been held he instituted for all Greece the famous Olympic Games.

But when Myrtilus, the charioteer, came to claim the reward that had been promised to him, Pelops treacherously refused. He killed Myrtilus and threw his body into the sea that bears his name.

In spite of this wicked deed Pelops continued to prosper. With Hippodamia as his wife he founded a great kingdom, so great indeed that all the southern part of Greece is to this day called after his name the Peloponnese or "Island of Pelops." Not only Pisa, but the great cities of Mycenae and of Argos came into his control. His power now was greater than it had ever been in Asia. Yet in his family he was not fortunate, though he died before he could see the terrible rivalry and the monstrous doings of his sons.

The eldest of these sons was Atreus, and it was he who inherited the great Kingdom that Pelops had founded. But his younger brother Thyestes continually plotted against him. Atreus' wife was called Aerope, and his sons by her were the famous princes Agamemnon and Menelaus. After their birth however Thyestes by his cunning acts won the love of his brother's wife, lived secretly with her and by her became the father of children. For some time the guilty secret was hidden, but in the end it was discovered. At first Atreus, in his fury, banished his brother from his dominions; but soon he thought of a revenge more cruel than banishment. He pretended that he wished to be reconciled with his brother and invited him to a feast in order to celebrate the occasion. Thyestes came, never suspecting the wicked outrage which Atreus intended to commit.

At the feast the two brothers spoke as though they had become friends, but at the end of the feast Atreus called a servant and ordered him to show Thyestes the dish from which he had just been eating. Thyestes looked and saw with horror that the meat which he had devoured was the flesh of no animal but human flesh. Atreus had killed the children of Aerope and Thyestes and had given the bodies, made unrecognisable in the cooking, to their father to eat. They say that at this deed, so horrible in its cruelty and impiety, the Sun itself turned backwards in its course, shrinking from the abominations of men.

Thyestes, when he realised what had been done to him, sprang up and overturned the table with his foot. Before he fled he called down a great curse on the house of Atreus, praying the gods that the blood of his children should be paid for by the blood of the children of Atreus, that treachery should follow treachery, that the very stones of the palace of Mycenae should preserve the memorial of the evil that had been done there. Then he fled from the Peloponnese, still fearing his brother's hatred, and in northern Greece, again through guilty love, he became the father of a son who was named Aegisthus. Much later Aegisthus returned to the plain of Argos and to Mycenae. There, though he was cowardly and scheming like his father, he helped to bring ruin on the greatest of Atreus' sons and on others as well.

All this, however, was still in the future. For the rest of his life, Atreus lived in security, though always he dreaded the effects of his brother's curse. On his death his Kingdom passed to Agamemnon and Menelaus. Agamemnon kept the fortress of Mycenae whose vast gates are flanked by great lions of stone, a fortress that governs the fertile plain of Argos and guards the mountain passes to the north. There he lived, the richest and most powerful of the Kings of Greece, with innumerable servants, armies and fleets at his command. His wife was the proud and beautiful Clytemnestra, and it was through his wife that in the end he was, in the moment of his glory, betrayed.

His brother, the golden-haired Menelaus, had Sparta for his Kingdom and there, beside the reedy banks of the river Eurotas, he lived with his wife Helen, whom all the youth of Greece had sought in marriage. It was to Sparta that Paris came with his Trojan ships.

HELEN

The birth of Helen was in every way remarkable. Her mother was Leda, wife of King Tyndarus of Sparta, a woman noted for her great beauty. Her father was, or rather appeared to be, a swan.

One day Leda was bathing in the waters of the river Eurotas. Zeus, the King of the Gods, saw her there and loved her. In order to be close to her he took upon himself the form of a white swan and he made a fierce eagle pretend to be pursuing him. Leda had pity on the fugitive bird and took him into her arms, while the eagle checked its flight and wheeled away screaming over the mountains. It was not immediately that Leda knew that the great white bird with powerful wings who had sheltered in her embrace was no bird at all, but the mightiest of the gods. In the end, however, when the time came for her to give birth, she gave birth not to babies but to two white eggs. Out of one of the eggs came Helen and her brother Polydeuces, or Pollux, as he is often called; from the other egg came Castor and Clytemnestra. It is said that Helen and Polydeuces were the children of Zeus and that the others were children of Leda's husband Tyndarus; but on this point there are several different accounts. We know certainly that Polydeuces and Castor, after many adventures on earth, were in the end received among the gods and given the power to answer the prayers of sailors in stormy seas. Sometimes they appear above the masts of ships like balls of fire; sometimes they ride on their white horses over the lessening foam.

As for Helen and Clytemnestra, they married the greatest kings of Greece. Clytemnestra married Agamemnon, the son of Atreus, and lived with him in the rocky fortress of Mycenae. By him she had three children, all of whom were, though in different ways, both famous and unfortunate. There were two daughters, Iphigeneia and Electra, and one son, Orestes. Until the time of the Trojan War everything prospered with her and with Agamemnon in their kingdom.

But when the time came for Helen to be married, the fame of her divine beauty had so spread throughout Greece that there was scarcely one of the heroes of the time who did not come to Sparta to ask for her as his bride. From the far north of Greece came Achilles, son of the goddess Thetis, the greatest warrior in the world. Of the youth and childhood of Achilles many stories are told, and two of these may be mentioned here. He was greatly loved by his mother who wished to make him immortal and, in order to do so, used to bathe his body in the waters of the river Styx. But, whether because it was the will of the gods or because of her own carelessness, she omitted to bathe his heels, since she held him by the heels as she dipped the body into the water. Thus there was one part of his body and one alone where Achilles might be wounded. Later, it is said, Thetis enquired from Zeus himself what the fate of her son would be, and Zeus told her that he might either live a long and prosperous life in his kingdom, enjoying both peace and happiness, but not to be greatly remembered after his death, or else he could have a short life, but one which would be for ever famous amongst men. It is said that Thetis begged her son to choose a long life for himself, but that he preferred glory above every other happiness and chose instead to live for a short time a life that would make him always famous.

Many others besides Achilles came to be the suitors of Helen. There was Antilochus, the strong son of Nestor, who lived in sandy Pylos. Nestor was the oldest and wisest of the kings of his time, and in his youth had known the great heroes of the past, Herakles, Theseus, Jason and the rest. In the Peloponnese he was only less powerful than Agamemnon himself. Ajax came also, a giant of a man and perhaps the strongest alive. With him came from Salamis his brother Teucer, the famous archer. Philoctetes came, carrying the bow and arrows of Herakles which, when he was a mere boy, he had been given by the hero just before his death. Yellow-haired Menelaus came from Sparta. And from the rocky island of Ithaca came Odysseus, the wisest and most resourceful of all men. So many indeed were the heroes, sons of kings and of gods, who desired to marry Helen that Tyndarus and Leda were at a loss to know how they would choose from them all a husband for Helen without giving offence to all the others who were passed over. It is said that in the end the wise advice of Odysseus was followed. What Odysseus suggested was that Helen should be allowed to choose freely herself from among her suitors the man whom she wished to marry, but that, before she made her choice, they should all swear on oath to protect her and her husband, whoever that might be, in the years to come. This plan was agreed upon, and Helen chose Agamemnon's brother, the yellow-haired Menelaus. It is said that in return for his good advice Odysseus received for himself as his wife the good and beautiful niece of Tyndarus, the famous Penelope.

So the heroes went back to their countries, having sworn that, if the need should arise, they would come together for the defence of Helen and of Menelaus. These two lived in Sparta happily together. One daughter was born to them, Hermione. They together with the rest of the Greeks and the Trojans might have lived out their lives in calm and in happiness, had it not been for the rivalry of the three goddesses and the faithless choice of Paris.

When Paris, with his Trojan followers, came to Sparta, they were received kindly and hospitably by Menelaus and his wife. In the king's great banqueting hall tables were set before them, loaded with meat and bread. The wine was mixed in golden cups and after the dinner was over a poet sang to the company of the great deeds done in old days, of the labours of Herakles, of the death of Meleager and of the Golden Fleece. The poet did not know that he was witnessing the beginning of a story which later would become more famous than any of these.

So, after feasting and the conversation, they retired to bed. Menelaus and Helen lay down in their room at the back of the gorgeous banqueting hall. For Paris and his companions beds were made beneath the high porch of the building. Sheep-skin rugs were spread for them, with purple coverlets. So they rested after their journey, but Paris stayed awake. He had seen Helen and found her more beautiful even than he had imagined. He thought nothing of the hospitality which had been shown to him, or of the dangers which he might bring upon his native land. For many days he stayed within the palace and then, when Menelaus was absent on a voyage to Crete, he took Helen away with him, set her on board his ship and, swifter than pursuit, made his way to Troy. Whether Helen came with him willingly or not, we do not know; but in Troy she was received as though she were his wife. The old King Priam welcomed her and supported his son in his act of theft, partly for the sake of Helen herself, partly because of Hesione, his sister, whom the Greeks had taken from him. Nevertheless in receiving Paris and Helen within his walls, Priam was receiving a curse which would utterly destroy him and his children and his city. It was as though a lighted torch had come within the town, indeed the very thing that the oracle had foretold.

THE GREEKS SET SAIL FOR TROY

When Menelaus returned from Crete to Sparta and found that Paris had treacherously taken his wife from him, he felt that all the joy in his house had departed. The statues in his high golden hall seemed to stare at him with lifeless eyes; the empty place in the bed where Helen had slept seemed to reproach him. Soon he determined on revenge and his great brother Agamemnon was not slow to come to his help. These two first gathered together their armies and their fleets, and at the same time they sent messages to the other kings and chieftains of Greece, commanding some and urging others to join the expedition against Troy.

Kings and warriors came together in such numbers that it would be tiresome to mention all their names. But there are some names which must be mentioned. From the far north of Greece came Achilles with fifty ships. He led into battle his own fierce troops, the Myrmidons, and he was accompanied by his friend Patroclus. He knew before he went that in this war he would lose his life, but this knowledge only made him fight the more fiercely and strive the more earnestly after glory. Among the shadowy mountains of his native land he left behind his old father, Peleus. He had a son too, Neoptolemus, who later was himself to fight at Troy.

From Ithaca and the islands of the western coast came the wise Odysseus. He left behind him his wife Penelope and his infant son

Telemachus. He did not know that it would be twenty years before he saw them again, and that then, when he did see them, he would find riotous princes usurping his house and his rights. There was none of the Greeks so full of resource as Odysseus or so good in counsel, unless it were, perhaps, the old King Nestor who came from sandy Pylos with his army and his strong son, Antilochus.

The great warrior Diomedes led an army from the enormous walls of the city of Tiryns, from the coasts surrounding this famous citadel and from the islands that lie beyond the gulf of Argos. He was one who, as we shall see, was not afraid to fight against the gods themselves.

From the island of Salamis came the giant Ajax, with his brother Teucer, the famous archer. Their father was Telamon, the friend of Herakles, who in the past had taken Priam's sister Hesione from Troy.

Eighty ships came from the great cities of Crete. They were under the command of the famous spearman Idomeneus. From Rhodes too and the other islands came ships and men; indeed from every great city, from Athens and from golden Orchomenos, from the plains and from the mountains, warriors came together for the war. The whole force was under the command of Agamemnon, whose kingdom was the greatest, and no such a force had ever before been gathered.

When all preparations were made the fleet assembled at Aulis, a harbour in central Greece, near the island of Euboea. Here, at Aulis, before the fleet sailed for Troy there occurred an event which might well have discouraged the Greeks, and here too Agamemnon was persuaded to do a deed which in the end was to bring upon himself and his family the greatest misfortunes.

Something which appeared certainly to be a miracle happened while the Greeks were waiting at Aulis for favourable winds to carry them over the sea to Troy. It was when the Greek leaders were sacrificing to the gods in a holy place where a bright spring gushed out of the ground beneath a plane tree. Suddenly they saw a large snake with blood-red markings on its back. It glided out from beneath the altar and made for the plane tree. In the tree there were some young fledgling sparrows who had struggled to the end of one of the branches and were cowering there, eight of them, or nine, counting the mother bird. All these little birds, with their pitiful chirping voices, the snake devoured, and then, as the mother bird came flying round, crying for her lost brood, the snake seized her by the end of her wing and ate her too. The gods then clearly revealed that this was an omen; for when the snake had eaten the young sparrows and their mother, it was turned itself to stone.

The Greeks stared at the sight in astonishment. Then Calchas, the prophet and soothsayer to the army, spoke. "Do not be afraid," he said, "you long-haired Greeks. Zeus himself has given us a sign. He took long to send it and we shall have to wait long for its fulfilment. Just as this snake has eaten the eight nestlings and the mother, to make nine, so we shall be for nine years fighting against Troy. But in the tenth year the city, with its broad streets, will be in our hands."

As the army listened to Calchas, some believed his words and thought with dismay that they would be, even if they survived the fighting, so long separated from parents, wives and children. Others could not believe that so great an armament as theirs could fail to be quickly successful even against Troy's high walls and against the valour of her defenders.

Yet difficulties met them at the very beginning. For long months they waited in Aulis for winds to fill their sails and carry them across the sea. It is said that the goddess Artemis was angry with the Greeks because Agamemnon had unknowingly killed a stag that was sacred to her. However this may be, no winds blew and the fleet was becalmed. At the prows of the beaked and painted ships the cables began to rot away. Food became scarce; the army grew weary of waiting; and soon the storms would begin to trouble the sea and the safe season for sailing be past. Once again Calchas spoke to the generals. "There is only one way," he said, "by which the goddess's anger can be appeased. It is a hard way, but it is a way that must be taken, if we are ever to set our feet on the windy plains of Troy. What the goddess demands is a sacrifice, and the sacrifice must be nothing less than the eldest and favourite daughter of King Agamemnon."

The prophet ceased speaking, and there was a hush in the council, as kings and chieftains looked in each other's faces and in the face of Agamemnon himself.

As for Agamemnon he thought of his daughter Iphigeneia, whom he loved, who used to sing to him in his palace, and for whom he had wished to choose as husband one of the noblest of the Greeks. How could he, her father, find it in his heart to become her murderer? At first he refused to do the bidding of the prophet. In the end, however, as the ships remained motionless in harbour, as the army began to grow mutinous and as Calchas continued to claim the sacrifice due to the goddess, Agamemnon, against his better judgment, allowed himself to be persuaded.

He knew that his wife Clytemnestra would never allow their daughter to leave home with such a fate in store for her, and he sent a messenger to say that he wished Iphigeneia to come to Aulis not for the dreadful purpose which he planned but in order to become the wife of Achilles. So this wretched girl left the golden palace of Mycenae bringing with her the dresses and ornaments of a bride, little knowing that she was coming not to her wedding but to her death.

When her father met her in Aulis it was hard for him to hold back his tears. Instead of greeting her gladly, as she had expected him to do, he turned his head aside from her and covered his face in the folds of his royal cloak. Nor did she find Achilles there to be her husband. Achilles did not even know that his name had been used for the deception. As the priests approached her, it did not seem that they came as they might be coming to celebrate a wedding. There were no bridal songs, no gay dresses, no shouting for happiness. Instead she found herself taken up in the hands of men as though she were an animal and hurried to the altar. Here Calchas was waiting, and at first he concealed behind his back the cruel knife. In sudden terror Iphigeneia turned to her father, but again her father hid his face from her. She struggled and tried to run away, but the priests held her fast. They bent back the graceful head with its long tresses of carefully combed hair, as though it was the head of some goat or heifer that they were preparing to sacrifice. So in her youth and beauty, in her father's presence, at the very time when she should have been a bride, she was foully murdered, so that the fleet should have fair weather and prosperous winds.

This wicked deed, prompted by superstition, was to bring ruin in the end on Agamemnon himself. Now his wife Clytemnestra, whom he had left behind as queen in golden Mycenae, became his bitterest enemy. Soon after the sacrifice of Iphigeneia, the son of Thyestes, Aegisthus, came back to the plain of Argos. Clytemnestra welcomed him, secretly received his love and with him began to plot against the rightful king, her husband Agamemnon.

Meanwhile in Aulis it seemed that the sacrifice, cruel as it was, had at least satisfied the anger of the goddess. Fair winds began to blow and at last the great fleet was able to set out for Troy.

On their way there the Greeks cruelly deserted one of their number, and this act also was to cost them dear. It happened that the fleet put in to the island of Lemnos in order to find fresh water. Here the hero Philoctetes was bitten in the foot by a poisonous snake. No healing herbs or draughts could cure his wound which became worse and worse. Moreover the effect of the poison in the wound was to produce a terrible smell, so sickening that it was unpleasant to be anywhere near the wounded man. In the end the Greeks left Philoctetes behind in spite of his prayers to them that they would look after and help one of their own comrades. The Greeks who so shamefully deserted him little knew that it was fated that Troy could never be taken without the help of the bow and arrows of Herakles, the famous bow and arrows that had been given to Philoctetes when he, then only a boy, had lit the funeral pyre on which the hero died and from which he ascended to heaven to join the company of the gods. Now for many years Philoctetes remained, still suffering from his wound, deserted on the island of Lemnos. But he kept with him the great bow of Herakles and in the end the Greeks, in their need for him, repented of what they had done. Before that time many thousands on both sides had fallen in battle. Now the Greeks, ignorant of the troubles in front of them, set on for Troy and in Troy the Trojans and their allies prepared to resist the invaders.

THE FIRST ACTIONS
OF THE WAR

The fleet sailed on past islands, some of which are rocky and pre-cipitous, waterless and uninhabited, while others are rich with vines and olives and herds of sheep and goats. On many of these islands grow all kinds of sweet smelling herbs, wild thyme, marjoram and many other flowers and shrubs. The warm wind would bring across the swelling waves the odour of these sweet herbs to those sailing still far from the shores where they grew. So sometimes the land could often be smelt before it could be seen. Yet it was not of these sweet and peaceful odours nor of the islands themselves that the Greeks thought as they pressed on in their black and painted ships to the destruction of the city of Troy.

It was at Sigeum that they made their landing. Beyond the long hills ran the rivers Scamander and Simois through the plain in which stood the huge walls of Troy with its wide streets, its towers and frowning battlements. But the Trojans were by no means con-tent to await a siege behind their powerful fortifications. A Trojan army was drawn up on the beach ready to oppose the landing. As the Greek ships approached the shore the Greeks, staring out towards the flashing arms, the wheeling chariots and dense masses of their enemies, tried to distinguish among them the tall figures of the warriors of whom they had heard, the figures of Hector and of Aeneas and the other princes of Troy. Soon they had to raise their shields to cover them from the showers of arrows that met the ap-proaching ships. But the helmsmen kept the ships straight on their course, and as ship after ship, with a grinding shock, ran upon the beach, so the warriors leapt out into the shallow water and began to fight their way inland through a storm of arrows and of spears.

They say that an oracle had revealed that the first of the Greeks to land on Trojan soil would certainly be killed. King Protesilaus either did not fear the oracle or else gallantly sacrificed himself for the good of his comrades. He had come to Troy leading an army from northern Greece and he had left behind him, in his half-finished palace, a newly-married wife, Laodamia, whom he loved more than all else. Now his ship was the first to reach the shelving shore and he was the first to spring from the ship on to the land. He fell dead at once, struck through the gorgeous armour on his breast by the heavy ashen spear hurled at him by Hector. They say that when the news of his death reached his home, his loving wife Laodamia became distraught with grief. She had a wooden image made of her dead husband and kept it with her in her widowed bed. Her father wished to cure her of her excessive sorrow and he ordered the image to be burnt, hoping that afterwards his daughter would forget to mourn. But this was not at all what happened. Laodamia could not bear to be parted even from this wooden semblance of her love, and she threw herself into the flames in which the image was being consumed. Some say that then the gods had pity on Protesilaus and Laodamia, and that in another world they were permitted to enjoy their love.

Protesilaus, then, was the first to die at the hands of Hector and of the Trojans. Many others also on both sides perished before the Greeks were able to land upon the shore, to form themselves into battle order under their commanders and gradually to push the defenders backwards towards the hills and towards their city that lay beyond the hills.

By the end of the day's fighting the Greeks had established themselves firmly on Trojan soil. They began next to build a stockade around their ships to protect them from any raids that the enemy might make. Then, before advancing on Troy itself, they attacked the towns along the coast and inland which acknowledged the power of King Priam. These towns were well defended, and few if any of them yielded to the Greeks without hard fighting.

In all these battles along the coast Achilles with his Myrmidons distinguished himself above all others. When he led his men against the enemy, it seemed as though a raging fire was going through dry crops of corn. He took twelve towns along the coast and eleven inland, one of which was Lyrnessus in which lived the beautiful girl Briseis. Her father and her brothers had been killed by Achilles, but she, given to him as a slave in the division of the spoil, loved the fierce and brilliant hero tenderly, as he also loved her. She too was to be the cause of great trouble to the Greeks, but it was through no fault of her own that the trouble came.

Meanwhile, as Achilles ravaged the coast and plain, Hector led his armies out from Troy and wherever he went it seemed that he was as invincible as Achilles himself. Old Priam and the people of Troy looked on him as their great defender and their champion. As he set out day after day to battle, his loving wife Andromache and his little child, Astyanax, would look at him with proud and wondering eyes. Of all the Trojans he was not only the strongest, but the kindest also and the most honourable. Often Andromache would beg him to spare himself and in particular to avoid battle with Achilles; but in her heart she knew that Hector was fearless and that he would follow his duty wherever it might lead him. Yet now was not the time for these heroes to meet. Instead they looked for each other, like lions looking for their prey, and each, where he went, was unconquered. So therefore for nine years the Greeks and the Trojans fought at the outskirts of the city. Sometimes indeed the Trojans would be pressed inside their walls; but then again they would issue out again, and the fighting would be renewed between the river valleys of the Scamander and the Simois, so that it seemed that neither would Troy ever be taken nor would the Greeks ever be driven back to their ships.

And as to the final issue of the conflict, the gods themselves were divided. Hera, the wife of Zeus, and Pallas Athene favoured the Greeks. Aphrodite, partly for the sake of Paris and partly for the sake of her own son Aeneas, was on the side of the Trojans. Ares, the god of War, who loved her, joined with her in this. So Zeus, the king of the gods, was perpetually pestered with the prayers and the complaints of his wife and of his children, some of whom urged him to give his help to Hector and his armies so that the Greeks might be driven into the sea, while others demanded that he should support Agamemnon and Achilles and allow them at last to sack the proud citadel of Troy. As it was Zeus gave his aid now to one side, now to another; for the time had not yet come for the decision to be taken. Before that time came it was necessary for many more of the Greeks and of the Trojans to lose their lives in this lamentable war. Indeed it was after nine years of fighting that the greatest slaughter of all took place because of the quarrel, so destructive to all, between Achilles and King Agamemnon.

BOOK TWO

The Wrath of Achilles

THE GREAT QUARREL

The reason for the quarrel between Agamemnon and Achilles was, in the first place, the god Apollo who sent a plague upon the army because Agamemnon had treated Chryses, Apollo's own priest, with discourtesy.

What happened was this. The Greeks had sacked the city where Chryses lived and made prisoners of its inhabitants. Among the prisoners was the young daughter of the priest and she, in the division of the plunder, was given to Agamemnon for his own.

Now old Chryses, in sorrow for the loss of his daughter, came to the Greek camp, bringing a full ransom and carrying in his hand a golden staff and the sacred crown that he wore as priest of Apollo. He spoke to all the Greeks, but particularly to the sons of Atreus, Agamemnon and Menelaus. "Great sons of Atreus," he said, "and all you other Greeks, may the gods who dwell in Olympus grant you your desire in taking the great city of Priam. But first, I beg you, show your reverence for Apollo, the Archer God; receive this ample ransom, and give me back my daughter."

The army applauded the words of the priest and would gladly have accepted his rich gifts and given back the girl to him. Agamemnon however thought differently. He spoke rudely to the priest and said, "Old man, don't let me find you any longer today about our hollow ships, or coming back here again another time. If I do, your golden staff and your crown will not preserve your life. So far from giving you back your daughter, I intend that she shall grow old in my house in Mycenae, far from her own country. Now be off with you! Do not make me angry, if you want to get back alive."

Trembling with fear the old man obeyed him. But when he came to the shore of the breaking sea he stretched out his hands and prayed to his master Apollo. "O hear me," he cried, "God of the silver bow! Reward me now for the temples I have built for you and for the fat thighs of oxen that I have sacrificed at your altars. By your weapons let the Greeks suffer for my tears!"

Apollo heard his prayer and came down in anger from the high peaks of Olympus. His bow was in his hand and the arrows clanged in the quiver at his back. He came like night falls, and very soon his presence was felt beside the ships of the Greeks. First he turned his anger against the animals—mules and dogs; but before long men too fell before his arrows. Man after man fell dead and by day and night countless fires were burning to consume the dead bodies.

So for nine days the Greeks suffered at the hands of Apollo, and then Hera, fearing that the whole army would be destroyed or be forced to sail home with Troy unconquered, put it into the heart of Achilles to call a council of the Kings and chieftains. When the council was assembled Achilles spoke first to their leader, Agamemnon. "King Agamemnon," he said, "so many of us now have died in the fighting and by the plague, that before long I fear we shall have to return home with our task uncompleted. Could we not therefore consult some prophet or oracle who could tell us why the gods are angry with us? Perhaps Apollo will accept some sacrifice, and so the army can be saved."

Then the prophet Calchas rose to his feet. "Lord Achilles," he said, "before I say what I wish to say, will you swear to protect me? There may be great men who will not like my words, and I dare not speak them unless I am sure that you will stand by me."

"Speak on," replied Achilles. "So long as I am alive, not one of the Greeks shall touch a hair of your head, not Agamemnon himself, if it is he that you fear."

This promise gave Calchas confidence. "Apollo is angry with us," he said, "because King Agamemnon has dishonoured his priest and refuses to give back his daughter, even though full ransom was offered for her. His anger will never cease until the old man's daughter is restored to him, and offerings are made by the army to Apollo's temple."

Now Agamemnon sprang to his feet. His heart was heavy with anger and his eyes blazed like fire. "As for you, Calchas," he said, "you have never once prophesied anything good. Always you have something evil to say, as on this present occasion when you claim that the gods blame me for keeping the bright-eyed daughter of Chryses. Indeed I had no wish to accept a ransom for her. I prefer her to my own wife Clytemnestra, whom she excels in beauty and intelligence and in all the works that women do. Nevertheless I will return her to her father, since I consider the safety of the army more important than my own desires. But you others must see to it that I am given a proper compensation for what I lose. It is hardly right that I should be the only one of the Greeks without a proper share in what we have won."

Achilles immediately replied to him. "Your avarice," he said, "goes beyond all bounds. How do you imagine that we are going to find you a special prize? All the spoils of war have already been divided and we cannot start dividing them all over again. No, give the girl back to her father and, if ever the Gods allow us to capture the great walls of Troy, we will pay you back three or four times the value of what you have lost."

Agamemnon looked at him in bitterness and anger. "Achilles," he said, "you may be a good soldier, and like the gods in battle, but you cannot trick me like this. It is I who am King here and Commander in Chief of the army. These are my terms. Find me something of equal value to what I am giving up, and I will say no more about it. If you do not, I shall take what I want for myself. Yes, I shall send my men to you or to Ajax or to Odysseus and I shall make away with one or other of the prizes that you have won in battle. This I shall certainly do, unless I am satisfied. I give you fair warning of it. And now let a ship be launched and let some responsible general, Ajax or Odysseus or Idomeneus, take the girl and take offerings with her and bring her back to her father, so that Apollo may look kindly on us."

Now the mind of Achilles was on fire with anger and again he leapt to his feet. "Have you absolutely no sense of shame?" he said. "Do you never think of anything but your own profit? How can you expect any of us to go on fighting for your sake? As for me, the Trojans never did me any harm, never robbed my herds or made war upon my men. Between their land and mine is a whole echoing sea and chain after chain of shadowy mountains. It was for your sake, you dog, and for the sake of Menelaus that I came here and have been in the front of the fighting ever since. And now you actually dare to threaten to take away the prize of war that the soldiers gave me. Yet in fact, when the plunder is shared out, it is always you who get the most. That is what you are good at, making yourself rich at the expense of other men's lives. When it comes to fighting it is I who bear the full brunt of it, and in the end am rewarded poorly for doing most. Why should I stay here to make you rich? Why do I not sail home again and become happy in my own country?"

Agamemnon looked at him with bitter hatred. "There is nothing to prevent you running away," he said, "if that is what you want to do. There are plenty of others here who respect me as they ought, and we can quite well do without you. I admit that you are a great soldier. But it was the gods who made you strong, and there is no need for you to claim all the credit for yourself. As it is you love nothing in the world but violence and fighting. Go home now with your ships and your Myrmidons. I am not frightened by your temper. But let me tell you this: just as Apollo is taking my prize from me, so I shall send to your tents and take from you the girl Briseis, who is your prize. So you will learn that I am stronger than you and in future others will not dare, as you have done, to oppose my will."

Now a great pain came over Achilles. His heart bounded within his shaggy breast, and he was in two minds, whether to draw his huge sword from his thigh, cut his way through the others and kill Agamemnon, or whether to curb his mounting anger. Already he was beginning to draw his sword when the goddess Athene, the daughter of Zeus, came down to him from heaven and stood at his side, invisible to all the rest, but visible to Achilles, who recognised

the goddess and said to her, "Why have you come to me, daughter of Zeus? Is it to see how I am insulted by Agamemnon? I tell you that this arrogance of his is going to cost him his life."

The grey-eyed goddess Athene answered him: "Remember," she said, "that I and the goddess Hera love you. You must take our advice. Be angry in words, if you will; but do not draw your sword. I tell you for certain that a time will come when Agamemnon will have such need of you that he will offer you three or four times the gifts and the prizes which now are in dispute."

Reluctantly Achilles thrust the huge sword back into its sheath. "It is right," he said, "to obey the gods, and the gods listen to those who obey them." Then Athene sped back to the company of the gods in Olympus, and Achilles turned again on Agamemnon. "You drunken brute," he said, "who look like a dog and fight like a trembling doe, you who never have enough courage to join in an ambush or fight in the front ranks, since it pays you better to steal what belongs to others, now listen to the oath that I swear. I swear by the kingly sceptre that I hold in my hands that the day will come when you will all yearn to have me at your side, when thousands of the Greeks will be falling before the spear of manslaughtering Hector, when you will be powerless to prevent the slaughter and when your heart will know all the bitterness of remorse for having treated dishonourably the best man among the Greeks."

When he had spoken, he hurled to the ground his sceptre which was studded with golden studs, and he sat down in his place.

Now Nestor, the old King of Pylos, old enough indeed to have been the grandfather of either Agamemnon or Achilles, rose to his feet and tried, though vainly enough, to heal the quarrel. "Alas! Alas!" he said. "What a terrible thing is happening to all the land of Greece! How delighted Priam and his sons would be, if they could see you two, the greatest of the Greeks, at variance with each other! Will you not listen to my words, the words of an old man who has known in the past great heroes like Theseus of Athens and Pirithous, his friend. Yet these great men used to listen to me and be persuaded by what I said. Agamemnon, do not take from Achilles the prize that was given him by the army. Do not insult the best of your soldiers. And, Achilles, though you are so great a warrior, you ought to show more respect to our Commander in Chief, one who rules over more men than you do. Kings have their authority from Zeus. Do you not see, both of you, that you are wrong? Only the Trojans can benefit from this quarrel."

"Nestor, my old friend," said Agamemnon, "what you say is, as usual, full of sense. But this man has no respect for authority. He wishes to be supreme. I am not going to be governed by him. Certainly the gods made him a good spearsman, but that gives him no right to insult kings."

At this point Achilles interrupted him. "And what a fool and coward," he said, "I should be thought, if I always and in every way gave in to you! You can order others about but not me any more. And here is another thing. As for the girl Briseis, the army gave her to me, and I shall not resist you if you take her away. But you cannot touch anything else of mine by my black ship. Come and try, so that the rest may see the result. I tell you that soon enough your blood would be pouring black about the blade of my spear."

With these words Achilles rose from the council. Patroclus, his friend, and all his men followed him, all resolved not to engage again in the war until their leader ordered them.

Then, at the command of Agamemnon, the wise Odysseus took the daughter of the priest Chryses in a swift ship back again to her father. He brought gifts with him and the proper offerings for the Archer god Apollo. The old man was pleased to see his daughter safe and sound, pleased too with the gifts and the offerings. Once more he prayed to Apollo, begging him now to spare the Greeks from the pestilence which was destroying them. And once more Apollo listened to his prayer. No longer did the funeral pyres burn for the dead in the Greek camp. Yet, though they were spared from the anger of the god, many more, because of the quarrel between Achilles and Agamemnon, would soon fall before the spears of Hector and the Trojans.

Agamemnon was far from forgetting the quarrel. He called for his two heralds, Talthybius and Eurybates, and told them to go to Achilles' tent and bring back with them the girl Briseis. "If he will not give her up to you," he said, "tell him that I shall come myself in full force to take her."

Trembling and abashed, the two heralds came to the camp of the Myrmidons, scarcely daring to address their words to Achilles. But Achilles received them courteously. "Heralds," he said, "you are welcome. My quarrel is not with you, but with Agamemnon who sent you. Only I ask you to remember this day on the day when Agamemnon will need me most and, with all his forces, will not keep Hector from driving him to his ships." Then he asked his friend Patroclus to bring out the lady Briseis and to give her into the keeping of the two heralds. Patroclus obeyed him and the girl was led away weeping.

ACHILLES AND HIS MOTHER

Then Achilles, in the pain of his heart, went by himself, leaving his companions behind him, to the shore of the grey sea. Here he sat down, looking out over the boundless deep, and, stretching out his hands, he prayed to his mother Thetis. "Mother," he said, "you it was who gave me life, but my life is destined to be only a short one. Since this is so Zeus ought at least to have given me honour. Yet now I am insulted by King Agamemnon."

As he spoke, the tears fell from his eyes. But his mother heard him from where she was sitting in the depths of the sea beside her old father Nereus, the sea god. She rose quickly, like a mist, through the grey salt water and came to her son, laying her hand gently on his arm. "My son," she said, "why are you weeping? Tell me, so that both of us may know."

Achilles groaned as he answered her. "Mother," he said, "you are a goddess and you know everything." Yet he told her the whole story of the quarrel, and at the end he begged her to go to Zeus himself, to clasp his knees and beg him to bring sorrow on the Greeks, to give aid to the Trojans so that Hector might drive the army of Agamemnon back to their ships and that Agamemnon might repent of his treatment of the best of all his warriors.

"My child," said Thetis, when he had finished, "indeed I have suffered in giving birth to you. I wish that you could sit here by your ships without tears and without any sorrow, since your fate is so brief, lasting for so short a time. As it is your life is not only shorter than that of others, but also more full of pain. Now indeed I will go to the snowy summit of Olympus and will speak to Zeus, the Thunderer, as you ask me to do, though yesterday he went with all the rest of the blessed gods to the stream of Ocean to join in a banquet with the blameless Ethiopians. But in twelve days he will return to Olympus, and then I shall speak to him. Meanwhile, you must preserve your anger and hold back from the fighting."

So Achilles stayed by his ships. Neither he nor Patroclus nor any of the Myrmidons took part in the war. Instead they spent their time in racing, in throwing the javelin or the discus, in singing and in feasting.

And after twelve days Zeus with the other gods returned to Olympus. Then Thetis rose out of the waves of the sea, ascended into the sky and found the Father of Gods and men seated apart from the others on the highest peak of the heavenly mountain. Thetis sank down at his feet. With her left arm she clasped his knees and, like a suppliant, she touched his chin with her right hand. "Father Zeus," she implored him, "if I have ever done you any good service now grant me my prayers and give honour to my son, who was born to have a shorter fate than most men. Now, as you know, King Agamemnon has dishonoured him by taking from him his prize. Avenge him, I beg you, and give your aid to the Trojans so that the Greeks may reverence Achilles and pay him the honour that is his due."

Zeus did not answer her at once. For a long time he sat still in silence, with Thetis clinging to his knees. Finally she spoke again. "Just nod your head," she said, "to show that you have granted my prayer. Or, if you will, refuse me. Then I shall know that with you I am given less consideration than any other one of the gods."

Zeus sighed and said, "Indeed you are causing me great embarrassment. This is certain to lead to more quarrels between me and Hera, my wife, who even now is constantly complaining that I favour the Trojans too much. You had better leave me now, or she is sure to notice what is happening. But to show you that I will grant your prayer, I will nod my head. This is a promise that can never be broken, and as I say so certainly shall I do."

Then Zeus bowed his head and, as he did so, the dark ambrosial hair swung forward and all Olympus shook.

So Thetis darted down from shining Olympus into the depths of the sea, and Zeus went to his own palace. As he entered it, all the gods rose from their chairs to show their respect for their father. Zeus sat down on his throne, but Hera guessed immediately that some plot had been made between him and the silver-footed goddess Thetis. At once she turned on him and said: "I know that some goddess has been scheming with you. This is what you always do. As soon as I am not there, you begin to decide things secretly behind my back. You never really take me into your confidence and tell me what you are going to do."

Zeus answered her and said, "Hera, you must not expect to know everything that passes in my mind. You could not bear the knowledge, even though you are my wife. I tell you first before all the others, when I have something which is fitting to be told. But when I reach a private decision of my own, it is not for you to question me about it."

Hera looked at him with her large eyes, like the eyes of oxen. "Great son of Kronos," she said, "I cannot imagine what you mean. Have I ever asked you questions about your private decisions or tried to interfere with you in any way? All the same I am terribly afraid that silver-footed Thetis has been using her arts on you and has persuaded you to help the Trojans in order to bring glory to Achilles."

"As for you," Zeus replied, "you are always leaping to conclusions. Perhaps you are right. If so, then this is my will. There is nothing you can do about it. I advise you to sit quietly in your place and to submit. For if I once was driven to lay my hands on you, not all the gods in Olympus could protect you."

At these words the ox-eyed Hera trembled and was afraid. She said no more, but sat in silence, though in her heart she was angry enough. Among all the gods there was silence, until the lame Hephaestus, the god of fire, spoke and said: "This is a sad business, if you two are going to quarrel simply for the sake of mortals. How can we enjoy our good food and drink, if our minds are on these other inferior things? I would recommend my mother to make peace with our father Zeus, or he may grow more angry still and then our dinner would be ruined. He might even hurl his thunderbolts at us, and then where would we be? No, mother, I beg you to ask his pardon, and then he will look kindly on us again."

As he spoke he carried to Hera a great cup filled with nectar, the wine of the gods, and urged her to drink and forget her anger. Then he began to serve all the other gods, beginning from the left, mixing their drinks for them in a golden mixing bowl. As they watched him bustling about in the banqueting hall, unquenchable laughter arose among the blessed gods. They sat cheerfully together, in no lack of food or drink or of the sweet music of the lyre, which Apollo played, while the Muses sang to his accompaniment. And when the bright light of the sun had set they departed each one to his own palace, palaces built for them by the cunning craftsman Hephaestus. Zeus himself lay down in the upper chamber where he was accustomed to sleep, and Hera lay beside him.

THE FALSE DREAM

So sleep came to the gods and to the warriors before Troy, to all except to Zeus. He stayed awake, pondering how he could avenge Achilles and have the Greeks slaughtered by their ships. What seemed to him the best plan was to send a false dream to Agamemnon. So he called to him one of the shadowy dreams that live in the house of Sleep, and when the dream came to him, he said: "False dream, go to the Greek ships and to the tent of Agamemnon. Say to him that now is the time for his soldiers to put on their armour and go into battle. Say that the immortal gods are now all of one mind. Hera's prayers have persuaded the rest. Doom is descending upon the Trojans and now he will be able to capture the city with its broad streets."

So he spoke, and the dream, going down to the ships, found Agamemnon sleeping in his tent. The dream stood at his head and put on the shape of the old counsellor Nestor, whom Agamemnon honoured most, and spoke to the sleeping King: "Are you asleep, great son of Atreus? This is no time for sleep, and certainly not for you, who have so many cares upon your mind. Now listen to me. I come as a messenger from Zeus who, though he is far from you, still watches over you and pities you. He bids me to tell you to make ready your forces at once for battle. Now the immortal gods are all of one mind. Hera's prayers have persuaded the rest. Doom is descending upon the Trojans and now you will be able to capture the city with its broad streets. Remember my words and keep them firmly in your mind when you wake from sleep."

So the dream slipped away and left Agamemnon with thoughts in his mind that were not going to come true. For he thought that he would take Priam's city that very day, little knowing what would really happen and that Zeus intended first to lay countless more sufferings both on the Trojans and on the Greeks in the hard and stubborn fighting. When he woke up, the divine voice was still ringing in his ears. He sat up on his bed, put on his soft tunic, and then threw his heavy cloak over his shoulders. He bound the bright sandals on his feet, slung round his neck his great sword with its silver-studded sheath, and took in his hand the royal sceptre of the house of Atreus. Then, as dawn was just beginning to show, he went out of his tent and walked among the Greek ships. First he came to the camp of Nestor and here, by Nestor's ship, he summonded a council of the chief leaders of the army— Ajax and Idomeneus, Menelaus, Diomedes and Odysseus. When he had told them of his dream Nestor spoke first and said: "If this dream had come to anyone else, we might have doubted it and thought it false. But as it is, it has come to King Agamemnon, our Commander-in-chief. I say therefore that we should at once call an assembly of the whole army and then lead out all our forces to battle in the plain before Troy."

The others approved of the old man's advice, and heralds went about the camp calling the soldiers to the assembly. They came together in their vast numbers to the meeting place, so many of them that it took nine heralds, all shouting at the tops of their voices, to make the troops settle quietly in their places and listen to the words of their commander. Now all of them were mustered except for the Myrmidons, the followers of Achilles. They, with their great leader, remained in their camp. Agamemnon spoke to them and said: "Soldiers of the Greeks, the time has come for our final attack on Troy. The first thing to do is for us all to have a meal, so that we may be fit for a day of battle. Sharpen your spears, see to it that your shields are properly fitted. Feed your swift horses well and make your chariots ready for action. We shall fight throughout the whole day, with no pause and no letting up in the fighting until night comes. The straps of your shields will stick to your breasts in the heat of battle; hands will weary on the spear shafts; horses will be soaked with sweat as they pull the polished chariots. Let me find no one hanging back from the war or cowering by the ships. If I do, he shall lie where I find him and be meat for the vultures and for the dogs."

When he had finished speaking, the army roared out its applause with a noise like the roar of the sea breaking in storm upon a rocky coast. They left the assembly to prepare their meal, to look over their equipment and to make ready for the great battle. Each man made offerings to the god whom he honoured most, praying that he might still be alive when the sun set. Agamemnon himself sacrificed a fat five year old ox to almighty Zeus and he invited the leaders of the Greeks to share in the feast. As the animal was being sacrificed Agamemnon prayed: "O great and powerful Zeus, God of the black clouds and dweller in heaven, I pray that before the sun sets in darkness I may bring down in flames the high palace of Priam, that my spear may rip through the brazen armour that covers Hector's breast, and that his friends and companions at his side may roll dying on the ground and bite the dust."

So he prayed, but Zeus did not grant his prayer. He received the sacrifice indeed, but in return he was planning death and destruction for the Greeks.

Now when the feast and the sacrifices were over, the captains and commanders led their men into the plain. They streamed out in innumerable hordes, like the flocks of birds—cranes or geese or long-necked swans—that can be seen along the rivers of Asia, filling all the meadows with their cries and the flapping of their wings as they wheel and turn about. But soon the officers had brought their men into battle order. Company stood by company in correct formation, and Agamemnon went along the ranks, urging on the troops to war. Then the whole army moved forward over the plain, and as they moved the dust rose into the air and the very earth shook beneath the tramping of their feet.

Meanwhile in Troy, Hector and the Trojan leaders were in the palace of Priam, discussing the conduct of the war. To them Zeus sent his own messenger Iris, goddess of the rainbow. She came in the appearance of one of the Trojan sentries who had been posted far out on the plain to watch for any signs of movement in the Greek camp. Standing before King Priam she said: "My Lord, this is no time for talking as one might do in peace time. Now the full flood of war is loosed upon us. I have been in many battles, but I have never seen a force to compare with the one that is now coming towards us over the plain to fight at our gates. Now, Hector, is the time to meet them with every single man of us who can bear arms."

Hector immediately recognised the voice of the goddess. He dismissed the meeting and gave the call to arms. The gates of the city were flung wide open and into the plain poured the armies of the Trojans and their allies, infantry, cavalry and chariots.

THE DUEL

So the two armies approached each other, the Trojans with a noise of shouting and the clashing of arms, the Greeks in a grim silence. Above them eddied the clouds of dust raised by their marching feet and the feet of their swift horses. Each side was bent on war, each side determined not to yield.

And now, when the armies were close to each other and on the point of joining battle, Paris stepped forward from the Trojan ranks, ready to challenge any Greek champion to fight in single combat. Over his armour he wore a panther's skin; his curved bow and sword were slung from his shoulders, and in his hands he held two sharp spears of bronze.

Menelaus saw him and when he saw that it was Paris striding out in front of the army, offering battle to the Greeks, he felt as glad as a hungry lion feels when he comes upon the body of a stag or a wild goat in the mountains. So, seeing Paris before his eyes, he felt sure of his revenge on the man who had wronged him. With all his armour he sprang down from his chariot and made his way through the first ranks.

But when Paris saw Menelaus coming forward to meet him, he turned pale and took a step backwards, like someone who has suddenly seen a snake on the ground in some wooded glade and who starts backwards in terror. So Paris felt his limbs tremble, and he made his way hurriedly back again behind the cover of the ranks of Trojans.

Hector saw him as he shrank back, and shouted out to him with bitter words: "You wretched Paris, you who are so good to look at, you who are so mad about women, you traitor! I wish you had never been born or had died before you found a wife. That would have been better than for you to bring shame on us all. Certainly the long-haired Greeks will laugh when they see us putting you forward as our champion, when you have nothing but your good looks to recommend you, no courage, no steadfastness. You took the wife of Menelaus and now you dare not stand up to him in battle. If you did, all your lyre-playing would not help you, nor would your good looks nor your curled hair nor all the gifts that Aphrodite has given you. You would soon be lying in the dust. But we Trojans are too considerate. Otherwise you would have been stoned to death long ago for all the trouble you have given us."

Paris replied to his brother. "Hector," he said, "what you say is right and I cannot complain about it. You have a spirit that is always resolute and energetic. It is like an axe cutting through wood. But you ought not to mock at the beautiful gifts of Aphrodite. The gifts of the gods should not be despised, even though one might have preferred to have had other gifts instead. And now I will do as you wish and fight with Menelaus. Let the others lay down their arms and let Menelaus and me fight in the space between the armies. Let us agree that whoever wins shall keep Helen and all her possessions. Then there can be a treaty of peace, so that the Trojans can live happily in Troy and the Greeks can return to their own land."

Hector was delighted with this proposal. He pushed back the front ranks of the Trojans and ordered them to sit down on the ground. Then he stepped forward towards the Greek army who still hurled javelins at him and shot arrows which rang upon his shield and upon his armour. But Agamemnon shouted out to his men to stop shooting. "Great Hector," he said, "has some proposal which he wishes to make to us. Let us listen to what he has to say."

So Hector spoke to the Greek army and told them of the offer that Paris had made. Menelaus replied to him. "One of us," he said, "must die, and it is good for the rest of you, who have suffered enough already through the quarrel between me and Paris, to make peace. But I do not trust the sons of Priam. Let Priam himself come and let us sacrifice to Zeus and to the Earth and to the Sun, and let both sides swear an oath that the winner of this battle shall keep Helen and her possessions, and that afterwards there shall be peace."

Both Greeks and Trojans were pleased with the words of Menelaus. Both sides longed for there to be an end to the bitter fighting, and now it seemed that, whatever the result of the battle, peace would be assured. But this was by no means the will of Zeus, who was determined that the fighting should become more furious still and more bitter than ever it had been.

Now the soldiers laid down their arms, unyoked the horses from the chariots, and prepared to watch the duel. Hector sent heralds back to the town of Troy to inform Priam of what had passed and to bring the animals for the sacrifice.

Yet before the heralds reached the city Helen herself had heard the news. Iris, the messenger of the Gods, came down to her from heaven, having put on the appearance of her sister-in-law, one of the beautiful daughters of Priam. She came to Helen in her rich palace and found her weaving a great purple web on which were shown the battles fought for her sake between the Trojans and the Greeks. Iris said to her, "Come with me, dear sister, and see what is happening in the plain. Just now the two armies were about to join together in battle; but now they are standing quietly in their places. The men are leaning on their shields and their spears are stuck into the ground at their sides. Paris and great Menelaus are going to fight together in single combat, and the winner is to take you for his wife."

As she spoke, Helen felt in her heart the sweetness of a longing for her former husband and for her native land and for her parents.

She put a white veil on her head and with tears in her eyes she left the gorgeous bedchamber and, accompanied by two waiting women, went out to the gate that overlooked the armies in the plain. It was the gate called the Scaean Gate and here on the tower above the gate were sitting Priam and the old counsellors of Troy. These men were now too old for battle; their fighting days were over; but they were still excellent in debate, good talkers and enjoying their talk as they sat there together, like grasshoppers chirping together melodiously in the sunny grass. When they saw Helen walking to the tower, they raised their eyes, and one would say to another: "No wonder that Greeks and Trojans have suffered so long for such a woman! Her face is like the face of the immortal gods. Yet all the same, and in spite of her loveliness, it would be better for her to sail away in her ships and not bring trouble on us and on our children."

Priam also saw her and called her to him. "Come here, my dear child," he said, "and sit by me, so that you can see your former husband and your friends and relations among the Greeks. I have never blamed you. No, it is the gods who are to blame for fastening upon us all the grievous load of this terrible war. Now tell me who is that huge man over there who towers head and shoulders above the rest. I don't think that I have ever seen anyone so fine looking or with such an air of authority. His bearing is the bearing of a king."

Helen answered him and said: "O my dear father-in-law, I both love and respect you. How I wish that I had died before I came here with your son and became the cause of so much trouble to you, leaving my own home and my little daughter and all my dear friends. But I had to do it, and now my heart is full of pain. Now I will answer your question. The man you see there is Agamemnon, the son of Atreus, a great King and good with the spear. Once he was my brother-in-law, disgraceful creature that I am—unless all that part of my life was a dream."

"So that is Agamemnon," said Priam, "the fortunate man, favoured by the gods and ruler over so vast a host. Now who is that other one near by? He is a head shorter than Agamemnon, but broader in the shoulders and chest. His armour is lying on the ground, and he himself is going the rounds of his troops. He looks like a great ram marshalling a herd of white sheep."

"That," said Helen, "is Odysseus, the son of Laertes, who comes from the rocky island of Ithaca. There is no one like him for wisdom and cunning and resourcefulness."

Here one of Priam's counsellors, the wise Antenor, joined the conversation. "I remember him well," he said. "Both he and Menelaus once came here on an embassy and I entertained them in my house. When we were standing up, Menelaus stood a head taller than all the rest; but when we were sitting down, Odysseus seemed the bigger man. They were quite different too in their style of speaking. Menelaus is a man of few words; he speaks simply and directly and makes his meaning plain. But when Odysseus got up to speak, he first of all looked all round him from under his shaggy eyebrows; he made no gestures with the sceptre that he carried, but held it stiffly. Indeed he looked as though he had never made a speech before. But then suddenly his great voice came from his chest; the words whirled about us like winter snowflakes; his eyes flashed. At such moments no one could possibly compete with him, and we wondered at him as we listened spell-bound."

Then Priam enquired from Helen the names of other leaders of the Greeks and she pointed out to him the mighty Ajax, Diomedes, Idomeneus and others. She looked in vain for her two brothers, Castor and Polydeuces. "Perhaps," she thought, "they would not join the army, because they feared reproaches for their sister's shame." She did not know that they were already buried in the earth of Sparta, in their own dear native land.

But now the heralds from the army came to King Priam to deliver their message. "Hector and Agamemnon," they said, "are calling for your presence at a solemn sacrifice. Paris and Menelaus are to fight together for Helen. The winner is to keep her and all her possessions; and after the battle we are to make peace, so that we may live undisturbed in Troy, and the Greeks will return to their own land."

Priam sighed as he heard the news, since, though he longed for peace, he feared for the life of his son. Quickly his horses were yoked to his shining chariot and he set out through the Scaean Gate towards the armies. He passed through the Trojan ranks and approached the Greeks. Agamemnon and Odysseus rose to greet him and in the space between the armies the animals were prepared for sacrifice.

When the sacrifices were made to Zeus, to the Sun, to the Earth and to the Powers under the earth, the kings called the gods to witness their solemn oaths. Each man in the armies, both Trojans and Greeks, prayed also. "Almighty Zeus," they prayed, "and you other immortal gods, if either side breaks this treaty, we pray that their brains may be poured out on the ground like wine, and the brains of their children too, and that their wives may pass into the hands of strangers."

So they prayed for peace, but Zeus did not intend to answer their prayers.

Then Priam spoke: "I myself," he said, "am going back to the towers of Troy. I cannot bear to watch while my dear son fights with great Menelaus. But I think that Zeus knows already which of the two is fated to die."

So Priam, and Antenor with him, mounted their chariot and drove back to the city.

Meanwhile Hector and Odysseus were measuring out the ground where the contest would take place. Then they put two pebbles in a bronze helmet, one for Paris and one for Menelaus. This was to decide which of the two should have the first throw with his spear. Next Hector took the helmet and, turning his head aside, shook it to and fro. The pebble that first leapt out was the one that had the mark of Paris on it.

Then Paris began to put on his beautiful armour. Round his legs he tied the splendid greaves with silver fastenings on the ankles. Next he put on his breastplate; it was one that he had borrowed from his brother Lycaon. Over his shoulders he slung a bronze sword with silver studs on the hilt, and then a great shield of toughened ox-hide. On his head he put a helmet with a nodding horse-hair crest, and then in his strong hands he grasped a heavy spear.

Menelaus armed himself in the same way, and now the two champions strode out from behind the ranks of their own men and stood facing each other on the measured ground. First Paris hurled his long-shadowed spear. It landed full upon the shield of Menelaus, but did not break through. The point bent on the strong shield.

Now Menelaus poised his spear in his hands and, as he did so, he prayed to Father Zeus. "King Zeus," he said, "give me my revenge on Paris who was the first to injure me. Let him fall before my hand, so that in the future men may tremble at his fate and may

shrink from doing harm to their hosts who have welcomed them kindly!"

So saying, he hurled his spear with such force that it pierced right through Paris's shield and through his breastplate. But Paris swerved aside and avoided death. The point of the spear tore the tunic on his skin and just grazed his flesh. Then Menelaus drew his sword and, leaping forward, brought it down with his full strength on his enemy's gleaming helmet. Paris was half stunned, but the sword, as it struck, broke into pieces and fell from Menelaus's hand. Menelaus groaned aloud and turned his eyes to heaven. "O Father Zeus," he said, "you are the most ungracious of the gods. Truly I thought that I had revenged myself on Paris for the wrong he did me; but now my sword is broken in my hands and I scarcely touched him with my spear."

And now, before Paris could recover himself, Menelaus sprang at him again and seized him by the great crest upon his helmet. Then he began to drag him backwards towards the Greek lines. The strap of the helmet pressed into Paris's tender throat and he himself was half strangled. Indeed Menelaus was on the point of dragging him off the ground and of winning all the glory of the victory. But Aphrodite, the goddess, saw what was happening to her favourite. It was she who caused the helmet strap to break, although it was made of stout ox-hide. So Menelaus was left with the empty helmet in his strong hand. He threw it behind him into the ranks of his own men, who took it up and kept it for him as a trophy. Then he rushed upon Paris again, longing to make an end of him with his spear. But Aphrodite easily, as gods are able to, saved him. She threw a thick mist around him and, while Menelaus searched for his enemy in the mist, she took Paris up and set him down on his soft bed in his own perfumed bedroom in Troy.

There Helen found him. She turned her eyes away from him and said: "So you have returned. I wish you had fallen at the hands of the great warrior who used to be my husband. You used to boast that you were a better man than he is, stronger in the arm and more skilful in the use of your weapons. Why then do you not challenge him again? But I should advise you not to. You would certainly be destroyed."

"Do not blame me, my dear wife," said Paris. "Menelaus has won on this occasion. It was the goddess Athene who helped him.

Another time I shall win. I have gods to help me too. But now let us enjoy our love together. I confess that I have never felt so fond of you and so deeply in love as I do now, not even at the time when I first took you from Sparta on my swift ship and we stopped together for the night on the island of Cranae."

Meanwhile as they talked together in their bedroom, Menelaus was going about like a wild beast searching for his prey. He looked for Paris everywhere in the Greek and Trojan ranks but nowhere could he find him, nor could anyone point him out. No one indeed would have hidden him out of kindness. They all hated him like black death.

Finally Agamemnon spoke. "Trojans and allies of Troy," he said, "it is plain that Menelaus is the conqueror. Now it is for you to fulfil your part of the bargain and to give us back Helen with all her wealth."

As he spoke all the Greek army applauded him.

THE TRUCE IS BROKEN

Meanwhile the gods were sitting in their heavenly palace, drinking nectar out of golden cups and looking down upon what was happening in the plain of Troy. Zeus indeed had no intention of allowing the fighting to stop, but now he spoke in order to irritate his wife Hera. "I know," he said, "that there are two goddesses, Hera and Athene, who are on the side of the Greeks. Yet they seem merely to be sitting here and looking on while the laughter-loving Aphrodite has shown herself most energetic in supporting her side. Only just now she has rescued Paris from the hands of that great warrior Menelaus. Still it is quite evident that Menelaus has won the battle, and now the city of Priam will be preserved and the Greeks will return home with Helen."

The words of Zeus made both Hera and Athene angry. They were determined that Troy should be utterly destroyed. Athene controlled her anger, but Hera could not do so. "Great Zeus," she said, "you surprise me. Do you wish me to have had all my trouble for nothing. Both I and my horses were covered with sweat at the time I went all over Greece summoning the great leaders to the war. And now is Troy to escape? You may do as you like, but certainly not all of us will approve of it."

Zeus spoke sharply to her. "What harm," he said, "have Priam and his sons done to you? Why should you be so determined to destroy their beautiful city? For my part I love old Priam and his people. He has always sacrificed to me as he should do, and in all the world Troy is the city that I love best."

"The cities that I love best," said Hera, "are Argos and Sparta and golden Mycenae. Destroy any one of these, if you will. I shall not stand against you. Yet I deserve some consideration too, since I am your wife. All I ask now is that you should allow Athene to go down to the battlefield and contrive matters so that the Trojans will break the truce."

This in fact was what Zeus wished to do and so he readily gave his permission to his child, grey-eyed Athene. She sped down to earth like a shooting star, and as the men on the plain saw the flash in the sky that marked her coming, they gazed at each other with wide eyes and they said: "What does this mean? Does it mean that Zeus is giving us peace, or is it war again and all the miseries of war?"

Meanwhile Athene had put on the appearance of a Trojan warrior and was searching through the Trojan ranks for the famous archer Pandarus. She found him standing among the spearmen whom he commanded and, taking him aside, she said: "Pandarus, why not win fame and gratitude from all the Trojans, and especially from Paris? There is Menelaus standing in triumph. Why not shoot an arrow at him and make an end of him? Come, take my advice and do so. Fit the arrow to the string, and then pray to Apollo, the god of Archery."

Pandarus was foolish enough to allow himself to be persuaded. He took out his great bow from its case. It was made out of the horns of an ibex which he himself had shot in the mountains. The horns measured sixteen hands, and they had been fitted together by a clever craftsman, who had polished them and given them golden tips. Pandarus pressed down the bow and strung it. Then, while his companions held their shields in front of him, he chose out a keen arrow that had never yet been used and fitted it to the string. He made his prayer to Apollo, then, holding tightly the notched end of the arrow and the bow-string he drew them back till the string touched his breast and the iron head of the arrow was on the curve of the bow. Taking careful aim, he loosed the arrow. The bow twanged; the string sang like a swallow and the piercing arrow leapt eagerly through the air among the press of men.

But the blessed immortal Gods did not forget Menelaus. Athene herself stood by him and warded off the arrow, turning it aside from the vital parts, as a mother brushes a fly aside from her child's sleeping face. The sharp point struck upon the golden clasps of his belt and pierced right through them. It pierced the armour underneath, and the tunic beneath the armour. The wound was a slight one, but still the purple blood gushed out over Menelaus's thighs and legs, running down over his well-shaped ankles.

Agamemnon shuddered when he saw the black blood. "O my brother," he cried, "are our oaths and our promises to end in your death? The day will come, I am sure of it, when Priam's city of Troy will fall into our hands. But what good will that be, if before then you have lost your life? How could I bear to return to Argos without you, my brother?"

But Menelaus comforted him and said: "All is well, my brother. Say nothing to discourage the army. My belt and my armour have taken the full force of the arrow and the wound can be cured."

Then Agamemnon sent for the famous doctor Machaon, who examined the wound and washed it, and put upon it some healing ointment which once the wise centaur Chiron had given to his father Asclepius.

Meanwhile the men on both sides were standing to their arms. The gods themselves were there to urge them into battle. On the Trojan side was Ares, god of War, breathing his spirit of dreadful violence into the army; and with the Greeks was the grey-eyed goddess Athene, no less resolute in her own cause. Now there were no thoughts of peace. Each side was full of hatred for the other, each longing to hear the groaning of men in their death agony.

Agamemnon went along the ranks of the Greeks, urging them on to battle. "Our enemies have broken the truce," he shouted, "and now Father Zeus will protect them no longer. Instead their smooth flesh will be devoured by the vultures and the dogs. We shall sack their city and take their women and children for our slaves." So he spoke, little knowing the trouble in store for his men, and for himself.

And now the two armies met together with a noise like thunder in the mountains. Shield pressed on shield; spears tore their way through armour; swords clashed together. Of the men who fell in that first onset one was a son of Priam. Great Odysseus struck him down with his long spear and his armour rang out as he writhed on the ground in death. And as Odysseus plunged forward the whole Trojan line began to give way. But the god Apollo, the friend of the Trojans, cried out to them: "Forward, horsemen and charioteers of Troy. These Greeks are not made of stone or iron. They have flesh that can feel your weapons. Moreover Achilles, the son of Thetis, is not with them. He is nursing his anger by his ships."

So Apollo put fresh heart into the Trojans, who surged forward again into battle, while on the other side the goddess Athene was encouraging the Greeks.

THE DEEDS OF DIOMEDES

It was on this day that Athene gave to Diomedes, the great son of Tydeus, such strength and valour and audacity that he stood out above all the other warriors and won for himself immortal fame. He raged through the Trojan ranks like a wild lion, and his shield and helmet shone like that star which in the summer months is brighter than all other stars as it rises washed from the streams of Ocean.

So Trojan after Trojan fell before the spear of Diomedes. He stripped the armour from their bodies and gave their horses to his followers, who drove them back to his ships. He himself pressed on with the attack and wherever he went the enemy fell back before him.

Now when Pandarus saw Diomedes come raging over the plain like a winter torrent that sweeps away the hedges and the dykes, driving whole companies of men before him, he bent his bow, fitted an arrow to the string and shot him in the right shoulder. The point pierced through the plates of his armour and the black blood spouted out over his breast. Pandarus shouted out in triumph: "See, Trojans, the best of the Greeks is wounded, nor will he last long, I think. Now, forward again into battle and drive them before you!"

But Diomedes was not for long out of the action. He withdrew a little from the battle and his faithful charioteer, Sthenelus, pulled the arrow out of his shoulder and bound up the wound from which the blood gushed out. Then Diomedes prayed to Athene: "O daughter of Zeus, just as you used to help my father in his battles, now, I pray you, help me. Let me kill Pandarus. Let him come within reach of my spear. So far he has only shot at me from a distance and now he is boasting that I shall soon be dead."

Athene heard his prayer and came to stand at his side. "Diomedes," she said, "fear nothing. Now I have filled your heart with all the courage of your father, he who once fought single-handed with fifty men and killed them all. And I have also taken the mist from your eyes so that you can tell the difference between men and gods. You may fight against any man, but, if the gods join in the battle, do not fight against them—or only against one of them. If Aphrodite comes to the war, you may wound her with your sharp spear."

Athene vanished from his sight and Diomedes once more charged into the front line. Now he was three times as fierce and bold as he had been before. He hacked men's arms from their shoulders; he dragged men backwards from their chariots; each throw of his spear stretched a champion on the bloody ground. He was like a wounded lion ravaging a sheep fold from which the shepherd has fled in terror.

The Trojan prince Aeneas saw him from the part of the field where he too was fighting bitterly. He went at once to find Pandarus and, when he had found him, said: "Pandarus, now is the time for you to use your bow and arrows. Are you not said to be the best archer in Lycia, better than all the archers of Troy? Now show

what you can do and shoot down that man over there, whoever he
is."

Pandarus answered him. "The man you mean is Diomedes. I
recognise him by his shield and his helmet. But he seems to be
protected by some god. I have shot at him already and hit him in
the right shoulder. I thought that I had killed him. Never before
have I had such bad luck with my bow. Now I wish that I had
taken the advice of my father who, before I left home to come to
Troy, was always telling me to leave my bow behind and to fight
from a chariot. I have eleven fine chariots standing idle in my father's palace, and swift horses to go with them. I wish I had taken
them instead of this unlucky bow with which today I have
wounded two of the best of the Greeks. But now both Menelaus
and Diomedes are back again in the battle. I have a good mind to
break my bow in two and burn it."

"If it is a chariot and horses you want," said Aeneas, "let us use
mine. They are the best horses in Troy and come from an immortal
stock. You may drive them and let me meet Diomedes with my
spear. Or, if you prefer, I will drive the horses and let you do the
fighting."

"The horses know you," said Pandarus. "It would be better for
you to drive them. I have failed with my bow. Let me see now
what I can do with my spear."

So they mounted the chariot and drove fast towards Diomedes.
Sthenelus, the charioteer, saw them coming and cried out: "Diomedes, my dear friend, be careful of your life. You have fought
enough already. Here come two great champions against you. One
is Pandarus and the other is Prince Aeneas."

Diomedes looked at him sternly: "Do not talk to me of fear," he
said. "My strength is still with me. But, if I strike down these men,
make sure that you seize their horses. They are the best horses in
the world and come from a race of horses that Zeus himself gave to
the first king of Troy. I mean to have them for myself."

As he spoke Aeneas and Pandarus were upon him. Pandarus
hurled his heavy spear and the point tore through the shield
of Diomedes, reaching the armour underneath. Then Pandarus
shouted out: "I have struck him, right through the side. He cannot last long now, and now I shall have the glory that I prayed
for."

But his boasting was in vain. Strong Diomedes stared at him

grimly. "My body is untouched," he said. "I think that you will not escape so easily from this spear of mine." So saying, he poised his spear and threw it. It struck Pandarus on the nose by the eye, and the point went through his teeth, cutting off the tongue at the root, and came out in his throat below the chin. Pandarus fell headlong from the chariot and, as his shining armour rang upon the ground, the horses reared and shied in terror. So Pandarus died and was more unlucky with the spear than he had been with the bow.

Now with a great shout Aeneas sprang down from the chariot and stood over the dead body of Pandarus, covering it with his shield and his spear. He seemed like a strong lion at bay, as he stood there ready to face all who approached him. Diomedes then picked up a great rock, so big that it would have taken two ordinary men, such as men are today, even to lift it. But Diomedes lifted it easily and hurled it at Aeneas, striking him on the hip bone, tearing the muscles and breaking the bone itself. Great Aeneas felt his legs give way beneath him; he supported himself on the ground with one hand, and darkness came over his eyes. Indeed he certainly would have been killed there before he could recover himself, if his mother Aphrodite had not seen the danger of her son. She sped down from Olympus to his side and threw her arms round him to protect him.

Diomedes recognised the goddess but still pressed forward. He thrust at her with his spear and pierced through the fragrant robe that had been made for her by the Graces. He wounded her on the wrist and out of the wound flowed some of the ichor, or immortal blood, that runs in the veins of the gods. Aphrodite screamed with pain and dropped the body of her son. She fled from the battle, and as she fled, Diomedes shouted after her: "Daughter of Zeus, it would be better to leave war alone in future. Is it not enough for you to be spending your time in breaking the hearts of weak defenceless women? Leave warfare to men."

As for Aphrodite, she fled back to Olympus to the palace of Father Zeus and there she complained of the treatment she had received. But Hera and Athene mocked at her and Athene said: "It looks as though Aphrodite has been persuading some other woman to desert her husband, and has somehow managed to scratch her slender hand on the woman's golden brooch."

Zeus smiled at this and said to Aphrodite: "My dear child, war is not your business. You should leave that to Athene or to Ares."

Meanwhile Diomedes was searching everywhere for Aeneas, but Apollo had taken him up from the ground and carried him to safety inside the city. Here he cured his wounds and soon the great warrior was back again in the fighting. But he had lost his famous horses, for Sthenelus had obeyed his master's orders and had driven them back to the tent of Diomedes.

And now the Trojans were being driven back towards their city walls. But powerful help was at hand for them. Apollo called to the war god himself, Ares, and said: "Ares, murderous god, you who sate yourself on the blood of men and rejoice in the noise of falling towers and of burning cities, come now and drive this man Diomedes from the battle and give your help to the Trojans."

Then Ares took upon himself the shape of one of the leaders of the Trojan allies. In the thick of the fighting he stood by Hector and urged him on against the Greeks. In his hand he held a tremendous spear and wherever he and Hector went Panic followed them. With this powerful aid Hector himself fought with twice his usual courage. Aeneas also was spurred on to even greater efforts, and now gradually the Greeks began to give way.

Diomedes recognised the War God fighting at Hector's side and he said to his followers: "My friends, we must retreat a little. See how Hector is destroying our men. But there is nothing strange in that, for Ares himself is with him. We cannot fight with the immortal gods. Fall back, therefore, but keep your faces to the enemy."

For some time the other Greek champions, Odysseus, Ajax, Menelaus and the rest stood like rocks against which the sea surges and beats, but finally they too had to give way before the Trojans. They retreated in good order, still fighting fiercely, but still, as they retreated, Hector killed man after man, and man after man fell before the great spear of Ares at his side.

From Olympus Hera and Athene saw how the Greeks were being driven back. They came in indignation to Father Zeus and said: "See how this murderous Ares is slaughtering the gallant Greeks. It is Apollo and Aphrodite who have let him loose. Will you not allow us to stop him and drive him from the battle?"

Zeus, since he hated the god of War and his savagery, gave his consent and the two goddesses came down to the plain and to the fighting. Hera put on the shape of Stentor, one of the Greeks who had a voice which was as loud as the voices of fifty men together. Using his voice she shouted out to the Greeks, urging them to resist and to fight back at the advancing Trojans. And Athene went to look for Diomedes. She found him a little withdrawn from the battle. He was cooling the wound which he had received from Pandarus, wiping away the blood, and had, for the time, laid aside his heavy shield, since, what with the sweat and the fighting, its straps were cutting into the flesh of his shoulders. Athene stood by him and said: "How different you are from your father Tydeus! He was smaller than you, but how he used to fight! Nothing would stop him. And now here you stand, in spite of the help I promised you, idle and useless! Are you tired already? Or are you afraid?"

"Goddess," said Diomedes, "I recognise you and will speak freely. I am neither tired nor frightened. I am only doing as you told me to do. You told me not to fight with any of the gods except with Golden Aphrodite. Now Ares is leading the Trojans and from him I ordered my men to fall back."

Athene smiled at him. "Dear Diomedes," she said, "I never doubted your courage. Now I am with you and you need not fear Ares or any other god. Be confident and drive straight at him in your chariot. He is a mad bully and a traitor. Only yesterday he promised Hera and me that he would fight on the Greek side, but now he has been won over by Aphrodite and Apollo."

With these words she took the place of Sthenelus in Diomedes' chariot. Sthenelus was glad enough to be relieved. She took the reins and the whip in her hands and drove the swift horses forward to the place where huge Ares, his face and arms spattered with the blood of the slain, was stripping the armour from a fallen Greek. Athene made herself invisible, but Ares saw Diomedes approach and came straight for him, brandishing his enormous spear. Over the horses' necks he thrust at Diomedes, but Athene caught the spear in her hand and pushed it upwards, so that it missed its mark. Then Diomedes thrust with his spear and Athene drove it forward to the lower part of the War God's belly. It struck home, and tore through the flesh. Diomedes drew the spear out of the wound, and, as he did so, Ares let out a great yell of agony, as loud as the noise made by nine or ten thousand men shouting together in battle. Both Greeks and Trojans stood still in terror as they heard the dreadful sound. And Diomedes saw for a moment the face of the

War God twisted in agony. Then like a rushing black cloud of storm he swept upwards and away into the broad heaven.

In Olympus, still clutching his wound, he came before Father Zeus and began to complain. "Father Zeus," he said, "are you not shocked at the way your daughter Athene is behaving? Can you not control her? See how she rouses mortals against the gods. If I had not managed to escape, I might be lying there now on the plain among the dead bodies."

"Don't come whimpering to me," said Zeus, "you, who are always changing sides. You are the god whom I dislike most of all, since you enjoy nothing except violence and fighting. Also you are as bad-tempered and ungovernable as your mother Hera. But since you are my son I will cure your wound. Otherwise I should have done nothing for you at all."

So Zeus called for a divine ointment which healed immediately the wounded flesh of Ares, who bathed himself, put on fresh clothing, and sat down sulking among the gods.

Meanwhile Hera and Athene also withdrew from the fighting, and still the battle swayed backwards and forwards on the plain.

HECTOR PREPARES FOR BATTLE

All day they fought, and at nightfall the Trojans withdrew within their city, while the Greeks went back to their ships. Heralds carried messages from one side to the other and it was agreed that there should be a truce while each army collected its own dead for burial. And so throughout the night, by the glow of innumerable fires, the dead bodies were brought back either to Troy or to the Greek camp. Men wept great tears as they dragged from the bloody plain the bodies of friends and companions in arms. In Troy itself there were wives, sisters, mothers and aged fathers to mourn over their dear ones, but the families of the Greeks were far away beyond the echoing sea and beyond the ranges of many mountains.

And now Zeus summoned the immortal gods and spoke to them. "Listen to me," he said, "and abide by what I say. I will not allow any of you any more to take part in the fighting. It is decreed by Fate that no help is to reach the Greeks until they are fighting among their own ships. This is also my will, and it must be obeyed. I warn you that if any one of you disobeys me, that one will be hurled out of heaven with the blast of my thunderbolts."

The gods listened in silence. Hera and Athene indeed would have wished to argue with the Almighty Father, but his look was so severe and his words had been so full of force that they did not dare to speak openly. Afterwards indeed they complained to each other. "This is the doing of Thetis," they said, "who has won Zeus over to her side in order to avenge her son Achilles." But there was nothing that they could do against the clear orders of the Father of Gods and Men.

Early in the morning the warriors armed themselves and prepared for battle. After the fighting of the day before the Greeks felt certain that Priam's great city was almost in their hands. On the other side the Trojans and their allies were determined to resist.

In Troy Hector summoned the captains and the princes to battle. When fully armed himself he came to the palace of Paris, and found Paris himself with Helen sitting beside him in their gorgeous bedroom. Paris was still looking at his beautiful armour and was testing his curved bow in his hands. Hector looked at him sternly. "Still not ready for battle?" he said. "Yet all this fighting has come upon us because of you. Other men are dying for you at our very walls. Do you intend to wait here until the city itself is on fire?"

"Hector," said Paris, "what you say is quite right. Indeed I should have been ready before, and now Helen also has just been urging me to join in the battle. I agree with you both, and I think that today things will go better than they did yesterday. Will you not wait a moment for me to get ready? If you cannot, I will hurry and catch up to you before you leave the town."

Hector made no reply to this, but Helen spoke softly to him and said: "Dear brother Hector, I am indeed a shameless wicked creature. I wish that a storm had carried me away on the very day that I was born and had hurled me into the middle of the sea. Then I should not have come here to cause such trouble to you and to my own people as well. And my next wish would be to have had a better husband than this man. For he pays no attention at all to the reproaches of others. But now come in and sit down for a moment. It is you who have to bear all the worry and the toil of battle for the sake of faithless me and my accursed husband."

"Helen," said Hector, "I thank you for your kindness. But you must not ask me to come and sit down now. My place is with the army who miss me if I am not there. Make your husband hurry, so that he can catch up to me before I leave the city. Now I am going to my own home to say good-bye to my wife Andromache and to my little boy Astyanax."

So Hector went to his home, but he did not find his wife there. She had been to the temple to pray for her husband's safety, and now she was waiting by the Scaean Gate to speak to him before he led out the Trojans to the plain. She saw him coming from a distance and she hurried towards him. Behind her came a maid carrying the little boy in her arms. Hector smiled as he saw his son, but he said nothing. Andromache put her hand in his. As she spoke the tears flooded to her eyes. "Dear husband," she said, "must you always be fighting? Will you not think of your child and your wife? We could not live without you. And now, if you stand every day in the front of battle, there will surely be a time when all the Greeks will attack you at once and kill you. I would rather die than be without you. Indeed I have no one else left. My father was king in woody Thebe, but Achilles took his city and killed him, though he was too noble a man to strip him of his arms, and he gave him an honourable burial. Afterwards the nymphs planted elm trees around his tomb. I had seven brothers too, and all of these were killed by great Achilles in one day. At the same time he took my mother prisoner, and, though he allowed us to ransom her, she died afterwards in our house. So you, Hector, are father and mother and brothers to me, as well as my dear husband. Have pity on us. Do not leave your wife a widow and your child an orphan. Stay here today on the tower and defend the city from here."

"If I were to behave like a coward," said Hector, "I should be ashamed to meet the Trojans and their wives and daughters. In any case I could not do as you say. I have learnt not to give in, but always to stand in the front ranks, winning fame for my father and for myself. Nevertheless somehow deep down in my heart I know that the day will come when holy Troy and Priam and his people will be destroyed. And I do not feel so much pain for the fate of Priam or of Hecuba or of all my brave brothers who will be beaten down into the dust as I feel for your sake, and at the thought of some Greek dragging you off to slavery. I cannot bear to think of you in Greece, working in another man's house, with people pointing at you and saying: 'That is the wife of Hector, who led the Trojans in the fighting around Troy.' And your sorrow will come over you again as you feel the lack of me who would have protected you. I pray that I may lie deep in my grave at that time, and not hear your cries as you are dragged away."

As he finished speaking Hector turned to his little boy to take him in his arms. But the child cried and buried his head in his nurse's breast. He was frightened at the sight of his father in his glittering armour with the great helmet and the horsehair crest nodding dreadfully above it. Both Hector and Andromache laughed, and famous Hector took the helmet from his head and put it down upon the ground. Then he kissed his son and swung him to and fro in his arms. He prayed also to Zeus and to the other immortal gods. "Zeus and all you gods," he said, "I pray you make this boy like me, strong and brave, a famous King of Troy. And when he comes back from battle let people say of him: 'Here comes one who is an even better soldier than his father was.' "

Then Hector kissed his wife and said to her: "Dear wife, you must not alarm yourself about me. No one will send me to Hades before my time. But no man alive, however brave or however cowardly, can escape what fate has in store for him. And now you must go back to the house and see to your work there. War is men's business."

So Hector took up his helmet and his spear. Andromache went back to her house and, as she went, she often turned round to look at him and great tears fell from her eyes. When she got home, she and her servants all mourned for him, for they thought that he would never come back alive from the battle.

Meanwhile Paris had caught Hector up. Now he too was fully armed, but he excused himself for being late. "Brother," said Hector to him, "you can fight well enough. Only you are apt to give in too soon and not keep on to the end. Now let us go. Fight well today, and I shall hold nothing against you if Zeus and the immortal gods allow us to return in victory."

So Hector led the army out into the plain and in front of them was the army of the Greeks drawn up for battle. Now Zeus thundered from Olympus and the warriors stood still, not knowing what the omen might mean or to which side Zeus would give his aid.

A TROJAN VICTORY

And now once again the two great forces hurtled together and the air was filled with the noise of clashing shields and swords, of the whinnying of horses and of the cries of the wounded and of the dying. All through the morning of this day men fell on either side in the rain of spears and arrows and in fighting hand-to-hand. But in the afternoon Zeus gave fresh strength to the Trojans and the line of the Greeks began to waver. No more could great Agamemnon, or Ajax or Idomeneus hold their ground, as Hector led his men in charge after charge against them. They began to retreat over the plain backwards in the direction of the wall and deep ditch that protected their ships.

But old Nestor was left behind in the retreat. One of his chariot horses had been shot in the head by Paris and now this horse, plunging and writhing on the ground, had made it impossible to control the other two horses that drew the shining chariot. Nestor himself had drawn his sword and was hacking at the reins in order to free the wounded animal, when he saw Hector himself in all the pride of his victory come driving towards him over the plain.

Then certainly the old King Nestor would have lost his life and Hector would have taken from him the famous shield that he carried, if Diomedes had not seen his peril. Quickly he drove up to Nestor and said to him, "My old friend, you are not a match for these young warriors. Your horses are too slow. Come and take the reins in my chariot. You will see how swift are the Trojan horses that I took yesterday from Aeneas. Let our charioteers look after your horses while you and I stand against Hector, and let us show him that my spear is as thirsty for blood as is his own."

Old Nestor was willing enough. He took the reins and drove the horses towards Hector who himself was yearning for the fight. Diomedes was the first to throw his spear. He missed Hector but struck his charioteer right through the breast so that he fell out of the chariot and threw the horses into a panic. And now Diomedes would have pressed on, but from Mount Ida there came a sudden roar of thunder and Zeus hurled down a thunderbolt which tore into the earth in front of the horses that Nestor was driving. The air was full of the smell of sulphur. The horses shied and reared up in terror. Nestor, terrified himself, turned to Diomedes and said: "Diomedes, it is no use fighting against Zeus. We must turn the horses round and fly. There is no help for it. Zeus is more powerful then we are."

"You are right," said Diomedes, "but I cannot bear the thought that soon Hector will be boasting over us and saying : 'Diomedes could not face me in battle. He was so frightened that he ran to his ships.' "

"Both Trojans and Greeks," said Nestor, "know well that you are no more a coward than was your father Tydeus. But today Zeus is allowing Hector to do what he wishes with us."

Then Nestor turned the horses and they drove back in flight after the rest of the Greeks towards the ditch and fortifications that guarded their camp. As they went the Trojans shouted in triumph and surged after them. Hector cried out to his men: "See how Diomedes, the best warrior of them all, is running away like a woman. Now is the time to make certain of our victory. Their wretched walls will be no defence to them, and as for their ditch our horses can easily jump it. Let me but once get among their hollow ships. I shall burn the ships with fire and cut down the men as they go staggering about in the smoke."

Then Hector called to his chariot horses and spoke to them by name. "Xanthus," he said, "and you, Podargus, and Aithon, and noble Lampus, now is the time to repay me for all the care and kindness which you have received from Andromache; for she always gave you your food of honeyed wheat and mixed wine and water for you to drink, and saw that you were satisfied before she gave me my food, although I am her husband. Now put out all your speed. Let us see whether we can capture Nestor's famous shield and the great breastplate of Diomedes which was made for him by the god Hephaestus."

So speaking, he swept upon the fleeing Greeks. Nestor and Diomedes indeed escaped, helped as they were by the swift horses of Aeneas, but in the space between the ships and the surrounding trench chariots and men were huddled together in a disorderly mass, and among them the sword and spear of Hector fell like lightning, as he raged forward irresistibly, determined to set fire among the ships. And indeed he might have done so that very day if Hera had not put it into the heart of Agamemnon to rally the troops once more.

Agamemnon stood by the black ship of Odysseus, which was in the middle of the line of ships, and he shouted out so that his voice carried far along the whole line. "Shame upon you, Greeks!" he shouted. "What has happened to us? What has happened to all our boasting? We used to say that each one of us was a match for a hundred Trojans, and now the whole lot of us cannot stand up to this one Hector. O Father Zeus, has there ever been another great king who was so cast down from his hopes and from his glory? At least grant me this prayer. Save my army from utter destruction."

Zeus heard the prayer of Agamemnon. He put fresh heart into the Greeks. Diomedes sallied out again beyond the wall, and with him were Agamemnon and Menelaus, Ajax and his brother Teucer. Teucer stood under the cover of his brother's shield, and, looking out from under this protection, he would shoot his arrows among the Trojans, each time picking out one of their foremost champions. Eight of them he shot down, one after the other. Then he aimed an arrow at Hector. This time he missed his mark but he hit one of the sons of Priam, who dropped dead in the dust, with his head falling over sideways like the head of a poppy in a garden when it is weighed down by its seed and by the moisture of a summer shower. "Let me try again," said Teucer, "to kill this mad dog," and once more he aimed an arrow at Hector. But Apollo turned the point aside, and the arrow struck Hector's charioteer full in the breast, so that he fell headlong from the chariot.

In grief and fury for his loss, Hector leapt to the ground. Teucer was just fitting another arrow to his bow, but Hector picked up a great jagged piece of rock and hurled it at him before he had time to take aim. He struck him on the collar bone, numbing his whole arm and shoulder. The bow dropped from his hands and he sank down on his knees. His life was saved however, since great Ajax covered him with his shield while his comrades lifted him up and carried him back to the ships.

And now once more the Trojans drove forward and the Greeks were pressed back to the trench that they desperately attempted to defend. That day they were saved by the coming of night, for now the bright sun set in the stream of Ocean and drew darkness over the earth. Hector, though unwillingly, was forced to withdraw his troops, while the weary Greeks thanked the immortal gods for this respite from the bitter fighting.

Hector did not lead his army back to the city. Instead he called an assembly in the plain near the river, where the ground was not covered with dead bodies. "Listen to me," he said, "my Trojans and my gallant allies! I thought that this day we would set fire to Greek ships and destroy these invaders. They have been saved by darkness and not by any courage of their own. Now we shall attack and not cease till we have driven them into the sea. Meanwhile let men go back to Troy and bring us out sheep and oxen for our evening meal. Let them bring wood too, so that we may have fires to burn all night long. Guards must be set, and we must keep an eye on the enemy, in case they may try to escape this very night. Tomorrow we will attack in full force, and I wish I were as certain that I should never die or grow old as I am certain that tomorrow will be a day of evil for the Greeks."

The Trojans shouted their applause and did as Hector commanded. They unharnessed their sweating horses and tethered them by their chariots. Wood and provisions were brought from the city. Soon their innumerable watch fires sparkled over the plain, like the stars shining around the moon on a windless night when all the mountain tops and headlands and rocky defiles stand out clearly and the great spaces of the upper air yawn open in their fathomless extent, so that every star in heaven is shining and the shepherd rejoices. So shone the Trojan fires between the ships and the stream of Scamander. A thousand fires were burning, and round each of them sat fifty men in the gleaming firelight. The horses stood by their chariots, munching the white barley. So they waited for the dawn.

THE EMBASSY TO ACHILLES

And now, while Hector and the Trojans planned the assault which on the next morning they would make upon the Greek camp, the Greeks themselves and all their leaders suffered a grief and a despair which were almost unendurable. Not only had they failed to take Troy upon that day, but they had lost numbers of their best men and now they were penned within the fortifications of their own camp.

When the sentries had been posted on the walls Agamemnon called a Council of the chief men in his army. As he rose to speak the tears poured from his eyes. "Zeus," he said, "has been the most cruel of the gods to me. He promised that we would bring down the high walls of Troy, but now he has changed his mind and is giving the victory to Hector. What are we to do? Are we to get on board our ships tonight and sail back to Argos, or are we to remain here till the ships are burnt and we ourselves are slaughtered by our ships?"

The others listened to the king in silence. Then Diomedes rose to speak. "Agamemnon," he said, "you are free to run away if you like, and so are all the rest of the long-haired Greeks. But I shall never give in, no, not if you all go back to Argos. I and Sthenelus, my charioteer, shall still stay here and fight, even if we have to fight alone."

This speech of Diomedes put fresh heart into the Greeks, and they shouted out that they too would stay and fight to the end. Then old Nestor spoke. "My lord Agememnon," he said, "I am an old man, and it is right for you, great king as you are, to listen to my advice. The noble Diomedes has spoken well. He is a true son of his father Tydeus, whom I remember well in my young days. But here is another thing that we can do. It was because of your action, King Agamemnon, that we have been without the help of great Achilles, whom Zeus loves so much that he will not protect us now that Achilles is out of the fighting. Will you not now be reconciled with him and offer him gifts if he will relent from his anger? I think that today's battle would have gone very differently if Achilles had been on our side."

To this Agamemnon replied: "Nestor, what you have said is true. It was the gods who drove me to that state of mad folly when I quarrelled with Achilles. And now I will tell you what I will do to satisfy him and to make up for my insults to him. I will give him back the girl Briseis whom I took from him and with her I will send seven women of great beauty and skilled in all kinds of useful work, women whom I took prisoners on the island of Lesbos. I will give him also ten talents of gold, twenty shining cauldrons, and twelve fine racehorses all of which have won prizes. All this I will give him now, and later on, if the gods allow us to sack the great city of Priam, let him fill his ship with gold and take the pick of the spoil. And when we return to Greece I will offer him my daughter in marriage and will honour him no less than I honour Orestes, my son. And with my daughter I will give him riches and seven of my finest towns, all lying near the sea coast. Let him only relent and put an end to the quarrel and serve with me again. He ought to do so. No man has a right to be always unyielding."

"Lord Agamemnon," said Nestor, "you have spoken well and generously. Now let us send to Achilles some of our best men to tell him of your offer. We have with us old Phoenix whom Peleus, Achilles' father, made tutor and guardian to his son. He must go now and use his influence. Great Ajax should go also and wise Odysseus with his soothing words."

To this proposal all the others agreed. Phoenix went at once to Achilles, but Ajax and Odysseus first had their supper and then walked together to the camp of the Myrmidons along the shore of the breaking sea. As they went they prayed to Poseidon, the god of the sea, that their words might be able to soften the proud heart of Achilles.

Soon they came to his tent and there they found Achilles playing on a lyre and delighting himself with the songs he sang of the great deed of heroes. Opposite him sat Patroclus with his eyes fixed on his friend's face as he waited for him to finish the song. Phoenix too was in the tent, but he had not yet spoken with his old pupil.

Odysseus, with Ajax following him, stepped forward and Achilles immediately sprang to his feet, still holding the lyre in his hand, and hurried to greet them. "Welcome," he said, "to you both. Of all the Greeks you are the two whom I love most, and I am happy to have you under my roof. And now, Patroclus, you must bring out bigger cups and better wine. For these two are some of my greatest friends."

Patroclus did as his friend asked him. They all sat down together in the firelight and poured out their libations to the immortal gods. Then Ajax nodded his head to Phoenix, encouraging him to speak, but Odysseus in fact spoke first and said: "Achilles, I drink to you and wish you well and thank you for your hospitality. And yet we are in no mood for eating and drinking. Today we have only just escaped with our lives and tomorrow we may lose them. Hector and his arrogant Trojans have carried everything before them and have beaten us back to our ships. And now they wait eagerly for the dawn and Hector is already boasting that tomorrow he will burn our ships with fire and butcher us beside them. Will you not rouse yourself, therefore, and help us in our need? Will you not forget your quarrel with Agamemnon, who now is ready to offer you every honour and a hundred times the value of what he took from you?"

Here Odysseus paused and then, speaking slowly, he told Achilles of what Agamemnon had promised to give him. Finally he said: "And if, Achilles, you are not moved by the gifts of King Agamemnon, then think of us other Greeks in the army. Think of how we should honour you if you came now to help us. Think too that now is the time when you might win immortal fame by killing great Hector himself in all his confidence. For now he would fight with the gods themselves."

But here Achilles interrupted him. "Odysseus," he said, "my noble and wise friend, let me tell you at once how my mind stands. For I hate like hell itself the man who keeps his intentions secret and says something different from what he means. Not Agamemnon nor all the rest of the Greeks will ever make me change my mind. I have stayed awake all night and I have fought all day in his service, and what reward did I get for it? He has injured me and I shall never forgive him. If now he wants to save his life, he must depend on you and the others. As for me, I shall sail back to my own country and be happy there. Tell him that I do not want his gifts, that I do not want to marry his daughter. All over Greece there are beautiful and noble women whom I might marry and with whom I could live happily and at peace. Now I think that life itself is worth more than all the wealth that Troy enjoyed in the days of peace before the Greeks came here—more than all the gold in Apollo's temple at Delphi, or the fabulous riches of Egyptian Thebes. The goddess, my mother, has told me that Fate has given me the choice of two roads—either to fight here and never to return home, or else to live quietly in my own land and be happy, though not famous for ever. Now I shall go home and I advise you also to do so. This is my last word, and I should wish you to report it to the Greeks tonight. But Phoenix can stay here with me, and, if he wishes, take ship with me in the morning."

When Achilles ceased speaking the others remained for some time in silence, looking anxiously at each other; for Achilles had refused them utterly. Finally the old warrior Phoenix spoke. The tears fell from his eyes, so much he feared for the Greek ships. "Dear child," he said, "will you not listen to me? Will you not remember how your father Peleus put you into my care? I have always loved you as though you were my own son, and you loved me too. When you were a little boy you would never take your food from any hand but mine. You have often sat on my knee and spilt wine over my clothes when you were learning how to eat and drink. And later, when we came to this lamentable war, your father begged you to be guided by me, since he knew that I would never give you bad advice. Even now, if Agamemnon had not shown that he was ready to yield to you, I should not be advising you to accept his offers. But Agamemnon repents. He offers you great gifts and he has sent to you the noblest men among the Greeks, who are your friends, in order to show his respect. My child, it is not right to be so unyielding. Even the gods yield to prayers, and prayers indeed are the daughters of Zeus who go about the world seeking to do good. It is right to receive them into our hearts. Think too of how the Greeks will honour you, if you save them in their great peril. I beg you, dear child, to be persuaded."

But Achilles replied to him, "Old friend, my mind is made up. It is no use trying to touch my heart by recalling old times and so taking the part of Agamemnon whom I hate. Nor do I care what the Greeks think of me. I have sworn not to join in the fighting though all the ships go up in fire, unless Hector is so bold as to attack my own men and my own ships. Now I advise you to stay the night here, and tomorrow we will decide whether to sail home or not."

Ajax then turned to Odysseus and said: "Great Odysseus, let us be going. We must tell the others our news, bad as it is, since they are waiting for us. As for Achilles, his heart is as hard as a rock, and he will not listen to us, though we honour him and wish to show ourselves his friends."

So Ajax and Odysseus left Achilles in his tent and Phoenix with him. They went back on the way that they had come and found King Agamemnon and the other leaders of the Greeks eagerly awaiting them. When Odysseus told them of how the spirit of Achilles was still utterly unyielding and how he refused to join in the battle, there was a long silence. Finally Diomedes spoke and said: "Agamemnon, your generous offers have only made Achilles prouder than he was before. Let him go, I say. And tomorrow all of us must fight in the front line, encouraging our men by our example. There are others beside Achilles who are not afraid of Hector, and there are gods also on our side."

A RAID ON THE TROJAN CAMP

Then the rest of the leaders of the Greeks went to their ships, and, having seen that the sentries were posted, refreshed themselves with sleep. But Agamemnon could not sleep, so many were the thoughts that came to his mind and tormented it. Sometimes he looked out over the plain and saw the fires of the Trojan army encamped outside their city. There were countless fires burning, and from the Trojan camp came the noise of flute playing and of singing. And then when Agamemnon turned his eyes towards his own army and towards the Greek ships, he tore his hair and he wept bitterly at the thought of the danger that surrounded them. Finally, in his sleepless mood, he left his bed, bound his bright sandals on his feet, threw over his shoulders a great lion-skin cloak that reached to his ankles, and, taking his spear in his hand, set out in the night in order to consult old Nestor and to discuss with him the plans for the morrow's battle.

But he had not gone far from his tent when he was met by his brother Menelaus. Menelaus too had found it impossible to sleep, and now the brothers decided to call yet another council of war in the tent of Nestor. Agamemnon went one way and Menelaus another. They woke all the great captains of the army and all met together quietly, while the troops were still sleeping, near the place where Nestor's black ships were drawn up on the shore.

Now when they were all together Nestor spoke. "Is there any of us," he said, "who has the courage to go out towards the Trojan camp and find out what their plans are? It would greatly help us to know whether they intend to stay where they are or to return to the city before attacking us in the morning. A brave man, willing to take the risk, might steal into their camp, and perhaps take a prisoner who could give us news. Such a man would not only be honoured by us, but would also be properly rewarded."

He paused and immediately Diomedes replied to him. "Nestor," he said, "I am willing to take on this adventure. But I should like it better if someone would come with me. In these affairs two are better than one."

Many of the Greeks immediately volunteered to go with Diomedes into the Trojan camp. There were Menelaus, Ajax, Odysseus and many others. Out of these Agamemnon told Diomedes to choose as comrade the one whom he would prefer himself. In his heart he hoped that he would not choose his brother Menelaus, since the task was dangerous. Diomedes did not hesitate. "Since you allow me," he said, "to choose my own comrade, I shall choose the godlike Odysseus. He is ready to take any risk and he keeps a stout heart in all difficulties. Moreover Pallas Athene loves him. He and I could go through fire together and come out safe. He is full of resource and has a brain like lightning."

"There is no need," said Odysseus, "to talk about me. These men here know both my virtues and my faults. Let us be going. Most of the night has gone and we have no time to waste."

Then Diomedes borrowed from one of the others a great two-edged sword, since he had left his own sword in his tent. On his head he put a leather helmet, without plume or crest. Odysseus borrowed from the hero Meriones a sword, a bow and a cunningly made helmet. Inside it were a number of leather straps, so that it fitted tightly to the head, and the outside was decorated with rows of white boars' tusks.

So the two men went out and as they went Pallas Athene sent them a lucky omen, a heron on the right. They could not see the heron in the darkness, but they heard it croak. Then Odysseus prayed to Athene and said: "Hear me, daughter of Zeus, you who always stand at my side in danger, you whose notice I can never escape. Help me tonight and bring us back safe to the ships after we have done some great deed and made the Trojans suffer."

Diomedes also prayed to the goddess. "Hear me too," he said, "daughter of Zeus, and stand by me as once you stood by my father Tydeus when the Thebans set an ambush for him and he killed fifty of them with his own hand, because you supported him. Support me now, and when I return I will sacrifice to you a broad-browed heifer with horns gilded for the sacrifice."

So they prayed and Athene heard their prayers, for of all men these two were the ones whom she loved most. Then they went on like two lions in the black night, treading among the dead bodies, the blood and the abandoned weapons on the ground.

Meanwhile in the Trojan camp Hector also had been making his plans. He had called together a meeting of the Trojans and had offered great rewards to anyone who would go as a spy among the Greek ships, to find out whether the ships were guarded or whether the Greeks, after their defeat, were thinking of sailing away.

Among the Trojans there was a man called Dolon, a rich man, not handsome to look at, but fast on his feet. It was he who undertook the adventure. "I shall go right through the Greek camp," he said, "to the tent of Agamemnon, and I shall bring you back the news you want. Only I ask for my reward the horses and chariot of Achilles, since these are the best there are in the Greek army."

Hector, in his confidence, replied: "No other Trojan except you shall ride behind those horses. I swear it by Zeus himself."

Then Dolon slung his curved bow over his shoulders and put on his head a cap made of ferret-skin. He covered himself with a grey wolf skin as a cloak, took a spear in his hand and set out towards the Greek camp.

He went fast and Odysseus was aware of him in the distance. He whispered to Diomedes. "Here comes someone from the Trojan army either to spy on us or to rob some of the dead bodies on the plain. Let us allow him to go a little way past us. Then we will spring out on him and, if he runs, we will head him off from his own army and drive him towards our ships."

So they lay down and hid themselves among the dead bodies. Dolon never saw them, but ran past, and, when he had gone a little way they sprang to their feet and ran after him. He heard their footsteps and for a moment he stopped still, looking backwards, thinking that Hector had sent messengers after him with more instructions. Soon, however, he knew that they were enemies and turned to run. But Odysseus and Diomedes followed in his tracks like sharp-toothed hounds that chase a hare turning and twisting and screaming before them through the woods. And if Dolon tried to run towards the Trojan camp, they headed him off and drove him towards the Greek outposts. Finally Diomedes was within spear's throw and he cried out: "Stop, or else you will feel my spear in your back." At the same time he threw his spear, but deliberately missed the man. The bright weapon flew over his shoulder and stuck quivering in the ground. Now Dolon's courage failed him and he stopped still, shaking and shivering with fear, while Diomedes and Odysseus came up to him and tightly seized his arms. Dolon burst into tears and, as he spoke, his teeth chattered together. "Take me alive," he begged, "and I will promise you a great ransom. In my house I have stores of gold and bronze and well-shaped iron. Only spare my life."

Odysseus looked at him grimly and said: "We will speak of that later. Now answer my questions. What are you doing here? Was it Hector who sent you out to spy upon our camp?"

"Yes," said Dolon, "and he promised me the chariot and horses of Achilles if I came back with the news he wanted."

Odysseus smiled. "A great prize indeed," he said. "But those horses are difficult to manage and difficult to drive for anyone except Achilles himself. Now tell me in what part of the field did you leave Hector. In what way are the sentries posted? What are the plans for tomorrow?" Dolon, still terrified, answered the questions of Odysseus. Among other things he told him that the Trojan allies were sleeping separately from the main Trojan army and he pointed out the place where was the camp of the Thracians under their king, Rhesus. "Rhesus," said Dolon, "has the most beautiful and the biggest horses that I have ever seen. They are whiter than snow and run faster than the wind. His chariot too is made of silver and gold, and he has some wonderful golden armour, more suitable for gods than for men to wear. I promise you that I am telling the truth. You can leave me here bound and go and see for yourselves. I stake my life on it."

"There is no need for you to stake your life," said Diomedes, "since we shall take that in any case. If we spared you, you might come out to spy on our camp again."

Dolon was stretching out his hands and beginning to speak, but Diomedes struck him on the neck so great a blow with his sword that he cut off his head which fell in the dust with his lips still moving in speech.

They took his ferret-skin cap, his bow and his cloak of wolf skin, and Odysseus raised up these spoils to Athene and prayed to her. "Goddess," he said, "receive these spoils, since it was to you that first we prayed. And now help us as we go to raid the Thracian camp."

Then he hid the trophies under a tamarisk bush and he twisted reeds and marsh plants together at the top of the bush so as to mark it and make the place easy to recognise when they were on their way back.

And now they went forward again among the dead bodies and soon came to the place where the Thracians were encamped. There was no guard set and the men were sleeping quietly, overcome with the fatigue of fighting. Their armour was piled on the ground at their side, and by each man was a pair of horses. Rhesus himself was sleeping in the middle and his great white horses were tethered to the rail of his splendid chariot.

Odysseus whispered to Diomedes. "There is the man, and there are the horses that Dolon told us of. Now quickly draw your sword and start killing the men, or else leave that to me and get the horses out."

Diomedes sprang forward with his sword drawn and, like a lion falling upon a flock of sheep or goats, began a grim slaughter of men. On all sides was the noise of hideous groans and all the ground was red with blood. Twelve men Diomedes slew and, as he slew them, Odysseus took each body by the foot and dragged it aside so as to leave a way clear for the horses, since he feared that they might cause trouble by refusing to tread over the dead bodies of those who had tended them. King Rhesus himself was the thirteenth man whom Diomedes slew. He was breathing heavily in his sleep, since Athene had sent him a terrible dream. He dreamed that Diomedes, the son of Tydeus, was standing at his head, nor did he wake from the dream until his sweet life had left him.

Meanwhile Odysseus had tied the horses together with thongs and, using his bow as a whip, had driven them out into the open. Then he whistled to Diomedes, who came out to join him. They took a horse each, mounted, and rode back like the wind on the way by which they had come.

Scarcely had they gone when one of the Thracian leaders, a relation of King Rhesus, woke from sleep and saw the empty place where the horses had been. Then he saw the slaughter that Diomedes had made and the dead body of the king. He cried out and roused the whole camp. Hector with his Trojans came running up and they looked with amazement at the deeds which those two men had done.

Meanwhile the two rode on through the night, leaving the crying and the shouting behind them. When they reached the place where they had killed Dolon, Diomedes dismounted, took up the bloodstained arms which they had hidden, and gave them to Odysseus, so that he might make an offering of them to Athene.

So they drew nearer to the Greek ships where the other leaders of the Greeks were anxiously awaiting them. It was old Nestor who first heard the sound of their approach. "My friends," he said to the others, "unless I am deceived, I hear the sound of horses. How good it would be if it were Odysseus and Diomedes riding in with horses captured from the enemy. Yet I fear it may be the Trojans themselves, and that something has happened to our best two warriors."

The words were hardly out of his mouth when the men themselves arrived. They jumped down from their horses laughing and their friends crowded round them and shook them by the hand. Nestor was the first to speak. "Glorious Odysseus," he said, "where did you get those horses? Never in my life have I seen finer ones. They shine like the sun. Did you really take them from the Trojans, or has some god given them to you? For Zeus loves you both, and so does Pallas Athene."

Odysseus answered him. "Nestor," he said, "the gods are stronger than we are, and a god, if he wanted, could give us even better horses than these. These we took from Rhesus, the King of Thrace. We killed him and twelve of his men; also on the way we killed a spy who was coming to our camp."

So, laughing, he drove the horses in among the Greek ships, and the other Greeks went with him, cheered by his success. Then they went into the sea to wash the sweat from their necks and thighs, and, after they had rubbed themselves down with olive oil, they took a meal and poured out to Athene libations of the cheerful wine.

THE BATTLE IN THE PLAIN

But as soon as Dawn had risen from her bed to bring light to gods and to men, the Greeks roused themselves for battle, knowing that now there must be no cowardice or hanging back from the fight if they were to keep Hector from setting fire to their ships upon that very day.

Agamemnon himself gave the call to arms. Then he put on his own armour of shining bronze. First he bound on his legs his beautiful greaves, fitted with silver over the ankles. Then he put on his breast the breastplate that had been sent him as a gift by the King of Cyprus when he heard of the sailing of the expedition to Troy. The breastplate was made of bands neatly fitted together—ten bands of dark blue enamel, twelve of gold and twenty of tin. At each side, reaching up to the place where the neck went through, were three coiling snakes, glittering with all the colours of the rainbow. Over his shoulders he slung his great sword, studded with gold on the hilt, and with a sheath of silver. Then he took up his huge man-covering shield. It was made of ten circles of bronze; the boss was of blue enamel and round this were twenty white shining studs of tin. On the shield was painted a Gorgon's head with grim eyes, and on each side were Terror and Panic. On his head Agamemnon put his helmet with its high crest and the horse hair plume dreadfully nodding above. In his hands he took up two strong well-pointed spears. So the King of Golden Mycenae went out shining into battle, and stood at the head of his army by the trench, with the chariots and the charioteers drawn up behind them, ready for action if they should push the Trojans back.

The Trojans on their side were marshalled by great Hector, by Aeneas, whom they honoured as a god, and by the three famous sons of Antenor. As he moved among his men, now here, now there, Hector in his blazing armour shone out fitfully like the lightning of Zeus, or like a baleful star that appears and reappears from behind the clouds.

And now the two armies fell upon each other like reapers in a rich man's field, cutting down the corn or barley in swathes. So all the morning men fell on each side and neither side would give way. But when it came to the time when a woodman in the hills would be weary of his task of felling trees and would begin to think of rest, then the Greeks began to break through the Trojan ranks and to force them back from the trench. Shouting to each other they pushed forward, and in front of them went Agamemnon, like a raging fire through the dry woods. Many were the captains and warriors whom he slew that day, and among them were two sons of Priam who had come out to battle in one chariot.

So the Trojans fell back before Agamemnon. By mid-day they had been pushed back to the old tomb of Ilus and the fig-tree half-way across the plain, and still Agamemnon pursued them, shouting his terrible war cry, his hands and unconquerable arms covered with the blood of those whom he had slain. On he swept, like a lion running amok among a herd of cattle at dusk, and he drove them back to the oak tree and the Scaean Gate.

Zeus meanwhile was watching the battle. He had withdrawn Hector from the fighting and he sent to him his messenger Iris who came to him and said: "Hector, this is my message from Father Zeus. So long as you see Agamemnon in the front line, take no part in the fighting yourself, but order your men to hold firm and encourage them to do so. But once Agamemnon is wounded, Zeus will give strength to you and to the Trojans, so that you may kill and kill until you reach the Greek ships and until the darkness comes."

Hector then jumped down from his chariot and, taking two

spears in his hand, went among the Trojan ranks, calling on them to stand firm and to yield no further ground. The Trojans obeyed him, and now in the forefront of their ranks, ready to meet the savage onset of Agamemnon, stood the two noble sons of Antenor, Iphidamas and Coön. Iphidamas had been brought up in distant Thrace, and the king who had brought him up there had offered him the hand of his daughter, so as to keep him always at home, so much he loved the youth for his beauty and his valour. But no sooner was the wedding over than Iphidamas heard of the expedition against Troy. He left his bride behind and came at once to fight against the Greeks.

Now he faced King Agamemnon and, thrusting at him with his spear, struck him full on the belt beneath the breastplate. But, though with all his weight he pressed his blow home, the spear point bent on the silver buckles of the belt. Agamemnon dragged the spear shaft out of his grasp and leapt towards him with his sword raised. He struck him on the neck so that his limbs were loosened and he fell to the ground in the sleep from which there is no waking. Hard indeed was his fate, dying there in defence of his country, far from the wife whom he had just married, but whose love he had never enjoyed.

And now Agamemnon began to strip the dead body of its glorious armour, but when Coön, the elder son of Antenor, saw what had happened to his brother, his eyes were dimmed with grief for it. He fell upon Agamemnon with his spear and struck him in the arm below the elbow. The point went clean through the flesh and Agamemnon shuddered as he felt the blow. Yet, wounded as he was, he did not give in. Coön had now taken hold of his brother's foot and was trying to drag the body back behind the Trojan lines. Agamemnon rushed at him and struck him with his spear below the shield. Then, springing forward, he cut off his head, there, upon the body of Iphidamas. So these two sons of Antenor both perished at the hands of Agamemnon.

And still, so long as the blood ran warm from his wound, Agamemnon pressed forward against the Trojans; but when the blood had dried and ceased to flow, the pain became unbearable and he could fight no longer. He mounted his chariot and ordered his charioteer to drive him back to the ships. As he went he cried out to the others: "Now it is for you, my friends, to fight on and save our ships. Zeus has not allowed me to fight all day."

Now when Hector saw that Agamemnon was wounded and was retiring from the battle, he shouted out with a great voice to the Trojans and their allies: "Now is the time to show our full strength. Now Zeus himself will give us the victory he had promised." And he plunged into the battle like a whirlwind that comes from the upper air and churns up the violet waters of the sea. Man after man he killed and behind him came the other Trojans, fired by his example.

The Greeks fell back and soon their retreat would have turned into a rout and they would have been driven again to their ships in that first onset if Odysseus had not called out across the ranks to Diomedes. "What has happened to us," he shouted, "in heaven's name? At this rate Hector will be among our ships before we know where we are. Come, my dear friend, and stand beside me, and let us show that we can resist."

Diomedes replied: "Certainly I will stand and endure the fight. Yet it seems to me that Zeus has now given his own strength to the Trojans and has determined on their victory."

So Odysseus and Diomedes stood firm and the Greeks rallied again. But Hector, looking along the ranks, saw where they stood and, shouting out his war cry, bore down on them with his picked Trojan warriors at his back. Even Diomedes shuddered as he saw great Hector in his flashing bronze. He turned to Odysseus and said: "Things look black for us two. Here comes great Hector in all his strength. We must stand firm and drive him back."

As he spoke he hurled his long-shadowed spear at Hector's head and struck him full on his helmet. The point did not pierce through the metal to the flesh, but Hector was stunned by the blow. He fell back quickly behind his men and sank to his knees, supporting himself with one strong hand on the ground, while everything went black before his eyes.

Diomedes shouted out in triumph and sprang forward, but now Paris, who had hidden himself behind the tomb of Ilus on the plain, aimed an arrow at him and shot. The arrow went through the flat part of Diomedes' foot and pinned it to the ground. Paris laughed as he came out from his ambush and cried out: "I have hit you, Diomedes, and I wish my arrow had pierced you in the lower belly below your breastplate and robbed you of your life. Then the Trojans would have had a rest from your savagery."

Strong Diomedes replied: "You bowman, you coward, you runner after women! I wish you would stand and face me with sword and spear. As it is, you have only scratched my foot. I might have been wounded like this by a woman or a careless boy. My weapons are different. If you faced them you would soon find yourself more sought after by the vultures than by the girls."

As he spoke Odysseus came to his side and covered him with his shield. Diomedes sat down and drew the sharp arrow out of his flesh. Pain stabbed through him as he did so. His charioteer supported him to his chariot and drove him out of the battle.

And now Odysseus was left alone, since all the rest had turned in flight. "Now what," he said to himself, "will happen to me? It would be shameful to run away, yet it is a bad thing also to be caught here by myself, now that Zeus has filled the other Greeks with fear. I know however that only cowards withdraw from fighting. The brave man will stand firm and either kill or be killed."

As he deliberated thus with his own great heart the Trojan companies swarmed up to him and surrounded him, like hunters with their hounds who surround a wild boar. And as a wild boar turns from side to side with his gleaming tusks, dealing death as he charges now here now there, so Odysseus, surrounded by his enemies, fought back at them and every thrust of his spear brought wounds or death. Many were the men he killed until at length a Trojan captain (Socus was his name), with a mighty throw of his spear, pierced through the bright shield of Odysseus and tore away the flesh from his side, though Pallas Athene kept the point from any vital part. Even then Socus turned to run; but Odysseus hurled his own spear and caught him between the shoulders, piercing his heart, so that he fell headlong to the ground in death. Then Odysseus pulled out the spear from his own wound and, as he did so, the dark blood flowed in a stream. The Trojans saw the blood and they shouted to each other and all together set upon the wounded man.

Then great Odysseus began slowly to give ground and at the same time he shouted for help. Three times he shouted and his voice was heard by yellow-haired Menelaus, who immediately turned to Ajax and said: "I hear the voice of brave Odysseus crying for help. It must be that the Trojans have cut him off by himself in the retreat. Let us hurry to the rescue. How we would miss him, if anything happened to him!"

So the two of them charged through the Trojans and came to

the place where Odysseus was still standing, with the blood pouring from his wound, keeping the Trojans at bay, though they pressed on him from all sides. Huge Ajax covered him with his shield and before his blows the Trojans gave way, while Menelaus took Odysseus by the arm and led him out of the battle to his own chariot in which they made their way back to the ships.

Meanwhile the Trojans were hurling their sharp spears at Ajax, who covered himself with his great shield and slowly gave way before them, though from time to time he would turn upon his enemies and charge, while they in their turn gave way to him, so much they feared his dauntless spirit and his strength. Stubbornly he withdrew as the shower of weapons fell upon his shield and armour. It was like when a donkey turns off the road into a field and starts to eat the crop. The boys who are in charge of him beat him with their sticks and throw stones at him, but the donkey goes on eating and, if he moves at all, he moves slowly. So Ajax retreated stubbornly from the enemy while the other Greeks were being swept over the plain by victorious Hector.

THE BATTLE BY THE SHIPS

Meanwhile Achilles had been watching the battle from the high stern of his black ship. He had seen the Greeks push the Trojans back almost to their city walls, and now he saw them routed and streaming back to the shelter of the trench and the wall that surrounded their ships and their camp. In the distance he saw old Nestor in his chariot and with him a wounded man. This was Machaon, son of the great healer Asclepius, a brave captain and himself an excellent doctor. Nestor had rescued him from the invincible hands of Hector and was carrying him out of the fighting to safety.

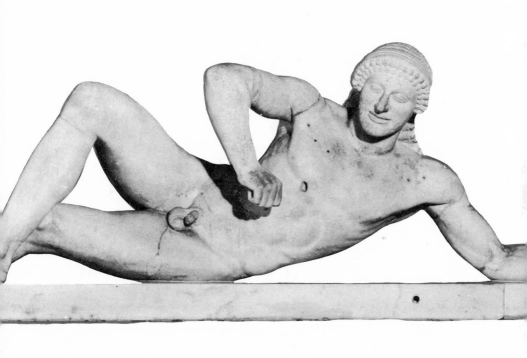

Achilles called to Patroclus and said: "Patroclus, dear friend, now I think that the Greeks will soon be begging at my knees. They are overwhelmed. But will you go now to Nestor's tent and find out who is the wounded man that he is bringing out of the battle? He looked to me like Machaon, but I could not be certain, as the horses dashed past me so quickly."

So Patroclus went along the shore to Nestor's tent. The old man himself was inside and on the table in front of him was a great silver cup which he had brought from home. It was studded with gold and had four handles on the tops of which were the figures of doves feeding. Most men could scarcely lift it when it was full, but Nestor lifted it quite easily.

Now Patroclus stood in the entrance to Nestor's tent, and the old man rose to greet him and to invite him to eat and drink. But Patroclus excused himself. "My lord Nestor," he said, "you must forgive me for not waiting. Achilles is expecting me to return to him. He sent me to inquire whether it was not Machaon whom you were bringing back in your chariot."

Nestor replied: "Indeed it was Machaon. But why is Achilles so anxious over him when our whole army is in such straits? Agamemnon also has been wounded. So have great Diomedes and mighty Odysseus, and many others of our best and bravest. Is Achilles going to wait until we are all destroyed? I myself am an old man, yet I have taken my share in the fighting. How I wish I had the strength that I had in my youth when once I captured fifty chariots from the invaders of my country and killed their leader. And now what use to anyone is all the courage and strength of great Achilles? Later on, I am sure of it, he will weep and be ashamed when all our army is destroyed. You are his great friend. Will you not go and ask him to relent from his anger and to help us? Or let him at least allow you to take his place and lead the Myrmidons into battle. Let him give you his armour to wear. Then the Trojans would think that you were Achilles himself, and they would fall back and give us time to recover ourselves. Now too the Trojans are tired with fighting. If you led a fresh force against them you might drive them back to their city."

So Nestor spoke and Patroclus was moved by his words. He set out to run back to the tent of Achilles, but on his way he came upon another of the Greek captains, Eurypylus, limping out of the battle. He had been wounded by an arrow in the thigh and he could scarcely drag himself along. The sweat poured from his head and shoulders, and blood streamed from his wound. Patroclus went up to him to support him. His heart was full of pity for the Greeks who were dying far from their country and on whose white flesh the dogs of Troy would soon be feeding. Sadly he asked Eurypylus about the battle and Eurypylus replied: "Noble Patroclus, there is no hope now for the Greeks. Our best men are dead or wounded. Great Hector is irresistible and the Trojans grow stronger as our men weaken. Help me, I beg you, to my ship, and tend my wound, since I know that you are skilful in this, and our own doctor, Machaon, is lying wounded himself in his tent."

"I am on my way back to Achilles," said Patroclus, "but I cannot leave you without help." And so he took Eurypylus to his tent, cut the arrow head out of the wound, washed it and put upon it healing herbs. Soon the wound began to dry and the blood ceased to flow.

Now while Patroclus was visiting Nestor and tending the wound of Eurypylus, the Greeks and Trojans fought on. In front of their trench and wall the Greeks rallied for a short time, but still Hector and his Trojans were irresistible and now the Greeks were penned inside the wall that protected their ships and the Trojans, dismounting from their horses and chariots, were forming up on foot for the assault. Paris led one of their companies and Aeneas another; but their strongest troops were under the command of Hector and of the warrior Polydamas. These were the troops whom Hector now urged on to the assault. But, just as they were about to advance to the trench, an omen appeared to them. They saw an eagle on the left, flying towards them and carrying in its claws a blood-red snake. But the snake was not dead. It writhed round in the eagle's claws and bit it in the neck, so fiercely that the eagle in pain dropped the snake down among the Trojan troops and then screamed as it made off on the currents of the air.

The Trojans shuddered when they saw the gleaming snake writhing on the ground in front of them, and Polydamas at once spoke to Hector. "Hector," he said, "you know that I am not afraid of the enemy, nor am I afraid to speak my mind, even if I happen to disagree with you. This omen was sent to us by Zeus, and it came just at the moment when we were going to advance. The eagle thought that he had the snake safe in his clutches, but he was forced to drop it and fly back to his nest in pain. So now, even if we succeed in storming the Greek wall, we too shall in the end have to retreat and shall suffer in our retreat. Therefore, I say, let us not advance today, but wait for more favourable signs."

Hector looked at him fiercely. "I tell you," he said, "that Zeus has promised me victory. You cannot put me off by your talk of the senseless doings of birds. To fight for one's country is worth all the omens in the world. Now follow me, and do not try to keep the others back, or else I shall strike you down with my own spear."

Then, shouting out to his men, Hector led the assault upon the wall. With a noise like the roaring of the sea his troops followed him, and Zeus sent out a wind which blew up the dust before them, half blinding the Greeks. Company after company swept across the trench and up to the wall.

Here indeed the Greeks fought back. They were led by huge Ajax and by his brother Teucer, the famous archer, by Idomeneus of Crete and those others of the great captains who had not been wounded. Arrows and spears fell thick among the attacking Trojans. Yet still it was impossible to hold Hector back. He picked up from the ground a great rock, pointed at one end though thick at the other, so big that nowadays it would take two men even to lift it up into a waggon. But Zeus gave Hector strength and he handled it as easily as if it were a small stone. Standing with his legs planted wide apart he hurled it at the centre of the strong bolted gate in the wall, and the blow broke the gate from its hinges, splintering the wooden panels and crashing through the bolts. The great double doors fell inwards and Hector himself, with a look on his face like black night, sprang into the breach. He held two spears in his hands and his armour shone like a star. None but a god could have withstood him as he swept through the gate. Behind him came his men, eager as wolves, and, as the Greeks fell back, still fresh parties of Trojans swarmed over the wall along its whole extent. Now the fighting was for the ships themselves and Hector, in his great voice, began to call for torches to set the ships on fire.

But now the Greeks stood firm, shoulder to shoulder in their gleaming bronze. They knew that if they were routed here they could hope for no mercy, nor would they ever be able to return to the wives and children they had left behind them in their own land. So the battle was renewed inside the wall and here the fighting was as fierce as ever it had been in the plain.

Yet still Zeus gave fresh power to Hector, for he was determined that on this day fire should be set to the Greek ships, so that he might keep the promise that he had made to Thetis, the mother of Achilles. It was only up to this point that Zeus would give Hector his aid, for in the end he had decided that the Greeks should be victorious. But now out of all those warriors Zeus was giving the greatest glory of all to Hector, since indeed he had not much longer to live and already the day of his fate was close upon him.

Now he fought like the War God himself or like a destroying fire that rages through the forests. His eyes flashed beneath his grim brows and the dreadful nodding crest of his helmet. Through the dense ranks of the Greeks he burst like a thunderbolt and forced them backwards to the first row of ships drawn up along the shore. Here once more the Greeks rallied. Great Ajax took his stand on a ship's deck, and strode from one deck to another, shouting out his commands and urging the Greeks to stand, since no further retreat was possible. In his hands he held an enormous spear of the kind that is used in sea battle and with this huge spear he kept the Trojans back. Twelve men he wounded with his spear, all eager to have the glory of being the first to set fire to the ships, and all the time, though his limbs were soaked with sweat and though spears and arrows fell in a rain upon his shield, he kept shouting to the others: "Fight on! Fight on! The sea is behind us and our country is far away. Nothing can save us except our own right hands."

Yet there came at last a time when even Ajax had to fall back. Hector swept down upon him and with one blow of his great sword cut right through the shaft of the spear, so that Ajax, left without a weapon, had to retire from the prow of the ship where he had stood. Immediately the Trojans hurled their blazing torches into the ship and soon the flames spread over the wood and leapt up into the sky. And now indeed it seemed that irreparable disaster was facing the Greeks, and that there among their ships they would perish every one of them before the unconquerable might of Hector. Yet at this very moment the fortune of the battle was about to turn, for Patroclus was putting on the glorious armour of Achilles and making ready to lead the Myrmidons into the fight.

THE LAST FIGHT
OF PATROCLUS

At about the time that Hector was storming the wall, Patroclus had come back to the tent of Achilles. Hot tears were running down his cheeks. Swift-footed Achilles pitied him when he saw him and said: "Why are you crying, Patroclus? You look just like a little girl, running beside her mother and plucking at her dress, asking to be lifted up. Have you had bad news from home, or what is it?"

"O, Achilles," said Patroclus, "you cannot blame me for weeping. The whole army is being destroyed and already the best of the Greeks are lying wounded. Great Diomedes is out of the battle; so is Odysseus; so is Agamemnon himself, and many more. Is there nothing to be done with you, Achilles? This unending rage of yours is spoiling you. What will people say in future times, if you do nothing to help your comrades in their great need? But, if your heart is still as hard as a rock, or if you are afraid because of some prophecy from the goddess your mother, then at least allow me to lead the Myrmidons into battle. And let me wear your armour, so that at first the Trojans may take me for you. They are tired out already with fighting, and, if I joined the battle with fresh troops, I might throw them back from the ships and from the camp."

Patroclus spoke urgently to his friend, little knowing that what he was begging for was his own death. But Achilles was moved by his words. "I am certainly not afraid of any prophecies," he said. "It is simply that I will not bear the insults of Agamemnon and his ingratitude for all that I have done for him. Yet perhaps you are right and I ought not to remain angry for ever. Go, then, put on my splendid armour and lead the Myrmidons out into the battle, now that the Trojans are engulfing the Greeks like a black cloud and our friends are driven back to the edge of the sea, and the whole air rings with the shouts of manslaying Hector urging on his troops to the final assault. Take the Myrmidons, therefore, my friend, and save the ships. But you must do exactly as I tell you. When you have swept the Trojans back from the ships you must return to me here. Then the Greeks will honour me all the more. Do not chase the Trojans over the plain towards their city, or some evil may come to you from one of the immortal gods, from the Archer Apollo, perhaps, who loves the Trojans. So be sure that, once you have saved the ships, you return here to me."

As he spoke they saw in the distance the fire leaping up to the sky from the ship of Ajax. Patroclus hurried to put on the famous armour and Achilles went out of his tent to call the Myrmidons together for the fight.

Soon Patroclus was armed. He took all the weapons of Achilles except his long and heavy spear, which no Greek except Achilles himself was able to handle. This spear had been made from an ash that grew on Mount Pelion and had been given to Peleus, Achilles' father, by the good centaur Chiron, a formidable weapon that had brought death to many.

Next Patroclus called for the charioteer Automedon and told him to yoke Achilles' horses to the shining chariot. These horses, Xanthus and Balius, were a pair that flew like the wind, and indeed they were divine horses, since the West Wind was their father. Alongside these horses went Pedasus, a famous horse that Achilles had captured in the war. He was only a mortal horse but he kept up with the immortal pair.

Meanwhile Achilles had drawn up the Myrmidons in battle order. They were eager enough for the fight, as they stood there under arms, shoulder to shoulder and shield to shield. And before them went Patroclus and Automedon, each resolved to win glory by fighting in the forefront of the battle.

But Achilles went back to his tent and there he opened a beautiful chest which his mother Thetis had given him before he sailed and had filled with tunics and thick cloaks and fleecy rugs. In this chest he kept a finely wrought drinking cup from which no one but himself was allowed to drink and from which he made his libations only to Father Zeus, using other cups when he poured out wine in prayer to the other gods.

Now Achilles washed his hands in fresh water and filled this cup with wine. Looking up at the sky as he poured the wine on the ground, he prayed: "Father Zeus, you listened to me when I prayed to you before. Now, I beg you, grant me this prayer also. My friend has gone out to battle with the Myrmidons. Give him victory, far-seeing Zeus, and strengthen his heart so that Hector may know that Patroclus can fight by himself, even when I am not with him. And when he has swept the Trojans back from the ships, let him return back to me safe and sound with his armour and with his men."

Zeus listened to the prayer of Achilles. Half of it he granted, but not the other half.

And now from between the ships the army of Myrmidons burst out upon the enemy. With a great voice Patroclus cried out to them: "Now show how you can fight, comrades of Achilles, and bring honour to him who is the best warrior among the Greeks, with the best troops under his command." So the Myrmidons, shouting their battle cry, fell upon the Trojans, swarming out upon them like wasps disturbed from their nest, who fly recklessly upon the disturbers and will not rest until they have avenged themselves.

And when the Trojans saw Patroclus in his gleaming armour with Automedon beside him, they believed that it was Achilles himself who had returned to the battle, having made up his quarrel with King Agamemnon, and every man looked round for some way of escape from the sheer destruction which threatened them. They fell back from the burning ships, and the Greeks quickly put out the flames.

Patroclus, carried behind the fleet horses of Achilles, raged among the broken Trojan ranks, killing on every side. Hector himself, experienced as he was in war, saw that the battle was lost. Leaping into his chariot he drove out over the ditch and the destroyed wall, fearing that he might be cut off before he reached the plain. There in the ditch many chariots were overturned and many men lost their lives in the headlong retreat. But Patroclus was carried by the divine horses of Achilles, and they easily leapt over the ditch and hurried forward in pursuit of Hector, for it was against Hector most of all that Patroclus yearned to fight. But Hector's horses also were fast and they carried him out of danger. The full fury of Patroclus turned upon the Lycians, allies of the Trojans, who fought under the command of their king Sarpedon, whose father was Zeus himself and whose mother was the daughter of the great hero Bellerophon. Sarpedon had been the first to climb the Greek wall, when Hector broke through the gate, and all day he, with his friend Glaucus, had fought in the front ranks. Glaucus

indeed had been wounded by the great archer Teucer, the brother
of Ajax, in the fight by the ships, but he remained still with his
troops, encouraging them to battle. Sarpedon had killed many men
that day, and now, when he saw his Lycian troops being driven in
disorder before Patroclus, he cried out to them to stand firm. "Let
me see myself," he said, "what sort of man this is who has done
such harm to the Trojans this day." And he leapt down from his
chariot, advancing towards Patroclus on foot. Patroclus too jumped
down from his chariot and came to meet him, brandishing his huge
spear. Just as two crook-clawed vultures scream and fight together
on the top of a rocky cliff, so these two came together in battle and
neither of them would yield.

All day Zeus, from his heavenly seat, had kept his eyes fixed on
the fighting. Now he sighed deeply and said: "Alas! Now I know
that it is fated for Sarpedon, whom I love most of all men, to die at
the hands of Patroclus. Yet I will save his body and set it down in
the rich land of Lycia, far from this lamentable battle, where his
friends will give him burial." Then Zeus, in honour to his son, sent
down to the earth drops of blood falling like rain.

Now Patroclus hurled his first spear and struck down dead the
charioteer who stood at King Sarpedon's side. Sarpedon cast next
and missed Patroclus with his spear; but he struck the horse Pedasus in the right shoulder and the horse collapsed in the dust and,
heaving a great sigh, breathed out its life. The other two horses
reared up and sprang apart, entangling the reins; but Automedon
quickly cut the thongs of the harness, separating the immortal pair
from the dead horse who had been their stable companion.

Sarpedon once more hurled a spear but the point flew over Patroclus's left shoulder. And now Patroclus forced his own spear
home. It struck Sarpedon in the upper part of the stomach near
the heart, and he fell with a crash like an oak falls or a high-
standing pine which woodmen have cut down in the mountains.
He clutched at the wound with his hands, and all the ground was
wet with his blood. Breathing his last, he cried out: "Dear Glaucus,
now is the time to show your courage and your strength. Fight for
me now, and save my body from the Greeks." As he spoke, his life
left him.

Pain and grief filled the heart of Glaucus as he heard the words
of his dying friend. He clutched his wounded arm which was too
weak to hold a spear and he prayed to the Archer God Apollo.

"Hear me," he said, "Lord of the Silver Bow! Our best man is dead and I am powerless to defend his body. Even Zeus has not helped his own son. Heal my wound, therefore, I pray you, that I may at least fight for him now that he is dead."

Apollo heard the prayer of Glaucus and immediately the blood dried and the pain departed from his wound. And now both Trojans and Lycians joined in the fight for the body of Sarpedon. Hector himself stood at Glaucus' side. Shame and anger filled his heart at the thought of the death of his great ally. But Patroclus still raged forward and with him was towering Ajax and all the companies of the Myrmidons.

For long they fought together, and Zeus, looking down on the battle, was in two minds whether he should now allow Patroclus to be slain at the hands of Hector, or whether he should let him live a little longer, so that he should do more harm still to the Trojans. He decided that for a short time he would let him live. Then gradually the Greeks pushed back the Lycians and the Trojans from the body of Sarpedon. They stripped off the splendid armour and would have taken the body also, but Zeus surrounded the body with a mist, and Apollo lightly took it up into the air away from the battle. He washed the wounds with water and anointed them with ambrosia. Then he dressed the body of great Sarpedon in imperishable garments and set it down in the rich land of Lycia, far away from the fighting.

And now both Trojans and Lycians turned in flight. Patroclus, shouting his war-cry, drove his swift horses in pursuit. Zeus had made him over-daring; for, if he had remembered the orders of Achilles, he might now have returned safely and with honour to his friend. As it was he drove the Trojans before him right to the walls of Troy, and, in his pride, he determined that on that very day he himself would capture the city. But this was not the will of the immortal gods, and the city was guarded by Apollo himself.

Three times Patroclus climbed up to the wall, and three times Apollo thrust him back. Still Patroclus came on, raging like a demon, and then the god spoke to him with a terrible voice: "Go back, Patroclus! It is not fated that Troy should be captured by your spear, and not even by the spear of Achilles, who is a far better man than you."

Then Patroclus retired for a little from the wall, but still he was determined to go on killing the Trojans till night fell, and most of all he desired to fight with Hector. Again and again he charged into the battle like a savage lion. Man after man fell before his spear and now he surely thought that he was invincible. Yet it was not only against men that he had to fight, for the god Apollo was protecting the Trojans. Wrapped round in a mist he came in all his strength and terror and met Patroclus in the very thick of the fighting. Standing behind him, he struck him between the shoulders with the flat of his hand; he broke his great spear in fragments and hurled from his head the shining helmet to roll among the horses' hooves. Never before had this helmet, which used to cover the glorious head of Achilles, been seen to fall in the dust; but now Zeus allowed Hector to wear it for a short time, since his own death was very close. As for Patroclus, darkness swam before his eyes; stunned and dazed, he staggered backwards, and his legs, as in a dream, seemed to have lost their strength to carry him. And now Hector thrust at him with his spear, striking him in the lower part of the stomach, where death comes quickest. His body crashed to the ground, and Hector exulted over him. "Patroclus," he cried, "you thought that you would destroy my city, and sell the Trojan women into slavery. But all the time I, Hector, was there to protect them, and now the vultures are going to feed upon your body. Not Achilles himself could save you from my spear."

In a feeble voice Patroclus replied to him from the ground where he lay bleeding. "You can boast now, Hector," he said, "since Zeus and Apollo have given you the victory. It was they who conquered me. As for you, I would not have shrunk back if twenty Hectors had come against me. And now listen to my words. I tell you that you too have not long to live. Strong destiny is drawing near to you, and death at the hands of Achilles."

As he spoke death closed Patroclus' eyes; his soul sped out of his limbs and went down to Hades, lamenting its fate, leaving behind its manhood and its youth.

ACHILLES AND PATROCLUS

When Patroclus died the Greeks shuddered, and their whole army fell back. Quickly Hector stripped the body of its splendid armour, the armour of Achilles which the gods had given to his father Peleus, and Peleus in his old age had given to his son when he set out for Troy. This armour Hector put upon his own body, and was to wear it for a little time. So he stood resplendent among the Trojans and their allies. His heart yearned for battle and the gods put fresh courage in his spirit, fresh strength into his limbs. Shouting to his men, he charged forward, and first of all he determined to capture the divine horses of Achilles and his shining chariot.

Now these horses, ever since they had seen Patroclus fall in the dust, had stood still, with the tears streaming from their eyes. Automedon, their charioteer, had done all he could to make them move, using his whip, speaking to them softly and cursing at them; but they stayed stock-still, like a statue over the grave of a dead man; their heads were bowed to the earth; the hot tears fell from their eyes as they grieved for Patroclus, and their silky manes were draggled in the dust.

Zeus, looking down upon the battle, saw the two horses and pitied them. "Poor creatures!" he said to himself, "why did we give you to King Peleus, who is a mortal, you who are ageless and immortal? Why should you share in the sorrows of wretched men? For man is the most miserable of all things that breathe and go upon the earth. Now certainly I shall not allow you to fall into Hector's hands. Already he has the armour and still I am giving him glory in the battle. For I intend him to drive the Greeks over the plain until the sun sets and darkness comes down upon the earth."

So Zeus put strength into the horses' legs, and they flew off, fast as the wind.

And now Hector turned to the body of Patroclus. He wished to drag it away, to cut off the head and leave the flesh to be devoured by the jackals. But the Greeks had rallied. Huge Ajax stood like a tower, covering the body of Patroclus with his shield. At his side was yellow-haired Menelaus and the great warrior Meriones. More and more entered the fight. They made a wall of their shields, and not even Hector could break through the wall. And now Ajax sent a messenger to the Prince Antilochus, the son of Nestor, who was fighting at the other end of the battle line. When the messenger found him, he said: "Antilochus, I have terrible news to tell. I wish that it had never happened. Patroclus has been killed and our whole army will feel the lack of him. And now Ajax bids you to hurry to Achilles and tell him that his dear friend is dead. Tell him that we are struggling to bring his body back to the ships—just his naked body, since Hector has stripped it of its glorious armour."

When Antilochus heard the news, the tears stood in his eyes and for long he was unable to speak. Yet he did as he was asked to do and ran back towards the ships with bitter tidings for Achilles.

Now spear was locked with spear and shield with shield over the body of Patroclus.

Yet still the Trojan powers increased. Hector, Aeneas and Glaucus fought as they had never fought before. From Mount Ida Zeus sent lightning flashes down upon the plain, clearly revealing that now he was giving victory to the Trojans. Even Ajax was appalled, and at this advice Menelaus and Meriones took the body of Patroclus and began to withdraw with it towards the ships, while Ajax himself rallied the Greeks and covered their retreat. Thick mist overhung that part of the field where the fighting raged over Patroclus, though in other parts it was bright sunshine.

Menelaus and Meriones lifted the body in their arms and came with it out of the mist. On all sides they saw the Trojans advancing and they made what haste they could, fearing that they might be cut off. Behind them was the furious din of men and horses in battle. Man after man the Greeks were falling before the spears of Hector and of Aeneas. They scattered and cried out like a flock of jackdaws or starlings when a hawk bears down upon them. So they forgot their courage and were pressed back again to the ditch, and still the fury of their enemies increased.

Meanwhile Antilochus had reached the ships and come to Achilles with his bitter news. He found Achilles standing in front of his black ship and already his heart was distressed. "Why is it," he was saying to himself, "that the long-haired Greeks are once more being chased back over the plain? What can have happened? I dread lest my mother's prophecy may be fulfilled; for once she told me that, while I was still alive, the best of the Myrmidons would be killed. Oh, is Patroclus dead? Could he not obey me when I told him to come back here and not to fight with Hector?"

And now Antilochus stood before Achilles, with the hot tears pouring from his eyes. "Alas, Achilles," he said, "I have terrible news for you. Patroclus is killed and they are fighting round his naked body. Hector has stripped him of your armour."

As he spoke, the black darkness of unspeakable pain came upon Achilles. In his two hands he picked up the dark dust and poured it over his head and over his beautiful face. Then he threw himself on the ground and lay there, with his fine body stretched out, like a great statue fallen, and he tore his hair in his misery, while the women servants, girls whom he and Patroclus had captured, came out to him and, when they saw him, they wailed and beat their breasts. Antilochus, with the tears still falling from his eyes, sat down beside him and held his hands, since he feared that now, while he was sobbing his heart out, he might snatch a sword and make away with himself. Then Achilles cried out aloud with a dreadful cry, and his mother Thetis heard him in the place where she was sitting in the depths of the sea, with her sisters, the Nereids, beautiful goddesses of the sea, around her. At the sound of her son's voice she also cried aloud and she said to her sisters: "Oh, unhappy that I am! Unhappy to be the mother of the best and greatest of all men! I nursed him like a tender shoot in the corner of a walled garden; but he went to fight at Troy and I shall never welcome him returning home to the house of Peleus. Even his short life is filled with sorrow, and I can do nothing to help him. Yet I will go to him and find out what new grief this is that he has suffered."

So she left the deep sea cave and her sisters came with her through the surging waters of the sea. One by one they came up on to the beach where the ships of the Myrmidons were. Thetis stood by Achilles and gently spoke to him, "Dear child, why are you crying? Has not Zeus done for you as I prayed him? For now, fighting without you, the Greeks are being driven back to their ships."

Achilles groaned as he answered her. "Mother," he said, "it is true that Zeus has fulfilled my prayer. But what joy can I have in it? Patroclus is killed, the friend whom I honoured more than all others and loved like my own life. I have lost him, and Hector has taken the glorious armour that the gods gave to Peleus when you were married to him, a mortal. Now there is no will to live in my heart. I would rather die. Only first I desire to strike down Hector with my spear, and avenge the death of my comrade."

His mother wept as she listened to him. "My child," she said, "what you are saying is bringing on your own death; for in no long time after the death of Hector you too are fated to die."

"Then let death come quickly," said Achilles, "since I was not there to help my friend in his greatest need. Instead I was sitting here by my ships, a useless burden on the earth. But now I will go and find Hector, the slayer of my friend. After that I shall take whatever fate is sent me by Zeus and by the other immortal gods."

Then Thetis, the silver-footed goddess, answered him. "I know," she said, "that I cannot make you alter your mind. But now Hector is wearing your beautiful armour and you have no weapons with which to fight. Stay here till tomorrow's dawn, and then I will come back to you and bring you immortal armour which the god Hephaestus will make for me."

So saying she left him. Her sisters, the Nereids, went back into the depths of the sea, but Thetis sped through the air to Olympus in order to ask the craftsman of the gods to make armour for her son.

Meanwhile the Greeks were fleeing before Hector over the plain, and now it seemed doubtful indeed whether they would succeed in saving the body of Patroclus from the rage of his enemies. Three times Hector laid hold of the feet as he tried to drag it away, and each time great Ajax pushed him back again. But still Hector came on like a hungry lion whom shepherds try to drive from the body of a sheep or bullock, and certainly he would have seized the body and taken it back to Troy, if Zeus had not willed otherwise. He sent his messenger Iris to Achilles and told him to show himself, unarmed as he was, outside the wall. So Achilles rose from the ground where he was lying and over his shoulders the goddess Athene threw her own terrible aegis; she put a golden mist around his head and from the mist she sent out piercing beams of light. Achilles stood by the trench and shouted aloud his tremendous war cry. Athene cried out too, and the sound of those terrible cries was like the sounds of trumpets calling to the assault. The Trojans fell back in turn; their long-maned horses twisted round in the shafts and began to pull the chariots back; the charioteers trembled when they saw that awful light blazing from the head of Achilles. Three times Achilles let his cry ring out over the plain, and three times there was tumult and confusion in the Trojan ranks. And now Hera caused the sun to set. Night put an end to the battle and thus the Greeks were saved. They brought the body of Patroclus over the trench and laid it down on a stretcher. Hot tears fell from the eyes of Achilles when he saw the body of his faithful friend so terribly wounded by the sharp spear of Hector. He laid his man-slaying hands on his comrade's breast and he groaned aloud, like a bearded lion when a hunter has killed one of his cubs and he comes too late to save it. "Ah, Patroclus," he said, "I promised your father that I would bring you back safe and famous from Troy, rich with the riches that we would win there. But Zeus will not grant all our prayers. Now it is fated that both you and I must make the same earth red with our blood, here in the land of Troy, for I too shall never return home to my father and my mother. I, Patroclus, shall follow you beneath the earth; and so I shall not give you burial until I have brought here the arms and the head of Hector, who killed you. And on your tomb I shall sacrifice twelve young men, all Trojan nobles, to do you honour. Meanwhile the Trojan women whom we captured together shall wail for you day and night, and you shall lie here in honour by my ships."

Then he ordered his servants to put a great cauldron on the fire to heat water for the washing of the body. When the water was hot they washed the dead limbs and put ointment in the wounds. They laid the body on a bed and put a soft sheet over it from head to foot; over that they stretched a white cloak. And so throughout the night Achilles and the Myrmidons mourned for Patroclus.

ACHILLES PREPARES
FOR BATTLE

But no sooner had Dawn risen from the stream of Ocean, than the goddess, silver-footed Thetis, came to Achilles with wonderful armour made for him by the gods. She had been to Olympus, to the bright gleaming house of the lame god Hephaestus. There she had found him with sweat streaming down over his shaggy breast, as he hurried to and fro, tending his fires and blowing them to intense heat with his gigantic bellows. He made all the furniture for the houses of the gods, and now he was busy with some beautiful banqueting tables with golden wheels.

When he saw that the goddess had come to visit him, he collected the tools that he had been using and put them away in a silver box. Then he washed his hands and sponged his face and neck and shaggy chest. He put on his tunic, took his sceptre in his hand and went limping out to meet her. He had miraculous servants who attended on him. They were made of gold, but they looked exactly like real women, and could even speak and obey his orders and do all the work that women do. With these golden creatures to wait upon him, he sat down with Thetis and asked her what she needed from him.

Once more the goddess wept as she told him of her son's distress and of how he had begged her to find him armour, now that Hector wore the splendid arms of Peleus.

Hephaestus immediately agreed to help her. He went back to his workshop, took hammer and tongs in his hand and prepared the metals he needed for his work—bronze, tin, silver and shining gold. First he made a wonderful shield, strong enough to resist all weapons, five layers thick and decorated with all kinds of designs. On this great shield were engraved the sun and moon and the constellations, cities of men too, vineyards, minstrels and dancers. It was a wonder to see, and it seemed to give out its own light. Then the god made a breastplate which shone brighter than the gleam of fire. He made a strong helmet with a golden crest, and greaves of tin that fitted well over the ankles and round the legs.

This was the splendid armour that he gave to Thetis. Gratefully she took it from him and swooped down with it like a hawk from snowy Olympus.

She found her son by the ships, still weeping for Patroclus and clasping the dead body in his arms. Taking his hand gently, she said to him: "My child, he was killed by the will of the gods, and we must suffer it to be so, however much we may grieve. Now you must take this armour. It is altogether marvellous and such as no man has ever yet worn upon his shoulders."

So saying, she put the armour down in front of him, and it rang upon the ground. All the Myrmidons trembled when they saw it; they turned pale and scarcely dared to set their eyes upon it. But the more Achilles looked, the more he felt the anger rising in his heart; beneath his brows his eyes flashed like fire; carefully and with deep delight he handled the wonderful gifts of Hephaestus. "Mother," he said, "this is certainly the work of a god. No mortal could have made such arms. And now I shall make ready for battle. But I am afraid that the flies may come and settle in the wounds of Patroclus and that his body will begin to rot."

"Do not fear," said Thetis, "I shall see that his body remains fresh and pure. I shall put nectar and ambrosia upon his flesh and will make it incorruptible. But now you must call the Greeks to an assembly and make peace with Agamemnon. Afterwards prepare for battle, and I will fill you with unconquerable strength."

Then Thetis put nectar and ambrosia upon the body of Patroclus, and Achilles rose and went along the shore of the sea, shouting out to the Greeks to call them to the assembly. Quickly they came together, and among them came great Diomedes and wise Odysseus, both limping from their wounds and supporting themselves on their spears. Last of all came Agamemnon, and he too was still suffering from the wound that he had received from the spear of Coön, Antenor's son.

When all the Greeks were gathered together, Achilles rose and spoke. "King Agamemnon," he said, "I wish that you and I had never quarrelled for the sake of that girl. Only Hector and the Trojans have profited by it, and as a result of it many of the Greeks now lie dead. What is done cannot be undone, but for the future my anger is at an end. I propose that now you call the Greeks to battle. I shall be fighting with them, and I think that the Trojans will be more anxious to run away than to face my spear in stubborn war."

The Greeks cried out with joy when they heard this speech of Achilles. Then Agamemnon rose and, turning to Achilles, said: "Indeed I have myself cursed the day when I was so blinded by anger that I took away your prize and caused this feud between us. It was not I, I think, but Zeus and Fate and the Furies that caused the quarrel. Now I too relinquish my anger. Arm yourself, great Achilles, and lead the Greeks into battle. And it is still my desire to give you all those gifts which yesterday Odysseus promised you in my name. I will send them to you now, if you wish it so."

Achilles replied to him: "I thank you, King Agamemnon. As for the gifts, you may give them to me, if you think it right, or keep them. But now I cannot wait before joining in the battle. All delay is hateful to me until I am cutting down the Trojan companies with my spear. I want neither food nor drink until our losses have been avenged."

And with this he would have led the Greeks immediately into battle, so eager was he to avenge the death of his friend, and to be surrounded with blood and slaughter and the thick breathing of dying men. But now Odysseus rose and said: "Great Achilles, you are a stronger man than I am and better with your spear. All the same I have more experience than you have, and it is my advice that should be taken. There is a day's fighting in front of our troops and they cannot be expected to fight well on empty stomachs. Certainly we must mourn for our dead, but not by fasting, if there is fighting to be done afterwards. Therefore let every man first prepare his meal and meanwhile let the gifts be brought to Achilles' tent. Then we will sacrifice a boar to Zeus and to the Sun. After that let no one be found lingering by the ships. We will go into battle with every single man who can bear arms."

Though he still yearned to plunge immediately into the war, Achilles recognised the wisdom of what Odysseus said. He returned to his tent and there the Greek kings and chieftains attended him to make ready the sacrifice. Meanwhile the heralds of Agamemnon brought the gifts which he had promised. The lady Briseis came too, as beautiful as golden Aphrodite. When she saw the body of Patroclus with its deep wounds, she cried aloud and flung herself down beside the corpse. "Oh Patroclus," she cried, "you were alive when I went away and now, returning, I find you dead. So it is with me always—one suffering after another. I saw my husband, my father and my three brothers all killed before my eyes. Yet you were always kind to me. You told me not to cry. You told me that you would take me back with you and make me the lawful wife of Achilles, and give me a great wedding feast among the Myrmidons. Always you were gentle and kind to me, and always I shall weep for you."

So Briseis lamented, and the other women lamented with her. Some indeed were weeping for Patroclus, but others were in reality weeping for their own sad state as captives who had lost their fathers and their brothers and their husbands in the war.

The leaders of the Greeks, Agamemnon and Menelaus, Odysseus and Nestor, all urged Achilles to take some food before entering the battle, but he still refused. "My dear friends," he said, "my grief is too great. Do not, I beg you, ask me to eat or drink until today's sun sets."

So he waited, still mourning for his friend, while the others took their meal, and then, when the time came for the troops to muster, he began to put on his splendid armour. He fitted the greaves carefully to his legs; he put on the shining breastplate and slung over his shoulder the great bronze sword with silver-studded hilt. Then he took up the enormous shield which flashed out like a beacon light which sailors see burning on a headland in the dusk. He fitted the helmet on his head, and it shone out like a star. And all the time that he was arming himself his devouring anger burnt within his heart. He gnashed his teeth and his eyes flashed terribly beneath his brows. Finally he took the great ashen spear of Peleus which he alone could handle. Already his horses were harnessed and yoked to the chariot, and Automedon, the charioteer, had taken the reins in his hand. Achilles, shining like the sun, stepped into the chariot and, looking down at his divine horses, shouted to them fiercely: "Xanthus and Balius, my famous horses, this time repay the care that has been given to you. Bring back your master safe from the battle and do not leave him there dead, as you left Patroclus."

Then from under the yoke one of the swift horses answered him. It was Xanthus to whom the white-armed goddess Hera had given the power of speech. Xanthus lowered his head, trailing his long mane on the ground. "Great Achilles," he said, "we shall indeed bring you safely back again today. But the day of your death is drawing near. Nor must you blame us for being the cause of it, since it will come to you from powerful Fate and from the hands of a great god. And it was not because we were slow or unwilling that Patroclus died. Great Apollo destroyed him and gave the glory to Hector. So though we run with the speed of the West Wind, you also are fated to lose your life in battle with a god and with a man."

As he spoke the Furies cut short his words. Achilles answered him angrily. "Xanthus," he said, "there is no need for you to prophesy my death. I know well enough myself that I am doomed to die here, far from my father and my mother. Yet there is nothing in the world that can keep me from the war."

So saying he shouted to his men and drove the horses forward to the fighting.

THE ROUT OF THE TROJANS

Meanwhile Hector and Aeneas had drawn up their army in the plain. Once more Hector's comrade, the wise Polydamas, had given good advice, but his advice had not been taken. Polydamas had spoken to the leaders of the Trojans and said: "It is true that we have won victories in the time that Achilles took no part in the war. But now his quarrel with King Agamemnon is over and he is angry for the death of his friend. I fear that when he leads his Myrmidons into battle we shall lose many more men than we lost at the hands of Patroclus. My advice therefore is that we should retreat to the city and defend ourselves there behind our walls."

To this Hector had replied: "Polydamas, is this the time to talk of retreat, now when the gods have given us such a victory and when we have forced our enemies back upon their ships? Run away, if you like; but you will not find any Trojans to follow you.

As for Achilles, if he really has decided to fight, he may well be sorry for it. I shall not run away from him, but shall meet him face to face. No victory is certain, and in war the man who expects to kill is often killed himself."

The Trojans had shouted out in favour of Hector and against Polydamas. Pallas Athene had taken away their wits.

Now they stood ready for battle in the plain and now Zeus summoned the blessed gods to Olympus. "Today," he said to them, "will be fought the greatest battle of the war, and today you may join in the fighting, each on the side which you prefer. For if Achilles were to fight alone in his anger, nothing could withstand him and he would take the high walls of Troy before the time that is fated."

So the immortal gods themselves went to war. On the side of the Greeks were Hera and Athene and Poseidon, the Earth-shaker. Strong Hephaestus went with them and Hermes, the Giver of Good Luck. On the side of the Trojans were Ares, the god of War, Phoebus Apollo and his sister Artemis, Leto, the great river god Xanthus and laughter-loving Aphrodite.

And now the blessed gods hurled the two armies together in battle. From heaven there rang out the terrible thunder of Zeus and Poseidon shook the earth. The woods and high crests of Ida trembled; the great walls of Troy quaked and the masts of the Greek ships were shaken like reeds. Down in the lower world the dreadful King of the Dead cried out in terror and lept up from his throne; for he feared that Poseidon would split the earth open above his head and let light in among the terrible dwelling places of the Dead, those vast decaying mansions were the ghosts flit to and fro and which are hated by the gods themselves.

So the armies rushed together and on each side the gods put courage and resolution into the hearts of their favourites. Achilles, flaming in his armour, searched in the battle line for Hector. It was Hector above all men that he longed to meet with. Yet the first to meet him from the Trojan ranks was Prince Aeneas, whose heart had been filled with courage by Apollo, so that he dared to stand out in front of the army to challenge Achilles with his spear. Achilles sprang to meet him, but first he cried out: "Aeneas, how is it that you have found the courage to face me, man to man? Have Priam and the Trojans offered you great rewards, waving fields of corn and vineyards, if you kill me? I think you will find that hard to do, and I advise you to turn back among your troops for safety, before safety is beyond your reach."

"Achilles," replied Aeneas, "do not imagine that you will frighten me with words as though I was a child. I know that you are a great warrior and that you are the son of a goddess, silver-footed Thetis. I also have a goddess for my mother and she is golden Aphrodite. One of these two today will mourn for her son. As for strength in war, Zeus gives it to a man or withholds it, since he rules over everything. Cease fighting with words, then, and let our bronze spears decide between us."

As he finished speaking he raised his great spear and hurled it at Achilles' shield. The metal rang out as the point struck it, and Achilles feared that the spear would pierce clean through to his body. He had forgotten that the handiwork of the gods is not so easily pierced by mortal strength. Through two of the layers that Hephaestus had made the spear passed, but there were three layers more and on the third layer the point was blunted and the ashen spear fell to the ground.

Next Achilles hurled his spear. It caught the shield of Aeneas at the thinnest part, near the edge, and went right through. Aeneas sank down, pushing the shield upwards above his head, and the great spear passed over his back and stuck in the ground. But it had come so close to him that he stood still for a moment with his eyes darkened in terror. Now Achilles had drawn his sword and with a tremendous shout, sprang towards him. Aeneas lifted up a huge rock, so big that it would have taken two men, such as men are today, even to raise it from the ground. But Aeneas handled it easily by himself. With it he would have hit the helmet or the shield of Achilles, and then Achilles would have been upon him with his sword; but the gods were watching the battle and now Poseidon, the Earth-shaker, exclaimed: "Though I favour the Greeks, I cannot bear to see the good Aeneas killed by great Achilles. Zeus himself would be angry at this, for Aeneas is destined to survive the war and to restore the fortunes of Troy in another country. He and his children after him will be great kings."

So Poseidon swept into the battle. He threw a mist over Achilles' eyes and picked up his spear from the ground, laying it down at his feet. Then he took hold of Aeneas and raised him lightly in the air, carrying him over the ranks of men, the chariots and the horses, and setting him down at the far end of the battlefield where the troops were on the point of going into action. Then he said to him: "Aeneas, it is madness for you to fight against Achilles. He is stronger than you and dearer to the immortal gods. If you see him anywhere in the fighting, avoid him. But once he is dead, you need have no fear, since no other Greek has the power to take your life."

Meanwhile the mist had fallen from Achilles' eyes and he looked about him in astonishment, finding his own spear at his feet and Aeneas vanished. "Indeed," he said to himself, "Aeneas must be dear to the immortal gods, who have saved him from my spear. Let him go. There are others who will not be saved."

Then, calling to his men, he plunged into the battle. On the other side Hector was encouraging the Trojans. "Do not be afraid of Achilles," he shouted to them. "Strong though he is, the gods do not always give victory to mere strength. As for me I shall certainly face him man to man, even though his hands are like fire and his spirit like shining steel."

Then he shouted out his war cry, but Apollo stood beside him and said: "Hector, do not by any means go and fight single-handed with Achilles. Stay in the ranks with the others and let him find you there." So Hector, obeying the voice of the god, went back into the ranks of men.

But there was nothing to hold back Achilles. With the first blow of his spear he split a man's skull in two. Next he killed one of Antenor's sons, shattering his helmet to pieces with his spear. And then he encountered Polydorus who was the youngest of Priam's sons and whom his father had forbidden to join in the fighting. But Polydorus was quick upon his feet and was showing his speed proudly as he rushed backwards and forwards among the fighters in the front line. Achilles however was a faster runner than any man alive. He swept down upon the young man and thrust his spear through his body. Polydorus fell dying to the ground, clutching the bloody wound with his hands.

When Hector saw his brother dying in agony, the tears came to his eyes and he could no longer bear to hold himself back. Brandishing his spear, he rushed at Achilles like a burning fire. Achilles sprang forward to meet him, joyfully finding at last the man who had killed his dear friend. Looking grimly on him from beneath his brows, he said: "Come quickly, for now your fate is upon you."

"Achilles," said Hector, "you need not try to frighten me with words. I know that you are the stronger man, but these things lie upon the knees of the gods. Though I am not so strong, they may allow me to kill you with my spear. It has been found sharp enough before now."

With these words he hurled his spear, but Athene was watching over Achilles. As with a breath of air she turned the spear aside and caused it to lose all its force, so that it fell at Hector's feet. Achilles rushed forward in his passion to kill; but the god Apollo, easily, as is the way of gods, hid Hector in a mist and bore him away.

Three times Achilles charged, thrusting with his spear at the empty mist. Then he cried out: "Hector, you dog, once more you have escaped me, though death was close upon you. But we shall meet once more, and then perhaps I too shall have a god to help me."

So saying he plunged once more into the fight and man after man fell before his sword and before his spear. He raged among the Trojans like a whirling wind that drives the flames this way and that when there is a forest fire along the dry slopes of the mountains. The earth ran black with blood; the hooves of his horses trampled over dead bodies and broken shields; the chariot wheels and the rails of the chariot dripped with blood as Achilles swept forward over the plain, dealing death on every side with his unconquerable hands.

The Trojan army turned in flight and was driven back to the ford of the eddying river Scamander, which the gods call Xanthus. Here Achilles cut the army into two. One part fled over the plain towards the city, while the other part was huddled together in a bend of the great river. These tried to escape by swimming, throwing away their armour and their shields, but still Achilles chased them into the river stream. Leaving his spear on the bank he went into the water with his sword and there he mercilessly destroyed these unarmed men as they cowered under the steep banks. The water ran red with their blood and all the air was filled with their crying and their groans.

Here, among many others, he killed Lycaon, a son of Priam. When first Lycaon saw him he ran to him and fell upon his knees, begging for mercy and promising a great ransom for his life. Achilles looked at him grimly and said: "Do not talk to me of mercy. Before Patroclus was killed I used to take prisoners and to accept ransom; but now not a single Trojan who falls into my power will escape with his life. No, my friend, you too must die. And why should you so complain? Patroclus died, and he was a better man than you by far. Consider me also, strong and beautiful as I am, the son of a great hero and with a goddess for my mother. Yet over me too hangs the stern necessity of death. Most surely there will be a morning or an evening or a noon when someone will take my life in battle, either with a thrust of the spear or with an arrow from the bow."

Still Lycaon knelt before him, hopelessly stretching out his hands; but Achilles struck him on the neck with his sword, burying the blade in the flesh. Out spurted the dark blood as Lycaon fell on his face. Achilles took the body by the foot and hurled it into the stream. "Lie there," he said, "and let the fish lick the blood from your wound. So may you all perish! Not the river himself can save you, nor shall I rest from slaughter till I have choked his silver streams with corpses."

Once more he sprang upon the Trojans, but now Xanthus, the god of the river, rose in anger. His voice came from the depths of the water and he said: "Achilles, you have shed too much blood already. My lovely streams are stained with it, and so many are the bodies that I can scarcely roll my river to the sea. Put an end now to the slaughter and leave me. I am horrified by your deeds."

"Great Scamander," said Achilles, "it shall be so, but not yet. I shall not cease killing until I have met with Hector face to face.

Again he plunged into the river, but now the god drew together all his streams and hurled himself upon Achilles. Roaring like a bull, he threw out on to the land all the dead bodies that Achilles had slain; then, arching himself up into a great wave, he bore down upon Achilles himself, falling with such weight upon his shield that Achilles could no longer stand upright. He seized hold of a strong elm tree to support himself, but the tree came out by the roots, tearing a great gap in the river bank. Then Achilles sprang on to the land and began to run, but still the river rose and followed him in a great wave arching black above his shoulders, roaring in anger as it sped in pursuit. Though Achilles was the greatest runner alive, the gods are more powerful than men and still the river gained upon him. Sometimes he would attempt to stand against the flood, but then the great wave would batter him to his knees, and, as he struggled up, the flowing water would circle his knees and wash the ground from beneath his feet. And now Achilles groaned as he looked up into the broad sky. "O Father Zeus," he cried, "will no god pity me and save me from the river? Indeed I would rather have been killed at the hands of Hector. He is the best man in Troy, and it would be no dishonour to die in fair fight with him. But now I am dying an unmanly death, caught up in a great stream of water."

But the gods were not unmindful of Achilles. Athene came to him and said: "Have no fear, Achilles. You are not fated to die by the river. The gods are on your side and soon the river will sink down again. As for you, do not rest from the fighting until you have driven the Trojans to their walls and taken the life of Hector."

As she spoke she put new strength into Achilles' limbs and he struggled forward through the flooded plain and the whirling waters where arms and dead bodies, branches of trees and the wreckage of chariots jostled together in the flood. Still the god of the river followed in pursuit, but now Hera called to her son Hephaestus, the God of Fire, and said to him: "Quick, my son! Bring fire upon the plain and drive Xanthus back! Burn the trees along his bank and scorch his waters with your consuming flames!"

Hephaestus was quick to obey. Running fire spread over the level ground, burning up the corpses and the arms. Fire blazed from the tree tops along the river bank. Down in the deep pools the eels and the fishes darting about in their cool homes felt the scorching blaze of the breath of Hephaestus. Soon the waters boiled and steamed and began to shrink away.

Then Xanthus cried out for mercy. "Put out your fires, Hephaestus!" he said. "I cannot stand against you. Give me peace now and I swear that I will help the Trojans no more, not even on the day when all their towers are swallowed up in the fires that the Greeks will make."

So, at his mother's bidding, Hephaestus withdrew his burning flames. Now the plain was dry as dust and the winding river flowed again in its usual channel.

Achilles gathered himself together, gripped his great spear in his hand and set out once more in pursuit of the Trojans who were fleeing to the shelter of their city.

THE DEATH OF HECTOR

Old Priam was standing on the city walls. In the distance he saw the Trojan army fleeing in terror before the savage might of Achilles and the Greeks who followed him. With a deep groan he went down to the gates and ordered the watchmen to set them wide open and to be ready to close them again quickly when the routed army had reached safety lest Achilles himself should burst in after them and massacre the Trojans in their own streets. And indeed this is what Achilles would have done, had it not been for Apollo who put on the shape of a Trojan prince who was fleeing from Achilles' spear. Achilles sped after him, but always the god kept a little way in front and Achilles wondered at the strange speed of foot that could outdistance him. So Apollo drew him away from the mass of the Trojans who poured back into their city and found safety there. They wiped the sweat from their bodies and refreshed themselves with drink, leaning against the beautiful battlements, while the main Greek army, with shields slung over their shoulders, approached the gates. But dark fate kept Hector outside the town, standing in front of the Scaean Gate alone.

And now Apollo spoke to Achilles and said: "Why do you pursue me, Achilles? However fast you run, you will never overtake me; for you are a mortal and I am a god. Now look back and you will see that the Trojans have escaped you."

Achilles spoke to him in anger. "Deceitful god," he said, "be sure that I would pay you back for this if I had the power. Had it not been for you I might have stormed the walls of Troy this very day."

And, turning away from him, he began to run back again towards the city, striding easily like a powerful racehorse that has outdistanced the others and confidently finishes the course.

Old Priam was the first to see him as he came running over the plain with his burnished armour, shining like a star. When the old man saw him, he groaned aloud and called down from the wall to his son Hector, who stood still before the gate, unshakably resolved to fight with Achilles. Stretching out his hands to him, the old man spoke in a pitiful voice. "Hector," he said, "dear child, I beg and beseech you not to stand and fight with that man. He is stronger than you by far, and he has a heart of steel. Many of my sons he has killed already, and even today I miss the sight of two others, Lycaon and Polydorus. Bitterly I grieve for them, if indeed they are dead; but how much greater would be my grief and the grief of all the Trojans, if you were to fall before Achilles! Come inside the walls, I beg you, and save us as you always have done. Have pity on me, your father, and think of the fate that is coming upon me in my old age—to see my wife and daughters dragged away by the Greeks, my sons all butchered and my palaces burnt with fire. And I myself shall lie dead among the ruins of my kingdom, and the dogs that I have fed at my own table will lick up my blood. When a young man is killed in battle and lies dead, he still looks beautiful with his wounds upon him. But there is nothing more pitiful than the sight of an old man with his flesh hacked to pieces and his grey hair and beard all foul with slaughter."

So Priam spoke in agony of mind, and Hecuba too, his wife, cried out to her son Hector from the wall. She drew her dress aside, showing him her breast, and she said to him: "Hector, my child, have pity on me! Think of how often I have given you milk from this breast and have put you to sleep. Do not fight with this man alone, my darling child. He is pitiless and, if he kills you, neither I nor your wife will be able to weep over your body and to bury you. Far away from us two the dogs will devour you by the Greek ships."

So Hector's father and mother wept as they begged him not to risk his dear life; but Hector stood firm, resting his bright shield on a protruding part of the wall, watching great Achilles draw near. "If now," he was thinking to himself, "I were to withdraw to safety, Polydamas would reproach me for not taking his advice this day and for not avoiding this disastrous battle. 'Hector trusted in his own strength,' people will be saying, 'and lost the army.' It would have been better far if I had taken his advice; but now at least I can preserve my own honour and either kill Achilles or be killed by him fighting in front of my city."

And now Achilles was upon him, looking like the God of War

himself, shaking in his hand his terrible ashen spear, brilliant in his armour like the rising sun. As Hector looked at him, his heart failed him and he turned to escape. But Achilles darted after him like a falcon, which is the swiftest thing on wings, chasing a dove and darting after her as she twists and turns in her efforts to escape. So Hector fled before Achilles, running beneath the walls of Troy. They swept past the fig-tree and past the two springs of Scamander with the beautiful troughs of stone where the wives and daughters of the Trojans used to wash their shining clothes in the days of peace, before the coming of the Greeks. Past these fair springs they ran, and they ran like champions. But this was no ordinary foot race with an ox or a shield for prize; here the prize for which they struggled was nothing less than the life of horsetaming Hector.

Three times on their swift feet they circled the city of Priam, and from Olympus all the gods were watching them as they ran. At last Zeus spoke to the other gods and said: "Alas! the man whom I see being pursued around the walls is one who is very dear to me. My heart is sad for Hector, who has so often burned sacrifices to me on the peaks of Ida and in the high citadel of Troy. He is a good man and I wish that I could save him from the hands of Achilles."

The bright-eyed goddess Athene answered him. "Father," she said, "how can you say such things? The man is mortal and the day of his fate has come. How then could you wish to preserve him?"

"It is true," Zeus replied to her. "Do with him as you wish," and Athene, who already had been longing for her father's permission, darted down from Olympus to the Trojan plain.

Still the two men ran with Achilles always heading Hector off from the town and towards the plain. It was like running in a dream, when the pursuer can never quite catch up with the pursued and the pursued can never quite escape from his pursuer, and both seem, though they are putting out every effort, hardly to be moving at all.

Now however Zeus took his golden scales. In one of the balances he put the life of Achilles and in the other the life of Hector. He held the scales by the middle and Hector's life sank downwards towards Hades. Apollo, who had strengthened his feet, now left him, but Athene came to the side of Achilles and said to him:

"Now, Achilles, the time for our triumph has come. Even Apollo cannot preserve Hector now. Wait here and recover your breath and I will go to Hector and persuade him to fight with you."

Achilles was glad when he heard her words. He stopped in his course and stood still, leaning on his heavy spear.

Athene then went to Hector and, putting on the shape and the voice of his brother Deiphobus, she stood at his side and said: "Brother, you are weary with running from great Achilles. Now let me stand by you and let us fight him together."

"Deiphobus," Hector replied, "I always loved you the best of all my brothers, and now I love you still more, since you are the only one who has dared to come outside the wall and stand at my side. Now let us see whether Achilles will kill the two of us or whether perhaps he may fall first to my spear."

So he and Achilles came near to each other. Great Hector was the first to speak. "Achilles," he said, "I shall run from you no longer. Now let us fight face to face and either kill or be killed. But let us first make a promise and call the gods to witness it. If Zeus gives me the victory, I will do nothing outrageous to your body, but will give it back to your friends for burial, once I have stripped it of its armour. Will you promise to do the same for me?"

Achilles glared at him and replied: "Hector, there can be no promises and agreements between men and lions or between wolves and sheep. So it is between you and me. There is nothing but undying hatred. Now is the time for you to show all the courage you have and all your skill with the spear; for now in a moment you will pay me back for all the pain I felt for my comrades whom you have destroyed."

As he spoke he raised his great spear and hurled it. But Hector was watching him closely; he sank down on one knee and the spear flew over his shoulder and stuck in the ground. He did not see, however, that Athene took it up and put it back again into Achilles' hands.

Now Hector prepared to throw his spear, but first he cried out: "You missed me, Achilles. It seems that you were over-confident. Now avoid this spear of mine if you can. I only pray that it may be buried in your flesh."

Then he hurled his long-shadowed spear and struck the shield of Achilles full in the centre. But the god's handiwork was not so easily pierced and the spear point was blunted on the massy metal. Hector was angry that the weapon had left his hand and done no harm to his enemy. He saw that Achilles still grasped a spear while he himself had no other to throw, and he shouted to Deiphobus, telling him to hand him a spear quickly. But when he looked round, Deiphobus was nowhere to be seen. Then Hector knew what had happened. "Alas!" he said. "Now it is certain that the gods are calling me to my death. I thought that strong Deiphobus was here with me, but he is inside the walls and I have been cheated by Athene. Now sad death is very close to me and can no longer be escaped. So it has seemed good to Zeus and to Apollo who used to love me and protect me. My fate is upon me, but at least I shall go to meet it and die bravely, so that those who are still unborn will hear how Hector died."

Then he drew his sharp and heavy sword and whirling it above his head, he swooped upon Achilles like an eagle that, from the height of the sky, swoops through the black clouds to snatch up from the earth a lamb or a cowering hare. Achilles rushed to meet him and his heart was filled with savage anger. He held his great shield before him and above the shield nodded the crest of the beautiful helmet that Hephaestus had made for him. In his right hand he poised his spear, and its glittering point shone bright as the Evening Star which shines through the darkness with the other stars and is the brightest and most beautiful of them all. So he came on with burning anger in his eyes and he searched the strong body of Hector for the spot where the flesh would most easily yield to his spear.

He saw that most of the body was covered with the flashing armour that he had taken from the dead Patroclus, but there was a place on the neck by the collar-bone, a place where death comes most quickly, which was unprotected. It was at this place that Achilles aimed as Hector charged upon him and with a powerful thrust he drove the heavy spear clean through the neck, cleaving the tender flesh but not severing the wind-pipe so that it was still possible for Hector to speak.

Hector fell in the dust and Achilles stood in triumph over him. "Hector," he said, "when you stripped the armour from Patroclus, you thought you would live to wear it. You did not remember that by the hollow ships there was a champion waiting, a mightier man that Patroclus, yes, I myself who have loosed your knees in battle. And now your body will be torn to pieces by the dogs and the vultures while the Greeks bury Patroclus with honour."

There was little life left in Hector and he spoke with labouring breath. "I beg you," he said, "by your own life and the life of your parents, do not let the dogs devour me by the ships. Take the gold that Priam will offer you in ransom and give him back my body so that the Trojans and their wives may give it burial."

Achilles looked at him grimly. "You dog," he said, "do not mention my parents to me or my life. I wish I had the heart to cut your body to pieces and to eat it raw, so much I hate you. Be sure of this. I shall accept no ransom, not if it were twenty times your worth in gold. Nor will anything keep the dogs and the birds from eating every fragment of your flesh."

Hector, now at the point of dying, spoke once more. "Indeed I know you for what you are. The heart in your breast is hard as iron, and I would never have persuaded you. Yet think what you are doing, lest the gods are angry with you on the day when you too, for all your strength, will lie by the Scaean Gate, killed by Paris and by Apollo."

As he spoke, death closed his eyes; his soul sped out of his limbs and went down to Hades, lamenting its fate, leaving behind its manhood and its youth.

Achilles spoke to the dead body. "Die!" he said. "As for me, let my death come when Zeus and the other immortal gods send it to me."

Then he drew his spear out of the wound and stripped the bloodstained armour from the body. And now the other Greeks came to see the sight. They stared in wonder at the size of Hector and at his beauty. Many of them stabbed him with their spears. "Look," they would say to each other, "it is much safer to come near Hector now than at the time when he was burning our ships."

But Achilles turned to the leaders of the Greeks and said: "Friends, we have won a great victory and the gods have granted us the power to kill this man who did us more harm than all the rest put together. Now there still lies unburied by my ships the body of my friend Patroclus, whom I can never forget so long as I live, and even in Hades, though the dead forget their dear ones, I shall still remember my comrade. Now let us go and bury him and as we go let us sing in triumph, for we have killed Hector, whom the Trojans worshipped as though he were a god."

Then Achilles did a terrible thing. He cut through the tendons of Hector's feet from heel to ankle, bound them with leather thongs which he threaded through, and fastened the thongs to his chariot. Then he mounted his chariot and drove back over the plain dragging the body of Hector behind him, with the dark hair streaming backwards, and the face that was once so beautiful jolted on the stony ground and in the deep dust. So Zeus allowed the body of Hector to be ill-treated by his enemies, there, on his own native ground.

Meanwhile old Priam and Hecuba and the Trojans had been watching from the walls. Now when they saw the head of Hector draggled in the dust they raised a loud and terrible cry as though the whole of towering Troy were going up in flames. King Priam struggled towards the gates, and his friends with difficulty held him back. "Ah, friends!" he said, "let me go. Let me go alone to plead with this savage man. He may have reverence for my age and for my grey hair. He also has a father who is old as I am and who loves him. Ah! how many of my sons has he killed in this fearful war? Yet for all of them I do not grieve as I do for this one, for Hector. How I wish that he had died in my arms! Then his mother and I could have satisfied our hearts with weeping for him."

So Priam spoke and the Trojans wept as they listened to him. Then Hecuba cried out to the women who were about her: "My child, how can I go on living now that you are dead? Day and night you were my joy and comfort. You were our great defence and the Trojans looked up to you as to a god. But now Fate and Death have overtaken you."

So Hecuba wept and lamented and the women joined her in the lament. But Hector's wife had not yet heard what had happened to her husband, or that he had remained alone outside the walls. She was sitting in her lofty house and weaving at the loom. She had just called to her servants and told them to put a great cauldron on the fire so that there should be hot water for Hector's bath when he came back from the battle. Little did she know that he was far indeed from the refreshment of baths and of changed clothing, lying dead upon the plain, destroyed by Athene and by Achilles.

Now she heard the noise of the crying and wailing from the

walls. Her limbs trembled and the shuttle dropped from her hand. Once more she called to her servants. "Come with me, two of you," she said, "and help to support me. I must go and see what has happened. That was the voice of my husband's mother that I heard, and now my heart is in my mouth and my legs will hardly carry me. I pray that what I think may not be true, but I am terribly afraid that Achilles may have caught my husband alone outside the walls. For Hector would never stay with the crowd; he always went out far in front of the rest and would let no one be as brave as he was."

Then she ran from the house as though she was mad and her servants followed her. She came to the tower above the gate, and, looking out over the plain, she saw her husband being dragged in the dust behind the swift horses of Achilles towards the Greek camp. Then the blackness of night fell upon her eyes; fainting, she fell backwards and her shining head-dress dropped to the ground, her bright coronet and the veil that golden Aphrodite had given her on the day that great Hector had come to her father's house to make her his bride.

As she lay there the noble women of Troy came to her and supported her head, and when she was able to speak she spoke to them between her sobs and said: "O Hector, Hector, I am unhappy. One evil fate has destroyed us both. Now you are going to the house of Hades and I am left a widow in your house. And the child whom we had together is still only a little boy. You will not be able to help him, Hector, since you are dead, nor will he be able to help you. Even if he escapes from this terrible war, there will be nothing in his life but sorrow and trouble. For when a child loses his father he loses his friends too. The other boys, whose fathers are still living, will push him away from their feasts. And he will come running to me in tears, Astyanax, who always used to sit on his father's knee and eat nothing but the best pieces of meat, and when he was sleepy and tired of play always slept in a soft bed in his nurse's arms and never wanted for anything. But now that he has lost his dear father, his whole life will be miserable. Astyanax, 'lord of the City,' so the Trojans call him, since it was you, Hector, who were the one protection to us all. And now, far from your parents, you lie by the Greek ships and the wriggling worms will eat your body after the dogs and the vultures have sated themselves. Naked you lie there, in spite of the fine clothing that I have here for you in your house. All this clothing I shall burn in the fire, since you will never wear it again."

So she spoke weeping and all the women lamented with her.

THE FUNERAL AND THE GAMES

Meanwhile Achilles, dragging the body of Hector behind his chariot, had led his troops back to their camp. Before they unyoked the horses they drove their chariots three times past the body of Patroclus to do him honour, and wept as they drove past him, so that all the sandy ground was wet with their tears. Then Achilles laid his man-killing hands on the breast of his comrade and cried out: "Rejoice, Patroclus, even though you are in the House of the Dead. I have done for you what I promised to do. I have dragged Hector here and shall give his body to the dogs to tear in pieces; and at your funeral I shall cut the throats of twelve young nobles of Troy to satisfy my anger."

Then he loosed the body of Hector from his chariot and let it lie face-downwards in the dust by the bier of Patroclus. The Myrmidons unyoked their horses and sat down to a great funeral feast. There were white oxen, sheep and goats to be eaten, and great fat hogs with their gleaming tusks. Cupfuls of blood were poured around the dead body.

But Achilles himself with the other kings went to feast with Agamemnon. When he arrived at the hut, Agamemnon told his servants to put a great cauldron on the fire, so that Achilles might wash the blood from his body and refresh himself. But Achilles refused. "I swear by Zeus," he said, "that no water shall come near my body until I have buried Patroclus. For I shall never, so long as I am alive, feel such pain as I feel now. I must eat, I know, though still all food is distasteful to me. And tomorrow, if King Agamemnon agrees, let men go out early and fetch wood for the funeral pyre."

Agamemnon willingly agreed. They sat down to their dinner and, when their hunger and thirst were satisfied, they went back each to his own camp. But Achilles lay down by the shore of the breaking sea in an open place where the waves came surging up on to the beach. Here he lay down and he groaned deeply as he lay there; but soon sleep came and enfolded him, making him forget his cares and his weariness, for his strong limbs were tired out by the fighting and by the chase of Hector round the walls of windy Troy.

Now in his sleep the ghost of Patroclus came to him, looking just like he had been when he was alive, with the same eyes and expression of the face, with the same voice and wearing the same clothes. The ghost stood by Achilles' head and spoke to him. "You are asleep, Achilles, and have forgotten about me, though when I was alive you used never to forget me. Bury me at once, so that I may pass through the gates of the House of the Dead. For now the other souls keep me out and will not let me pass the River. And give me your hand, I beg you. Once I have been burned in the flames I shall never come back again from Hades; nor will you and I ever sit apart by ourselves and talk as we used to do. Dreadful Fate has overwhelmed me, and it is your fate too, great Achilles, to die beneath the walls of Troy. One other thing I ask from you. Just as we grew up together in our youth, so let our bones rest side by side and our ashes be mingled in the same urn."

"Patroclus, dear friend," said Achilles, "why have you come to tell me this? Be sure that I shall do everything as you would have it done. But come nearer to me, so that we may embrace each other for a short moment and find comfort in each other's grief."

As he spoke he stretched out his arms to clasp his dead friend, but the ghost slipped away from him like smoke and with a thin cry disappeared beneath the earth. Achilles woke in amazement and cried out: "It is true then that even in the House of the Dead there is something of us that remains, though it is only a ghost and an image without life or sense. For all through the night the ghost of poor Patroclus has been standing by my head, weeping and lamenting, telling me what it wanted done. It looked just like Patroclus himself."

By crying out Achilles had woken the Myrmidons, and now he

and they mourned once more for Patroclus until dawn. But at dawn King Agamemnon sent out men and mules to fetch wood from Mount Ida. There they felled the tall oaks, cut the timber into lengths and brought it back to the place appointed by Achilles for the funeral pyre. To this place had come the Myrmidons with their horses and their chariots, escorting the body of Patroclus. From the wood that had been brought they raised a great pyre, a hundred feet high and a hundred feet broad. Sad at heart, they placed the body on the top, and all around the body they placed the carcases of sheep and oxen. There were four great war horses also that Achilles sacrificed at the pyre and there too he put jars of honey and of oil. Patroclus had had nine dogs as pets. Achilles cut the throats of two of these and put them also on the pyre. Then he did a terrible thing: he killed twelve Trojan prisoners, good and noble men, and put their bodies on to the flames so that they should burn with Patroclus. The wind fanned the flames into a great fire and Achilles cried out for the last time to his friend. "Farewell, Patroclus!" he said. "I have kept the promises that I made. I have killed twelve noble Trojans who will burn with you in the fire. As for Hector, I shall not give his body to the flames but leave it for the dogs to tear apart."

Yet for all this the dogs never came near the body of Hector. Day and night Aphrodite, daughter of Zeus, kept them away from him and over his flesh she poured an ambrosial oil of roses so that it should not be torn when Achilles dragged him over the ground. And Apollo folded the body in a purple cloud that covered the space where it lay and warded off the fierce rays of the sun, so that the skin should not be withered or corrupted.

Through the afternoon and through the night the fire burned, and at daybreak, as the flames sank down, they poured wine upon the ashes and carefully collected together the bones of Patroclus. At the orders of Achilles they put the bones in a golden urn and sealed it. "Let them lie there," he said, "until the time when I too have gone down to the House of the Dead. And let us build a mound for him that is fitting but not very big. Later those of you who are still alive can build a bigger tomb where my bones can be buried together with his."

Quickly the soldiers of the Greeks built the tomb for Patroclus and then Achilles brought out from his ships valuable and splendid prizes and prepared to hold funeral games in honour of his friend.

The troops sat down in a great circle and watched while the greatest and most skilful athletes in the army competed in the games.

The first event was the chariot race, and the first prize was a slave woman well trained in household matters and a great tripod, very exquisitely made. The second prize was a mare known to be good for breeding, the third prize a new copper vessel that had never been touched by the flames. And for those who came fourth and fifth there were prizes of two talents of gold and another cooking vessel.

The first to come forward for the race was Eumelus, who had some of the best horses in the army and was himself a famous charioteer. Others who competed were Diomedes, who drove the fine horses that he had taken from Aeneas, Menelaus, Meriones and Nestor's son, Antilochus. Before the race began Nestor gave long and careful advice to Antilochus. He told him that he would never win on the merits of his horses, since they were the slowest ones in the race, but that skill and judgment in racing are often just as valuable as speed.

Soon the horses were off and the drivers were shouting to the horses as they sped over the plain in a cloud of dust, vanishing from the eyes of the spectators. At the turning post Eumelus was ahead, but Diomedes was quickly overhauling him. Apollo, however, was angry with Diomedes and, just as he was going to overtake Eumelus, the god knocked the whip out of his hand. In despair Diomedes saw Eumelus's horses going ahead while his own began to slacken pace. But Athene was watching over her favourite. She brought back his whip to him and set it in his hand. Then she went after Eumelus and broke the yoke of his chariot, so that the horses ran on wildly and Eumelus himself was hurled to the ground. As he got to his feet, bruised and sore from his fall, he saw the chariot of Diomedes sweep past him, now certain to win the first prize.

Menelaus was not far behind, and behind Menelaus came Antilochus. Not far from the winning post the chariot track ran through a narrow gorge and at this point Antilochus whipped up his horses and, driving a little to the side of the main track, overtook Menelaus and began to come closer and closer to him so that he would force him off the course. Menelaus shouted out to him: "Antilochus, this is mad driving, wait till the track gets wider and then

pass me if you can. Otherwise both our chariots will be wrecked."

But Antilochus pretended not to hear, and drove even faster. Finally, fearing that they would both be killed, Menelaus gave way and Antilochus drove past him. Again Menelaus shouted out: "You are the most dangerous driver I have ever seen—absolutely without sense, and I shall complain about this foul." Then he lashed on his own horses and, as soon as the track became wider, they began to gain upon Antilochus and would have passed him if the course had been longer. As it was, however, Antilochus just managed to come in second, with Menelaus close behind him. Meriones came fourth, and last of all came Eumelus, dragging his broken chariot.

Achilles was sorry for him and said: "Eumelus is the best driver of them all and he has come in last, through no fault of his own. He ought to have a prize. Let us give him the second prize, since Diomedes certainly should have the first."

Everyone agreed to this except Antilochus who said: "Great Achilles, I came in second and I ought not to lose my prize. If you feel so sorry for Eumelus, you ought to give him something else."

Achilles liked Antilochus and he smiled at this. "Very well," he said, "you shall keep the mare and I will give Eumelus a splendid Trojan breastplate. Then everyone will be satisfied."

But now Menelaus, in great anger, came forward to swear that it was only by a foul that Antilochus had managed to beat him and he challenged Antilochus to swear on oath to the contrary. At this Antilochus began to be ashamed. "Forgive me, King Menelaus," he said. "You are older than I am and you know how young men sometimes go too far in the heat of the moment. I do not want to quarrel with you and I will give you the mare and also something else of my own, if it will please you and make you forget your anger."

Menelaus at once forgave him. "Antilochus," he said, "you have fought well in my cause and I respect both your father and yourself. And I know that usually you do not act so foolishly as you did today. So I will give you back the mare and will cease to be angry with you."

So Menelaus took the third prize and Meriones the fourth. There was no one to claim the fifth prize and Achilles gave it to Nestor, saying to him: "My Lord, accept this, I beg you, in mem-

ory of Patroclus. I think that you are too old now to compete yourself in the wrestling or the foot races, and I should like you to have
something by which to remember my dead friend."

Old Nestor thanked him. "You are quite right," he said. "There
was a time when I could run and box and wrestle with any man in
Greece. But I am not so quick on my feet as I was, nor so strong in
the arm. Now I thank you for your gift and for showing me the
respect which you never forget to show. I pray that the gods will
reward you."

And now came the other events. There was boxing, throwing the
javelin and throwing the discus. In the wrestling match the competitors were great Ajax and Odysseus. For long the two remained
gripped together and neither was able to move the other. The
sweat streamed from their bodies as each exerted his enormous
strength, and along their arms and on their ribs the flesh reddened
beneath the pressure of their holds. Finally Ajax said to Odysseus:
"My Lord Odysseus, we must allow each other a throw each and
then see to whom Zeus will give the victory." So he lifted Odysseus
off the ground, but Odysseus knew every trick in wrestling. As he
was raised in the air he kicked Ajax behind the knee and brought
him down on his back, himself springing on to his chest. There was
loud applause at this. And now in the next round Odysseus tried to
lift Ajax and throw him. He could hardly shift the great bulk, and
though, by crooking his knee behind, he tried to force Ajax backwards, they both fell to the ground together. They then prepared
for a third round, but Achilles prevented them. "You have both
won," he said, "and the prizes shall be equal." After their struggle
Ajax and Odysseus were glad enough to agree.

Next came the foot race. Among the runners was another Ajax
called Ajax the Smaller, since he was not such a giant of a man as
was the Ajax who had just wrestled; but he was a great warrior and
one of the finest runners among the Greeks. The other competitors
were the wise Odysseus and Antilochus, who was the best runner
among the younger men. The first prize for this event was a beautiful mixing bowl of silver; the second prize was a fine large ox, and
the third was a talent of gold.

This race was a very close one. Ajax kept just a little ahead of
Odysseus, but Odysseus was so near to him that Ajax could
feel his breath upon his shoulder. All the army cheered Odysseus
for the effort he was making and, as they approached the winning

post, Odysseus prayed to Athene, begging her to strengthen his limbs. Athene heard his prayer. She made his limbs lighter and at the same time she caused Ajax to slip and fall in a place that was all slippery from the dung of cattle that had been standing there for the sacrifices at the tomb of Patroclus. So Odysseus won the first prize. Ajax took the ox and, as he held it by its horns, he spat out of his mouth to filth into which he had fallen. When he recovered his breath, he gasped out: "Sure enough it was the goddess who made me lose, Athene who always looks after Odysseus as though she were his mother."

The others laughed at him. As for Antilochus, he took the third prize and, as he took it, he said: "Friends, it is always the same thing. It is the old ones whom the gods love. For though Ajax is only a little older than I am, Odysseus belongs to an earlier generation altogether. Yet he is tough enough. None of us could beat him in a race, except Achilles."

Achilles was pleased with the praise. "Antilochus," he said, "I thank you for the compliment and in return I will double your prize and make it two talents of gold."

So Antilochus took the two talents and was highly pleased with his prize.

The prize for the next event was the armour of Sarpedon, whom Patroclus had killed. Two men were to fight for this armour in single combat and the winner should be the one who first drew blood. Great Ajax and Diomedes were the two competitors here. Three times they charged at each other with their spears and at the fourth charge Ajax drove his spear right through Diomedes' shield; but the bronze breastplate warded off the point from his body. Then Diomedes lunged over the top of Ajax's shield and just managed to touch him on the neck. The army cried out in terror, fearing lest one or other of these two great champions should receive a serious wound, and Achilles stopped the fight and decided that the armour should be shared between the two.

Next came a contest in archery. Here the prizes were iron axes. There was a set of ten double-headed axes for the winner and a set of ten single-headed axes for the loser. The greatest archer in the army was Teucer, the brother of Ajax, but Meriones, the friend of Idomeneus, was not far his inferior. These were the two who now competed for the axes. Nor was the competition an easy one. A pigeon was tied by the foot to the top of one of a ship's masts a long way away from the arena. This was the target, and to choose the one who should shoot first, two pebbles were shaken together in a bronze helmet. Teucer's pebble was the first to jump out of the helmet, and he immediately put an arrow to his bow and shot. But he had forgotten first to pray to Apollo, the god of Archery, and so he missed the pigeon, though his arrow struck the cord by which it was tied and cut through it. The Greeks all cheered, since the shot was certainly a good one; but Meriones quickly snatched the bow from Teucer's hand and, as the pigeon, now free from its cord, shot up into the sky, he hastily made his prayer to Apollo and shot at the bird at the moment when it was high in the air above his head. The arrow went clean through the bird's wing and came down again to stick in the earth at Meriones' feet. The pigeon fluttered weakly down to settle on a ship's mast and from there fell dead to the ground. Everyone was amazed at such shooting and Meriones took the set of double axes.

And now the games were over. The Greeks went back to their tents to prepare for their evening meal and for their sleep.

THE END OF THE ANGER

But Achilles could not forget his dead comrade. At night he tossed to and fro on his bed, longing for the good and strong man who had been his friend, thinking of all the joys and sorrows that they had been through together, all the battles and expeditions on land and all the perils on the waves of the sea.

He would rise before dawn from his sleepless bed and would wander along the beach and promontories of the land. And when dawn came he would yoke his horses to his chariot, tie the body of Hector behind the chariot wheels, and then drag him three times round the tomb of Patroclus. Afterwards he would go back to his hut, leaving the body on its face stretched out in the dust. But Apollo still loved Hector, though he was dead, and kept the body fair and beautiful, guarding it from all corruption and from all the injuries that Achilles did to it in his rage.

Zeus himself was angry with Achilles for so shamefully treating his fallen enemy, and so were the other blessed gods and goddesses except for Hera and Athene who still hated the Trojans and the whole house of Priam. But Zeus would not be governed by his wife and by his daughter. He sent for the goddess Thetis and she came to him from the deep sea cave where she had been sitting with her sister nymphs. Then the Father of Gods and Men spoke to her and said: "I have done for you what you asked. Achilles has won great glory and is honoured by the Greeks more than ever before. Now I wish you to go to him and tell him that I am displeased with him for keeping the body of Hector, who was a good man and one whom I loved. Let him give it back. Meanwhile I shall send my messenger Iris to old Priam and tell him to prepare a ransom and to go and plead with Achilles."

Thetis, the silver-footed goddess, was not slow to obey. She darted down from the heights of Olympus and came to Achilles whom she found still mourning by his hut. "Dear child," she said to him, as she took his hand in hers, "will you not take any pleasure in life? Can you not eat and drink or find comfort in a woman's love? Your own fate is close upon you and it is only a little time that you have left to live." Then she gave him the message from Father Zeus and Achilles replied: "Let it be so. If Zeus commands me, I must obey. When they bring the ransom, they shall have the body."

Meanwhile Zeus had sent his messenger Iris, the goddess of the rainbow, to Priam in Troy. In the royal palace she found nothing but wailing and lamentation. Priam was sitting with his sons around him. The old man had befouled his head with dust and he covered his face with his cloak as the tears still streamed from his eyes. And all through the house his daughters and his sons' wives were crying out and weeping as they remembered Hector and all the other brave men who had fallen before Achilles and the Greeks.

Iris went up to the old man and spoke gently in his ear; but his limbs began to tremble when he heard her voice. "Do not be afraid, Priam," she said. "I have not come to you with news of evil, but have come to help you. I am the messenger of Zeus who, though he is far away, still cares for you and pities you. It is the will of Zeus that you should go to Achilles with a ransom for your son. You must go alone, but you need have no fear. Hermes himself will protect you and Achilles will do you no harm."

After speaking these words Iris vanished from sight. Priam at once told his sons to get ready for him a cart with mules to draw it. Then he went to his high-roofed bedroom with its panels and roof of cedar wood, and he called to his wife Hecuba and told her of the message which had come to him from Zeus. But Hecuba cried out in despair when she heard that he intended to go to the Greek ships. "Dear husband," she said, "have you taken leave of your wits, you whom everyone used to admire for your wisdom? How can you bear to go and put yourself into the power of that cruel and savage man who has killed so many of our sons? Certainly he will kill you too."

But Priam refused to be turned aside from his purpose. "Do not try to hold me back," he said. "I tell you that I saw the goddess with my own eyes, and I am going to do as she told me. Even if it is my fate to die by the Greek ships, it is a fate that I would accept. Once I have held my son in my arms and wept over him, then I do not mind if Achilles strikes me down with his murderous hands."

Out of the treasure chambers of his palace Priam then took twelve beautiful robes, with tunics and cloaks. He took ten talents of gold, two burnished tripods, four cauldrons and a drinking cup of very great beauty which had once been given to him by the Thracians when he had made a journey into their country.

So impatient was he to be on his way that he shouted angrily at his sons, at Paris and Helenus and Deiphobus and the rest, since they seemed to him to be slow in harnessing the mules to the cart. "All my best sons," he cried, "are dead and gone. You who are left are good for nothing but dancing and wearing fine clothes. I wish that all of you had died and left Hector alive, who was like a god among men and looked not like a man's son but like the son of a god. Make the cart ready immediately and load it with these treasures, so that I can be on my way."

Priam's sons trembled at the old man's angry voice. They hurriedly brought out the cart and harnessed the mules to it. Then they fetched the gifts which Priam had chosen for the ransom and loaded them carefully upon the cart. The old king mounted and took the reins. As he drove through the streets of Troy a crowd followed him, weeping and wailing as if he were going to his death. His sons and his old counsellors escorted him outside the city gates. Then they turned back and Priam went on alone.

As he crossed the plain towards the ships of the Greeks, darkness began to descend and suddenly through the darkness Priam saw approaching him a young man of great beauty. He stopped still in terror, fearing that this must be one of the princes or captains of the Greeks who would betray him. But the young man was no other than the god Hermes, guide to travellers and bringer of good fortune, whom Zeus had sent down from Olympus to protect King Priam. Hermes soon calmed the old man's fears and promised to accompany him to the hut of Achilles. Not yet did Priam realise that he had a divine escort; but when they reached the Greek camp, they found that all the sentries were asleep, since the god had exercised his power over them; and when they reached that part of the camp where Achilles had his quarters, they found the entrance barred by a great bolt made from the trunk of a pine tree, which could only be moved by the strength of three men. Hermes by himself easily drew back this bolt. Then he turned to Priam and said to him: "I, who have accompanied you here, am an immortal god. My father Zeus sent me to help you. But now I shall go no further with you. Go in yourself and pray to Achilles in the name of his father and of his mother and of his own son to have pity on your distress."

Hermes then returned to Olympus. Priam went forward to the hut and opened the door. Inside he saw Achilles with some of his companions about him. Automedon, the charioteer, was waiting on him and Achilles had just finished eating and drinking. Great Priam entered, and no one saw him until he was standing close to Achilles and until he had knelt on the ground and was clasping his knees and kissing his hands, those terrible murderous hands that had destroyed Hector and so many of the old man's sons. As they saw him they were filled with astonishment, and they listened still in amazement while Priam spoke. "Royal Achilles," he said, "think of your own father, who is an old man too, like I am. Perhaps he is being attacked by his neighbours and has no one near him to help and protect him; yet, even so, while he knows that you are alive, he will be glad at heart and every day he will hope to see his dear son again, coming back from Troy. But I have nothing to look forward to. I had nineteen sons, the best sons of any man in Troy. Most of them have fallen in battle and Hector, who was everything to me, who was the one great defence of Troy and the Trojans, has been killed by you fighting for his country. Now I have come with a splendid ransom for his body. Give him back to me, I beg you. Have reverence for the gods, Achilles, and have pity upon me, remembering your own father. Indeed I am still more to be pitied than he is, since I have forced myself to do something which no one else on earth has done: I have kissed the hands which killed my own son."

As he spoke, Achilles began to think with pain and longing of his own father. He took the old man's hand and gently moved him from his knees. Then both he and Priam burst into tears, Priam on the ground at Achilles' feet weeping for Hector, and Achilles weeping for his own father and for Patroclus. And when for the time he had had his fill of weeping, Achilles rose from his chair and took the old man by the hand to raise him to his feet, pitying and reverencing his grey hair and beard. "Indeed," he said, "I pity you. How you have suffered in your heart! You have dared to come alone to the Greek ships and to me who have killed so many of your fine sons. Now sit down, I beg you, and in spite of our grief, let us cease our lamentations, since they cannot bring back what is past. It is the will of the gods, who live in happiness for ever, that we wretched mortals should be in pain either constantly or from time to time. None of us can escape it. Consider my father Peleus. From his birth the gods gave him all their most splendid gifts. He had wealth and fortune beyond all other men; he was King of the Myrmidons; and, though he was a mortal, he had a goddess for his wife. Yet to him too the gods gave evil as well as good. He has no children to carry on his name, none except for me who am doomed to die young. Nor do I help to care for him in his old age, since I stay here, far from my own country, bringing harm to you and to your children. You too, sir, had the name of being happy with one of the greatest kingdoms in the world and with so many noble and brave sons. Yet ever since the gods brought this war upon you, you have seen nothing but battles and the killing of men. You must endure therefore and find courage to bear your fate. No weeping will ever bring your son back to life again."

Priam replied to him and said: "Do not ask me to sit down, Prince Achilles, while Hector still lies uncared for. Accept the ransom and let me see him with my eyes. And I pray that you yourself may return to your own land in safety, since you have spared my life."

Achilles looked sternly at the old man. "Do not hurry me or reproach me," he said, "lest my anger should return and I should sin against Zeus by treating you as I treated Hector. I have already resolved to give him back to you. Indeed I know that it was by the help of some god that you came here, for otherwise you could never have passed the sentries or drawn back the bolt at my gate. Do as I say, therefore, and do not anger me."

Priam trembled at his words and seated himself on a chair. Achilles then rushed out of doors like a lion. He gave orders for the ransom to be taken from the cart and for the body of Hector to be washed and anointed with oil and wrapped in fine coverlets. Then he lifted the body in his own arms and set it on a bier which his comrades raised up and put upon the waggon. When this was done he groaned aloud and spoke the name of his dear friend. "Patroclus," he said, "do not be angry with me if in the House of Death you learn that I have given back the body of Hector to his father. He has given me a noble ransom, and you too shall have your share of it."

Then Achilles returned to his hut and sat down opposite Priam. "Sir," he said, "I have done as you asked. Your son's body is lying on a bier and at dawn you shall see him and shall take him away. Tomorrow you shall weep for him when you bring him back into Troy. And indeed you have reason to weep."

After this food and drink were set before them, and when their hunger was satisfied, Priam looked long and carefully at Achilles and wondered at his size and beauty; for he looked like an immortal god. Achilles also gazed with admiration at Priam, noting his great stature, his noble looks, and listening to the words he spoke. Thus they found pleasure in looking at each other, but presently King Priam said: "Achilles, I would ask you now to let me retire to rest. Sweet sleep has never yet come to my eyes since the time that Hector lost his life at your hands, nor until now have I tasted food and drink."

Achilles rose and had a bed made for the old man in a covered place outside his own room. But before Priam retired to rest he asked him how many days they would require in Troy to hold the funeral of Hector. "I will promise you," he said, "that you will be left free to bury him as you think fit. There will be no fighting till the funeral is over."

Priam thanked Achilles and told him that the Trojans would mourn for Hector in their houses for nine days, on the tenth day they would bury him and on the eleventh build his tomb. "And on the twelfth," he said, "we will fight, if fight we must."

Then Achilles grasped the old man's hand to assure him that his promise would be kept and to free him from fear. He escorted him to the bed that had been prepared for him and himself lay down to sleep upon his own bed.

But before dawn Hermes, whom Zeus had appointed to protect Priam, came to the old man's bed and woke him. He wished him to pass through the Greek lines before the army was awake, and Priam obeyed the orders of the god. Hermes himself yoked the mules; he drew back the heavy bolt from the gate and he drove the waggon, with Hector's body upon it, as far as the ford in the eddying stream of Scamander. Now dawn was showing red in the eastern sky, and Hermes departed to Olympus, while Priam drove the horses on towards the city, carrying their sad burden.

King Priam's daughter Cassandra was the first to see him coming over the plain. She had climbed to the top of the wall and now she let her voice ring out over Troy. "Men and women of Troy," she said, "you who used to rejoice when Hector, our deliverer, came back from battle, come out and see him now."

Then every man and woman in the city came out into the streets, and when they saw the body of Hector, they were overcome by unspeakable grief, crowding round the waggon where the corpse lay. But Priam told his people to make way for him so that he could take the body to its own home. There would be time later, he said, for them to mourn for Hector, but first he must be mourned for by his own family.

So they brought the body into the palace and laid it down on a bed, and summoned the musicians to make their music, and to sing the dirges. And among the women Andromache, holding Hector's head between her hands, began the lament. "Husband," she said, "you died young, before your time, and you have left me behind you a widow with our little boy who will never grow up, I think, to be a man. Before then this city with all its towers will be folded up in flames, since you, Hector, its guardian and defender, have died.

And I shall be carried away into slavery, and you, my little son, will go with me, unless one of the Greeks seizes you by the arm and hurls you down from the battlements to your death, angry with you because Hector killed a brother of his or a father or a son. For there were many Greeks who fell before the spear of Hector, and in the hard fighting your father had no gentle ways. That is why all the people lament for him. But, Hector, my sorrow is greatest of all, because you did not die in bed, holding out your arms to me, nor did you speak to me your last words, so that I could have treasured them in my heart day and night as I wept for you."

So she spoke and all the women wept with her. Next Hecuba made her lament. "Hector," she said, "you were the dearest to me of all my sons. The gods loved you when you were alive and even in death they have taken care of you. For though Achilles dragged you around the tomb of his friend, whom you killed, you lie now in your palace fresh as dew, comely and beautiful, like one whom Apollo of the Silver Bow has gently visited in death."

Again the women wept with her, and then Helen made the third lament. "Hector," she said, "since Paris brought me here to be his wife (and I wish I had perished first), you have always been much the dearest to me of all my brothers in Troy. It is nineteen years now since I came here and left my own country, and in all that time I have never once heard from you an unkind or an ungracious word. Others have reproached me—your brothers, your sisters, your mother (though never your father, who has been as kind to me as if I were his own child). But you always stopped them from insulting me, so gentle you were to me in your heart, so kind and courteous in your ways and words. And now I weep both for you and for my wretched self, since I have no one left in all Troy to be kind to me or to care for me. Instead they all shudder at the sight of me."

So Helen spoke, weeping. And now Priam gave orders for the preparation of the funeral. For nine days the Trojans mourned over Hector and meanwhile they brought into the city from the forests of Mount Ida great quantities of wood to make the funeral pyre. On the tenth day they put the body on the fire and set it alight, weeping as they did so. They collected the bones together, wrapped them in soft purple cloths and put them in a golden chest. Over the bones, on the eleventh day, they raised a great mound. Then they set sentries on the walls, in case the Greeks should attack before the time, and they went back to the palace of King Priam where the funeral feast was to be held.

Thus all the proper rites were performed at the burial of great Hector.

BOOK THREE

The Fall of Troy

THE DEATH OF ACHILLES

After the death of Hector it might well have seemed that the Trojans would be no longer able to resist Achilles and the victorious Greeks. Yet they were wisely led by Prince Aeneas, and by the few surviving sons of Priam. Moreover now, in the tenth year of the war, reinforcements were at hand. Two great new armies came to strengthen the defenders of Troy. The first of these armies was led by Memnon, the king of the Ethiopians, the second was an army of Amazons, the women who fight from horseback like men, and was led by the Amazon Queen Penthesilea.

King Memnon was the nephew of Priam, and, like Priam's other nephew Aeneas, he was the son of a goddess. His father was Tithonus, the son of Laomedon; but Tithonus had been carried up to heaven before the time of Laomedon's treachery to Herakles. Yet, as we shall see, though he was made immortal he was not made happy.

It was Aurora, goddess of the Dawn, who fell in love with young

Tithonus, and used to rest with him in the woods and deep glades of Mount Ida. So much did she love him that she took him with her to her heavenly palace, and she begged Father Zeus to make him immortal. Zeus granted her prayer, but the prayer itself was an unwise one. Tithonus was indeed immortal, but she had forgotten to ask at the same time that he should remain, like the deathless gods, young and beautiful as he was. Thus, though Tithonus could not die, he did grow old, and, as he felt the weakness of age overcoming his limbs, as he saw the wrinkles on his face, dwelling day after day in the rosy palace of Aurora, he could not bear the thought of what he had been and of what he was. He begged Aurora to revoke her gift and to let him share the fate of all men and die. But even the gods cannot recall their gifts. So Tithonus grew older and older, more and more feeble in that splendid palace, losing his taste for sight and colours, for music, food and drink and every pleasure of his youth. In the end, they say, the gods had pity on him. Though they could not let him die, they changed his shape and turned him into a small insect, the cicada, which sings merrily through the summer days among the trees and rocks.

But long before this time a son was born to Aurora and Tithonus. This son was Memnon who became the king of the great nation of the Ethiopians. It was he who now led an army of ten thousand men to Troy, and both his army and his own presence, since he was a great warrior, encouraged the Trojans to renew the fighting. They fought on the more fiercely to preserve their homes and to avenge the death of Hector.

Memnon himself was not fated to live long, yet before he died, he won great glory. Many Greeks fell before his spear and before the spears of his Ethiopian warriors. In the front line of battle he killed with his own hand Antilochus, the gallant young son of Nestor and the friend of Achilles. At this loss the Greeks were sad indeed, yet the grief of none of them equalled the grief of old King Nestor himself. Distraught with longing for his son, he sent a challenge to Memnon, offering to fight with him in single combat. Memnon, however, was too chivalrous to use his great strength and his skill in arms against an old man still mourning for his dead son. Instead he chose to accept a challenge from Achilles, who also longed to avenge the friend whom he had loved. Yet not even Aurora could help her son against Achilles. Though Memnon fought bravely and well, his spear and sword could not pierce the imperishable armour of Hephaestus, and in the end he fell, slain by the invincible hands that had destroyed Hector and so many others.

Aurora wept for her son. She could not bring him to life again any more than she could give youth back to her husband; but she saved his dead body from Achilles and she begged Zeus to show her son some honour at his funeral. Zeus granted her prayer and, while the Trojans burned the body of Memnon on a high pyre, a miracle took place. The clouds of smoke that eddied up from the great fire that was devouring the body began suddenly to take on distinct shapes that looked different from smoke. As the onlookers stared upwards in amazement, they saw the smoke changing into the figures of birds. Soon the whole air was full of them; the wheeling flock flew three times round the pyre, then separated into two flocks which immediately began to fight bitterly together. So fiercely did they attack each other that nearly all of them were destroyed before they broke off the battle and flew away. These birds came to be called "the birds of Memnon" and for generations afterwards they would come each year on the same day to renew their battle over Memnon's tomb. So Zeus did honour to the son of Aurora, and in Memnon's own country the Ethiopians raised for him a wonderful and gigantic statue which had the power of making sounds. At dawn when the sun's first rays fell upon this statue, it would seem to speak in a melodious voice and in the evening, when the sun set, it would make a noise that was more like the noise of mourning.

So, even after his death, the name of Memnon remained famous on the earth, and round Troy the fighting continued as bitterly as before. The army of the Amazons, fierce women armed with double-headed axes, pressed the Greeks hard, but here again the Greeks were delivered by Achilles who, coming to close quarters, slew Penthesilea, the Amazon queen, with his sword. They say that when he stripped the armour from her body he was astonished at her beauty and wept for what he had done. Yet now his own fate was close upon him. As he led the victorious Greeks forward, streaming towards the Scaean Gate, the moment came which had been fixed for him at birth by the Fates. Though for long he had been irresistible, now he was in the hands of the gods, and though he expected that day to sack the city of Troy, once more the city was saved by Apollo. It was Paris who shot the arrow that killed great Achilles, but Apollo strengthened the archer's arm and directed the arrow to that part of the body where alone it would bring death. Achilles fell in the dust in front of the Scaean Gate, as Hector with his dying words had foretold, and the Greeks were dismayed when they saw their champion fall. Eagerly the Trojans surged forward to take the armour and the body of their great enemy and at first they forced the Greeks backwards in the fight. But Odysseus stood firm, and while he beat off every attack that the Trojans made upon him, great Ajax rescued the body and carried it back to the ships. Afterwards it was decided that the splendid armour of Achilles should be given either to Ajax or to Odysseus, since they had been friends of Achilles, had saved his body in the fighting and were among the greatest of the Greeks. There was much debate as to which of the two was most worthy of the armour, but in the end Agamemnon, Menelaus and the other leaders decided that it should be given to Odysseus. And now Ajax, great warrior though he was, could not bear what he considered was an unjust decision. He went out of his mind and fell upon a herd of sheep, imagining them to be the two sons of Atreus and the other generals who had awarded the armour to Odysseus. In his madness, he slaughtered these animals, and then, when he came again to his right mind, he was ashamed at what he had done and killed himself with his own sword, preferring to die rather than to live with the memory of how he had lost his wits and disgraced his own great name. The Greeks built him a high monument on the shore and in his own country of Salamis he was honoured ever afterwards for his strength and for his steadfastness in battle.

But first the Greeks mourned for Achilles as bitterly as the Trojans had mourned for Hector. By the sea coast and near the ships they raised for him a high mound where his bones were buried together with the bones of his friend Patroclus. His mother Thetis with her sisters, the nymphs of the sea, came to mourn at his funeral and the Greeks honoured their dead leader as though he was a god.

Old King Peleus did not know yet of his son's death and just before had allowed his grandson, Neoptolemus, the young son of Achilles, to sail himself to Troy that he might fight beside his father. But when Neoptolemus arrived, he found that of his great father nothing was left except the high funeral mound and an undying fame. Neoptolemus wept at Achilles' tomb, and then he flung himself fiercely into the war, soon showing himself to be a warrior worthy of his birth.

So the fighting continued and still the blood of men stained the waters of the River Scamander or was soaked up in the dusty ground.

THE FATAL HORSE

Calchas, the prophet, had foretold that the war would end in the tenth year, yet still the war dragged on, still the Trojans, led by Aeneas and by Paris, fought on behind their walls or in front of their city, and still the Greeks, for all that they could do, failed to win a decisive advantage.

And now another prophecy was made known to the army. Some say that it was again Calchas who made the revelation; some say that Odysseus and Diomedes captured Helenus, a son of Priam and the chief prophet of the Trojans, and that it was he who revealed to them that Troy would never be captured without the famous bow and arrows of Herakles. These were in possession of the warrior Philoctetes, whom the Greeks had cruelly abandoned on the island of Lemnos nine years before this time. On this rocky island Philoctetes remained, still suffering from the wound he had received from the bite of a snake, in continual pain and in continual anger with the Greeks who had deserted him.

Now in their great need the Greeks were ashamed of the cruelty with which they had treated this great warrior. Odysseus and Neoptolemus went to Lemnos in order to urge Philoctetes to return with them and to give them his help. They found him weak and tortured by the pain of his wound which had so corrupted his flesh that all men avoided him because of the dreadful smell of decay with which he was surrounded. At first he refused utterly to come to the help of the Greeks. And indeed the young Neoptolemus was so deeply affected by the story of his sufferings that he was prepared, against the wishes of Odysseus, to help Philoctetes to escape from the island and to return to his own country. But, just as this plan was about to be carried out, Philoctetes saw in a vision the great Herakles himself who, after his many labours, had become a god. Herakles ordered him to forgive his enemies and to sail at once to Troy, where the Greek physician Machaon would cure him of his wound.

So Philoctetes obeyed and went with Odysseus and Neoptolemus to the Greek camp, where Agamemnon and the rest received him with honour and gave him that share of the spoils which would have been his if he had been with the army from the beginning of the war. His wound was cured by Machaon who had the skill and the soothing ointments of his great father, Asclepius, the best of all doctors. Then Philoctetes, armed with the bow of Herakles, entered the battle, and among the many who fell to his arrows was Paris, the son of Priam, who was the cause of the whole war. Paris was not killed immediately by the arrow with which Philoctetes struck him, but he was mortally wounded and there was no doctor in Troy who could heal his wound. So he gave orders to his servants that he should be carried to Mount Ida to the nymph Oenone whom he had loved and who had loved him in the days before he was visited by the three goddesses and made the fatal judgment. Oenone had great skill in medicine and knew the virtues of all healing herbs. Messengers went in front of Paris to find the nymph and to beg her to assist her old lover in his extreme peril; but she was still angry with Paris for having deserted her and she refused to give him her help. When the messengers returned and told him of her refusal, Paris knew that he had no hope left. In a weak voice he ordered the men who were carrying him to turn back, so that he might die in Troy, and, when he was brought to his own palace, he had scarcely the strength to say farewell to his father and his mother and to Helen, for whose sake he was about to die. So he died in his bed of a wound from one of the arrows of Herakles. And no sooner was he dead then the nymph Oenone came to the city, having repented of the words she had spoken to the messengers that Paris had sent to her. Since they had left her, she had changed her mind and now she was ready to employ all her skill in attempting to save his life. But she had come too late. Paris

was dead. It seems, however, that, though he had treated her most cruelly, she still loved him, for, at the sight of his dead body, she stabbed herself with her own hand and fell lifeless at his side.

Paris had caused the war in which better men than he had lost their lives, and now that he was dead there might have been, perhaps, some hope of peace. But by this time nothing would satisfy the Greeks except the total destruction of Troy and, though the war had been started for Helen's sake, they would never have laid down their arms even if Helen with all her goods were restored to them. Yet though they fought on to avenge their own dead and to reach final victory, victory still escaped them, and in the end it was not by fighting but by a stratagem that the city was taken and the race of Priam utterly destroyed.

It was Odysseus who made the plan which was to lead to the fall of Troy. Under his orders the Greeks made out of wood the figure of a huge horse. The face and nostrils of the horse, its feet and hooves were beautifully carved. Its body was hollow and was of such a size that twenty armed men could hide within it. And this is what they did. Odysseus himself with Diomedes, Menelaus, Neoptolemus and others of the best of the Greeks climbed inside the wooden framework of the horse's gigantic body and there they waited fully armed, knowing that this desperate venture would end either in their own deaths or in the destruction of Troy.

For while these great warriors lay hidden inside the horse, Agamemnon, with the rest of the Greek army, had embarked on their ships by night and sailed away. They sailed just as far as the shelter of the island of Tenedos, which lies some twelve miles distant from the Trojan coast. There the fleet was out of sight, and when dawn came and the Trojan sentries reported that the Greek camp was deserted, all the Trojans believed that their enemies, exhausted and dispirited by their sufferings, had sailed back to Greece, abandoning finally the purpose of their great expedition. It was a day of joy and gratitude in Troy. The people came out of the city, singing and dancing and offering thanks to the gods for what they imagined was their deliverance. They came to the deserted shore where the Greek camp had been and looked at the huts, now empty, where famous men—Achilles, Agamemnon, Diomedes and Odysseus—had lived for so long. In particular they wondered at the huge wooden horse and made all kinds of guesses as to the purpose for which it had been made. Many of the Trojans wished at once to drag the horse inside the walls of their city, so that it might stay there for ever as a trophy and sign of their victory. There were others however who were in favour of hurling it into the sea or setting fire to it, so that there should be nothing left on the Trojan coast which could possibly remind them of the Greeks. Chief among those who wished to destroy the horse was Laocoön, the priest of Apollo. "Trojans," he cried out to the people, "have you taken leave of your senses? How can you be sure yet that our enemies have gone away? Is this what you would expect of Odysseus or of Diomedes? I believe that this horse has been made to deceive us. Either there are armed men inside, or else it is some kind of a machine which can be used against our walls. Whatever it is, I for my part still distrust all Greeks, even when they seem to be offering us gifts."

As he spoke he poised a spear and hurled it at the horse. The point stuck in the wood and the shaft quivered. A hollow sound came from the body and now, if the Trojans had not been blinded by the gods, they would have sawn through the wood and explored the hiding places within. So they would have saved their city and the high palaces of Priam. But this was not to be. And now other events were to confirm them in their folly.

When the Greeks had sailed away, they left behind them one man, named Sinon, promising him a great reward and instructing him to tell a false story so that the Trojans would take the horse inside their walls. Now this man Sinon, who had given himself up to a patrol of Trojan soldiers, was brought by them, with his hands tied behind his back, in front of the chief men of Troy. Sinon told his story well. He pretended that he was an enemy of Odysseus and that Odysseus had planned to take his life. Therefore, he said, he had been forced to hide from the Greeks and to throw himself on the mercy of the Trojans. As he spoke of his pretended sufferings, he wept what seemed to be real tears, and there were few who did not believe what he said. As for the horse, he told them that it was an offering which the Greeks had been commanded to make to the goddess Athene. If the Trojans were to destroy it, that would mean certain destruction for their city; but if they took it inside their walls, they would always have the protection of Athene and, in course of time, they would invade Greece itself and conquer the sons or the grandsons of those who had fought against them for so long. Calchas, the prophet, had warned the Greeks of this and it was for this reason that they had made the horse so big, in order that it should be difficult for the Trojans to drag it inside their walls.

This story of Sinon's was believed and so the Trojans, who had resisted Achilles and Diomedes and an expedition of a thousand ships, became the victims of a cunning plot. Still further were they deceived by the gods, for now Zeus no longer protected the city which he had loved and he allowed those gods and goddesses who hated Troy and the race of Priam to have their own way and to act as seemed best to them. Now either Athene or Poseidon sent monsters out of the sea in order to make the Trojans doubt the good advice that had been given to them by Laocoön.

The priest, accompanied by his two young sons, was sacrificing on the shore, when far out in the blue water there appeared two huge snakes swimming strongly towards the land with their blood-red heads projecting above the level surface of the sea. Soon they were on the beach and here they paused for a moment; their forked tongues flickered in and out of their mouths as they stared about them with blazing and with blood-shot eyes. Then they made straight for Laocoön and first the snakes twined themselves round the bodies of the priest's sons, crushing the boys to death in their huge and scaly folds. The wretched father hurried to the help of his sons, and then the snakes wound their coils about him too. In vain he tried to free himself; they pinned his arms to his sides and choked him as they coiled about his neck. Soon he lay dead beside the bodies of his sons, and then the snakes fled to the city of Troy and took refuge in the temple of Athene.

Now indeed the Trojans were confirmed in their wrong opinions. Everyone said that this fate had come upon Laocoön because he had insulted the goddess by hurling his spear at the horse which was sacred to her. Men, women and children hurried to bring the fatal horse into the city. Ropes were fastened to its neck; the ground was cleared so that it would be easier to drag, and hymns of praise were sung while this monstrous effigy, bearing inside it the best warriors of the Greeks, was taken into the doomed town. So big was the horse that it was necessary to destroy part of the walls near the gate in order that it should have room to enter. No one then thought of how these walls had preserved the Trojans for so long. Instead there was nothing but cheering and rejoicing, a noise that drowned the noise of clashing armour which came from inside the horse when three times it stuck on the very threshold of the city.

Here once more the Trojans were warned of the fate which was hanging over them. Priam's daughter Cassandra had been given the power of prophecy by Apollo himself, but later she had deceived the god and the god had become angry with her. He could not take away his gift, but he made it worthless. Cassandra indeed always prophesied truly, but Apollo made those who heard her always disbelieve her. Now once more she warned the Trojans of their folly, and once more no one paid any attention to her warnings.

So the horse was brought within the walls of Troy and all day the Trojans gave themselves up to feasting and rejoicing. Far into the night their feast continued; no sentries were posted on the walls or along the coast. Confident in their security and tired out from their exertions and their rejoicings, at length they slept in a city that was already almost in their enemies' hands.

For as soon as all was quiet, Sinon made his way to the place where the horse stood. He undid the cunningly contrived bolts, and pulled the timbers apart. Moonlight shone on the eager and expectant faces of the Greeks within, who now gripped their arms, descended from their place of concealment and went quietly through the sleeping city to the gates.

Meanwhile Agamemnon with the whole fleet had set sail from Tenedos. In the silent moonlight they had drawn their ships up on the beach that they knew so well. Silently they had crossed the plain, and now, when Odysseus, Diomedes and the rest opened the city gates to them, they joined forces together and swept into Troy, killing and burning as they went. Almost before the Trojans could arm themselves and long before they could make any plans for defence, the city was lost, high towers were crumbling in ruin and tall flames shooting upwards to the sky. In the moment of their triumph the Greeks showed mercy neither to young nor old. Small children and white-haired men were butchered in the streets and in their very beds. So great was the hatred that this long war had provoked, so bitter and outrageous the feelings of those who were at last victorious.

THE ESCAPE OF AENEAS

Prince Aeneas had gone to sleep that night in the home of his old father Anchises, a palace that lay back from the streets in a quiet and secluded quarter of the city. As he slept there came to him, whether as a dream or in a vision, the ghost of great Hector. He seemed to stand there before Aeneas's eyes and, as he stood, his face was wet with tears. All the wounds that he had received in defending Troy and in his last fight with Achilles were clearly visible on his body. His hair was matted together and covered with dust; his feet were pierced by the cruel wounds that Achilles had made before he dragged the body behind his chariot.

At the sight Aeneas himself wept or dreamed that he was weeping. He spoke first and said: "O Hector, you who were the light of Troy and our great defender, from where have you come, and what is it that has disturbed your calm face? Why do you appear with these wounds upon you?"

Hector heaved a deep sigh. He looked earnestly at Aeneas and said: "Alas! my friend, I have come to tell you to escape. Our walls are in the hands of the enemy. The city is on fire. Great Troy is falling. But you are fated to take the gods of Troy and to found in another country another city. So in the end from your Trojan blood there will come a power even greater than the power of Priam or of Agamemnon. Here in our own country there will be nothing but ruin and desolation; but, after many wanderings, you will find a place to rest and there Troy will be reborn."

With these words Hector vanished and Aeneas woke with the voice ringing in his head. He sprang up and went out on to the roof of the palace. There he stood still in dumb astonishment, for in all directions he saw the blaze of fires. Not far distant the great palace of Deiphobus, the son of Priam, was crashing to the ground in swirling sheets of flame. All the sky was lit up and the far away waters of the sea glowed red in the dreadful illumination. Then from all sides came the shrieks of women and children, the sound of trumpets, shouting and the clashing of arms.

True indeed were the words of Hector. These were the last hours of Troy. This was the end of the great glory of Priam and of the Trojan name. The Greeks were masters of the burning city.

Yet Aeneas did not at once do as Hector had told him and make his escape. Hurriedly he armed himself and rushed out into the streets. Fury gave him strength and courage, so that he was re-solved, if he could not save the city, at least to die fighting with the conquerors. Soon he gathered together a small band of Trojans who were as willing to fight as he was, and with them he made his way through the burning streets towards the great palace of Priam. As they went they fell upon every party of Greeks whom they met, nor was there anyone that night who could stand before the spear of Aeneas. He fought like a lion and was determined to fight on until his strength failed him or the weight of numbers bore him down.

So they reached the palace of Priam. Here everything was in confusion. Half the palace was in flames and beyond the flames the main army of the Greeks was surging forward, battering down the doors, killing the men and dragging off the women as prisoners. Beyond the burning buildings Aeneas saw the beautiful daughter of Priam, Cassandra, being dragged away by her hair. She was des-tined to be the slave of Agamemnon. Agamemnon himself and Menelaus were at the threshold of the inner chambers, shouting orders to their men. And closer at hand was a more terrible sight; for through the flames they could see old Priam clinging to the altar at his own hearthstone. Yet the holy altar could not preserve his life. Fierce Neoptolemus burst open the door, dragged the old man away from the place where he was seeking refuge and butch-ered him with his sharp sword. Then with one blow he severed the head from the body. So fate came to King Priam. He saw his city on fire, his palace falling to the ground, his daughters and his wife carried away into slavery and all his sons slain by the Greeks. He who had been the master of Asia, ruling over so many cities and peoples, now lay stretched out in his own blood, a huge body, without a head and without a name.

Aeneas looked at the sight with horror. His first impulse was to dash into the flames and either die there or die beyond them in battle with the Greeks; but then there came to his mind the thought of his own old father Anchises and of his wife Creusa and of his son Ascanius whom he had left behind in his palace. He turned back, resolved to protect them if he could or at least to share their fate.

On his way through the ruined palace he saw in the light of the flames Helen sitting by herself, in fear both of the Trojans and of the Greeks. And now the heart of Aeneas was filled with burning anger. It was because of her, he thought, that Troy, with its high towers, was going up in flames, because of her that Hector had died and that old Priam lay butchered on his own hearth. Why should she, who had done such evil to the men and women of Troy, be allowed to escape and to return to her own country? He drew his sword and was already moving towards her when suddenly there appeared to him the goddess, his mother, Aphrodite in her full splendour as she is seen by the gods themselves. She took his hand gently and spoke to him. "My son," she said, "you are being carried away by madness. Your first care should be for your old father, for your wife and for the little Ascanius. Up to now I have preserved them, but now it is for you to go to their help. And it is not because of Helen, nor because of Paris that Troy is falling. It is the gods themselves who are unmerciful, and strong fate that is bringing this city to destruction. See, I will take away the veil from your eyes, so that you may know that now there is no human power which could save Troy from the great gods who are its enemies."

As she spoke Aeneas seemed to see behind the raging forces of the Greeks the figures of enormous gods. Poseidon, the Earthshaker, was tearing down the walls. Clouds of dust and the roar of falling masonry followed every blow of his tremendous trident. At the Scaean Gate was the goddess Hera, urging on the Greeks to slaughter and to rapine; and on the high citadel stood Pallas Athene with a fierce light blazing from her terrible shield and breastplate.

Aeneas turned back to his divine mother, but she herself had disappeared. And now it seemed to him that the whole of Troy was crashing to the ground among the burning flames, like some great tree which, for long shaken by the blows of felling axes, in the end totters, while the topmost branches shiver, and then finally with a splintering crash falls and spreads its ruin over the ground.

So Aeneas obeyed his mother Aphrodite and went back to his father's house through the flames and through the lines of the

enemy. But when he reached the place and explained to old Anchises his plan of escape to the mountains, the old man refused to
go. "Go yourself, my son," he said, "and take with you your wife
and child. I have lived here too long. Already I am worn out with
age and I wish to die with the city where all my life has been spent."

"How could I bear to go," Aeneas replied, "and leave you here
to be killed as I saw Priam killed? No. If your mind is made up, I
shall die here with you, though first I shall bring death and vengeance on our enemies."

So saying, he fitted the shield to his arm and took his spear in his
hand. But first he prepared to say farewell to his wife Creusa and to
his small son Ascanius, who were weeping in sorrow and in
terror.

And now a miracle happened. Suddenly from the top of the
head of Ascanius a bright flame began to spring up. It burned
clearly and lapped the whole forehead of the boy with fire, yet the
fire did not scorch his skin. Old Anchises stretched out his hands
and prayed, as he looked up to the sky. "Almighty Zeus, if my
prayer can reach you, look down on us and help us. Show us what
is the meaning of this sign."

Hardly had he spoken when Zeus clearly revealed his will. There
was a clap of thunder on the left and then, as they stared upwards,
they saw a bright shooting star running across the sky. It crossed
directly over the top of their house and then plunged to earth in
the forests of Mount Ida, lighting up the trees and showing them
the way on which they should go.

Now Anchises hesitated no longer. "My son," he said, "lead
the way and I will go with you. O gods of my country, save this
house and save my grandson. Troy will be restored in him and in
his descendants."

Hurriedly then they took their flight. The old man was too
feeble to walk, so Aeneas carried him on his shoulders. The little
boy Ascanius clung to his hand and his wife Creusa followed in his
footsteps. To the comrades who were still with him Aeneas gave
orders to make their own way out of the burning city and to meet
him beyond the city walls at the sacred mound in the plain below
the slopes of Mount Ida. Then Aeneas himself with his family set
out, seeking the cover of darkness where there was any darkness;
and now Aeneas, with the precious burden on his back and clasping his son's hand, moved cautiously, fearing the slightest sound,

though at other times he had never feared the roar of battle but had always gone forward against the enemy.

So he escaped and, coming to the mound, found all his comrades gathered there. But there was one who was even more than a comrade to him who was missing. When at last he turned back to look for her, he saw that Creusa, his wife, was not there. In vain he cursed himself for not having made sure all the time that she was following him; in vain he tried to remember where on the way she might have lost sight of him in some dark alley or have been overcome with weariness; in vain he questioned his companions. No one had seen her. It seemed that some fate had snatched her from him.

So Aeneas put his father and his son into the care of his companions, while he himself went back again among the flames to look for his wife. Carefully he retraced his steps as far as his own house. He found the house on fire and the Greeks surrounding it. He saw the long processions of captured women and all the Trojan treasures being gathered together for division by the victorious Greeks. He saw the marks of blood and violence on every side. Still he went on searching for his wife and crying out her name in the darkened streets where she might have taken refuge. Then suddenly before his eyes he saw not her, but her ghost. She had the same gentle expression in her eyes, but she seemed bigger and taller than she was in life and a strange light shone from her face. "Dear husband," she said to him, "you must not mourn for me and you must not risk your life any longer in searching for me. All this has happened by the will of the gods, who do not wish you to take me away with you. Zeus himself has other plans for you. You will have many years of wandering and will cross a great waste of surging sea. In the end you will come to Italy in the far West and there by the river Tiber you will found a city and you will have a royal bride. Do not weep for Creusa whom you loved. I shall not fall into the hands of the Greeks. The gods are taking care of me, but now your fate is separate from mine. Farewell, dear husband, and remember me in the love you feel for our child."

She ceased speaking and disappeared into the thin air, though Aeneas longed to speak more to her and to hear her voice again. Three times he tried to fold her in his arms, but each time she slipped from his embrace, like a breath of air or like a fleeting dream.

Then Aeneas went back to his father and his son and his companions who were destined with him to save the great name of Troy and to found, after many adventures, a city in the West from which would come in due time a race of heroes, used to danger and to difficulty, who would build the high walls of Rome.

Meanwhile in the captured city all was havoc and destruction. The wives and the daughters of kings now passed as slaves into the victors' hands. Little Astyanax, the son of Hector, was killed, as his mother had feared, by a Greek maddened with hatred for the loss of some brother or friend slain by the spear of his great father. In their victory the Greeks forgot the difference between right and wrong. They were cruel and unmerciful, often not sparing even the temples of the gods. Thus the gods themselves were angry with them. Sufferings awaited them on their voyage home and in their very homes when they reached them.

So ended the great expedition against Troy.

THE VENGE-ANCE OF THE GODS

PROMETHEUS

According to the old stories the gods themselves, like men, have changed and altered. Just as men were once wild and savage, and just as they struggled amongst themselves, and still struggle, for power and supremacy, so, at the very beginning of things there was warfare and enmity and deceit among the gods. Even Zeus did not establish himself without difficulty; nor was he always perfectly wise and good. Not everyone believes these early stories, and there are some who say that it is wrong to tell such stories at all; for how can we believe that the gods ever did things which men themselves would be ashamed to do? However the stories are still told. One of them concerns the anger of Zeus with the good Titan, Prometheus, the friend and benefactor of mankind. But to understand this story it is necessary first to go back to the very beginning of all things.

First of all, they say, was Chaos, a wide-open yawning space, something in which it was impossible for any thing to be separated from or combined with any other thing; for indeed there were no things at all. But from Chaos there came Gaia, the Earth, the Mother of all things. And Gaia created from herself Ouranos, the great vault of the starry Heaven, to enfold her and to be her equal and her mate. Many children were born to Gaia and to Ouranos. First was the whole race of the Titans—father Oceanus, whose salt streams encircle the world, great Iapetus, who was the father of Prometheus, and many others, youngest of whom and most cunning was Cronos. And apart from these, Gaia bore a monstrous brood, the huge Cyclopes, who had one eye in the middle of their foreheads, and great creatures of enormous strength, the giants, each of whom had fifty heads and a hundred arms.

As for Ouranos, from the very first he hated all his children. As soon as they were born, he hid them away in the depths of the earth and would not allow any one of them to see the light. So they were restrained as it were in the very body of their mother and both they and their mother were angry. Then Gaia herself thought out a cruel plan. Out of her own body she formed a hard metal, either iron or flint, and from this she made a sharp sickle. Then she spoke to her sons and asked them to avenge her on Ouranos, so as to cut him off entirely from her, since it was he first who had done such shameful deeds and had imprisoned them from the light of day. But the sons all feared their father, all except Cronos who said to Gaia, "Mother, I will undertake to do this thing, since I care nothing for our father, whose name I hate; and it was he first who did wrong."

So Cronos took the sickle and when at night Ouranos came down from Heaven, to lie with his bride the Earth, he waited for him in ambush and with this sickle he cut off from him his male parts and hurled them from him into the sea. Now from the wound the drops of blood which fell upon the earth were fertile and out of them sprang the terrible goddesses, the Erinyes who pursue with vengeance all those who are guilty of shedding a father's or a mother's blood; and from the sea into which fell the outraged members of Ouranos there arose, from the very foam of the sea, a great goddess, lovely and powerful, the laughter-loving Aphrodite, who has her hold over the hearts of gods and men. Out of the sea sprang her immortal body and she came first to the island of Cythera and from there to Cyprus, and around her white feet the grass grew green and sweet flowers opened in their blossoms. Desire and Longing went with her, and she took at once her great place amongst the powers that be.

As for Ouranos, he withdrew to the Heaven which he had named. His sons, he said, had done a dreadful deed and this would not go unpunished.

And now Cronos became King among the gods; but it had been revealed to him by his mother, Gaia, that he was destined to lose his sovereignty and to be overthrown by one of his own sons. Cronos did his best, but unavailingly, to guard against this event. His wife was the Titaness Rhea and she bore to him great children, the goddesses Hestia, Demeter and Hera and the gods Hades, Poseidon and Zeus. Cronos, fearing the future, had no wish for any of his children to exist and, as soon as they were born, while they were still in swaddling clothes, he took them from their mother and swallowed them. This cruelty was something which their mother, Rhea, could not bear, and when the time came for her to give birth to Zeus, her youngest child, she determined to outwit her husband. And so, instead of giving Cronos the child, she gave him a large stone wrapped round in swaddling clothes and it was this stone which Cronos swallowed, thinking that it was his own son. Meanwhile Zeus was being secretly brought up in the island of Crete. Gaia herself took charge of him and instructed him in the arts of seizing power. So, after time had passed and Zeus had grown to his full strength, he fell upon his father Cronos and bound him with chains, overcoming him by superior force and by superior cunning. He forced him to disgorge from his belly all those children whom he had previously swallowed down, and first out came the stone which Cronos had believed to be Zeus himself. This stone was set down in Delphi and in later times was reverently anointed by the Delphians with oil.

And now, in place of Cronos, Zeus, with his great brothers and sisters, ruled. Not only did Zeus free the children of Cronos and Rhea, but also those monstrous creatures, children of Gaia and Ouranos, whom Ouranos had imprisoned in the deep places of the earth. And these sons of Heaven were grateful to him and gave him the lightning and thunder, weapons by which he could confirm his supremacy.

Still, however, there were quarrels among the gods and among the children of the gods, and still the house of Zeus was not so firmly established that it was unshakeable. There were still among the old Titans those who preferred the rule of Cronos to that of Zeus; there were still the great giants and earth-born creatures who, in their immense strength, believed that brute force could never be resisted and that sheer weight and size were more important than skill, intelligence and cunning. So, against Titans and giants, Zeus and the newer gods had to fight in order to preserve their power and authority. And in these fights it is said that Zeus was greatly helped by the advice of the Titan Prometheus, the cleverest of all his race, to whom his mother Gaia had revealed the truth that in the future victory would not go to ignorant force or to might but to those who were able to think and to plan ahead.

And so in the end the empire of Zeus was firmly established. The dreadful monsters who had refused to submit to him were either destroyed by his thunderbolts or bound and fettered underground. The other gods had their appointed places and, though they might quarrel amongst themselves, none of them would venture to oppose the will of Zeus. But Zeus, as is the way with those who have newly risen to power, was still jealous of others, still determined to insist upon his authority. In particular he was most grudging in his gifts to men and it was here that he came into conflict with the wise Titan Prometheus who had helped him to gain his position of absolute supremacy.

There are many different stories told as to how men themselves came into being. Some say that they appeared lying on the ground under the ash trees and so were, in some sense, the children of the nymphs who are the guardian spirits of those trees. According to others they were formed inside the earth by the gods out of earth and fire and all the elements that can be mixed with them. It is said too that they were actually created by Prometheus himself. However this may be, it is agreed that in the beginning man was a weak, ignorant and defenceless creature.

But Prometheus, for some reason of his own, loved this weak and pitiful race. He saw them living like animals in caves, adapting themselves as best they could to each day that came, and he it was who taught them how to distinguish the seasons, one from another, how to follow the risings and the settings of the stars, the beginning of civilisation. He taught them how to use numbers and how to form letters to serve as signs for the sounds they made in speech and so finally to become the means by which knowledge could be recorded and the beauty and strength of thought and

feeling be made to last for ever. He told them the way to tame wild animals, cattle and horses and dogs, so that they might relieve man's burden and help him in his work. He showed the sailors how to build boats that could float upon the waters and be carried forward on wings of sails. He taught them the meaning of the behaviour of birds and of their flight, so that by observing them they might know the future. In a word, it was Prometheus who gave men every art and every science; and finally he gave them the gift of fire. According to one story Prometheus stole the fire from the island of Lemnos where stood the forge and workshop of Hephaestus, the master craftsman among the gods; according to other stories he took the fire from the very hearth of Zeus himself on Olympus and brought it to man concealed in the hollow stem of a plant.

Now Zeus was a jealous god. He grudged men all the gifts that Prometheus had given them and he was angry with Prometheus for granting to these wretched creatures of an hour the ability to shape their lives into something better and to raise their thoughts up to the heaven itself. And so when he found that Prometheus had given to man this final gift of fire, he burst out into uncontrollable rage. He ordered his two invincible servants, Power and Violence, to seize Prometheus and to carry him to the highest peak of the dreadful Caucasus. There among the crawling glaciers, beneath the lashing hail and winds of storm, or, in the summer time, shelterless against the scorching heat of the sun, Prometheus was to be bound fast with unbreakable chains. The task of making these massive chains and of fastening them upon the victim's body was given to Hephaestus, and, though Hephaestus shrank from the dreadful deed of so torturing a brother god, he feared the power of Zeus and did not dare to disobey. Indeed he hated the skill of his hand, but he was forced to use it, and so he flung the hard chains around the immortal body of Prometheus and, with great blows of his hammer, nailed and fastened him to the towering rocks. He groaned as he did this work, for he pitied the good Titan; but the servants of Zeus, Power and Violence, merely mocked him for his weak spirit and hurled their insults at Prometheus himself. "You did good to men," they said, "against the will of Zeus. Now see if there is any help to be found in men." And they taunted him with his name, which means "Forethought." "You will need more forethought than you have," they said, "if you are ever to break out again into freedom from these eternal chains."

But neither to them nor to Hephaestus did Prometheus speak a word, and so they left him nailed against the mountain side, a god tortured at the hands of gods. And as for Prometheus, though his body was chained to the rocks, his mind remained stubborn and unconquered. Zeus had the power to control his body in unbreakable fetters, but not Zeus himself could alter or subdue his fixed and steady mind and persuade him that there was anything in this punishment but black ingratitude and base injustice. Zeus owed the very power he wielded to the help given him by Prometheus; nor had Prometheus ever rebelled against the power of Zeus; his only crime had been to help mortal men to escape from savagery and to raise themselves, by knowledge, higher than the beasts.

Now there were many of the gods who pitied Prometheus and among these was the Titan, Father Oceanus, who surrounds the world with his life-giving stream. He left the self-made caves of rock in which he lived and came up to earth to give Prometheus the best advice he could, urging him to make his submission to Zeus. "For Zeus," he said, "has absolute power, and it is useless to fight against it. Whether you are right or wrong, it will make no difference. Surely it is better to relax your anger and to speak humbly to one who is more powerful than you are. And, if only you will do this, I myself will go to Zeus and will beg him to forgive you and the other gods will join me in their prayers."

But Prometheus would have none of this intervention, which seemed to him both disgraceful and useless. Zeus, he considered, was behaving like some dictator, whose lust for power was forcing him beyond the limits. Zeus had already destroyed many of the older gods and for these now Prometheus began to feel pity. There was his own brother, Atlas, who, by the will of Zeus, stood in the regions of the west and carried on his vast shoulders the whole weight of the heavens, a difficult burden which he could never shake off. And there was the great hundred-headed monster Typhon, the child of Heaven and Earth, who had been blasted to ruin by the thunderbolt of Zeus and now lay, a useless frame, beneath the roots of Etna, though still his anger boiled and the hot heaving of his breath would, from time to time, force fire and molten rock into the air and devastate all the fields of smiling Sicily. And so Prometheus told Oceanus to beware lest, if he took the side of one of the older gods, some such a fate as this might fall upon him too. As for himself, he said, no power and no pain would ever make him bow the knee to the tyrant of the gods. For century after century Zeus might hurl fresh pain upon him but would never conquer his unyielding spirit. Nor was Zeus himself secure for ever in his power. For, just as Ouranos had given way to Cronos and Cronos himself had been overmastered by Zeus, so, said Prometheus, there was a moment fixed in the hidden and distant future when Zeus, if he made a certain marriage, would become the father of a son mightier than himself, one who would laugh at lightning and thunderbolts, since he would possess a weapon far greater than these, and who with a motion of the hand would brush aside the great trident of Poseidon, the earth-shaker. Prometheus, who was wise with the wisdom of his mother Earth, knew the secret of this wedding and who it was, if ever she became the bride of Zeus, that was destined to bear a child more powerful than the present supreme ruler of gods and men. But, said Prometheus, he would never reveal this secret—never, until he was released from these chains and restored to the honours he had before. Nor could any exercise of supreme power make him in any manner of way alter his mind.

So Oceanus returned to the deep sea caves where he lives remote from the quarrels of gods in heaven and of men on earth. He might have wished that Prometheus could have been less unbending in his spirit, but he feared for himself if he were to do more in the matter.

But Zeus, who hears everything, had heard the words spoken by Prometheus and knew that in the possession of this chained and helpless captive was a secret which, if it were not told, might at some time or other, near or far, mean the end of his own power and an ignominious fall. He could not bear to think that anyone could hold, or could be allowed to remain holding, an advantage over him, and so he sent down from Olympus his messenger, the god Hermes, to that crag in the Caucasus where Prometheus stood chained. Hermes came and delivered his message, which was that Prometheus must tell at once that secret of which he had been boasting; if he did not, punishment far more fearful than any he had yet known would come down upon him.

But Prometheus treated both the message and the messenger with contempt. "I hate and despise," he said, "your master Zeus, and I would rather be the slave for ever to this bitter barren rock than his trusted servant. I know the power of Zeus and, though I may feel it, I do not fear it. Let him let loose upon me all the fires of his lightning, all the blows of thunder from above and beneath the earth. Let him mix earth and heaven together over my head. Never, till I am released from these bonds, shall I reveal to him the thing he wishes to know and the thing which will, in the end, plunge him downward from his dictatorship."

Nor did any words that Hermes could speak have any effect upon the Titan's unbending pride. "Try," Hermes begged him, "to make your thought follow the meaning of your position. Be humble, since there is no help. For, if you persist in refusing to speak, Father Zeus will convulse this whole mountain with thunder and lightning. You will be buried in the depths of the earth and you will groan as the weight of the earth bears down upon you. And then, shattered and broken, you will be brought up to the light of day; and now, every day, the winged hound of Zeus, his great eagle, will fly to you and every day will tear the flesh of your body into rags, feasting upon your liver and gnawing it black; and every night the flesh will grow again to be destroyed and torn to fragments as the next day comes. There will be no end ever to these fearful pains, nor am I threatening anything that will not be done; for Zeus will bring every word I have spoken to actual fact."

But no threat and no certain knowledge could turn the mind of Prometheus. "You have told me," he said, "nothing that I did not know already. The hound of Zeus may tear my body into shreds; my frame may be broken and shattered beneath earthquakes and falling skies; my mind remains immortal and unsubdued."

So Hermes departed hurriedly, lest he might find himself involved in that terrible convulsion of nature that he knew was now to fall upon the mountain where still Prometheus stood to challenge a superior power. And soon indeed came the crashing and reverberation of thunder, the roar and howling of winds, the quaking of the earth and the loose-flung torches and solid sheets of burning and corroding lightning. Yet in this shattering storm and conflagration of nature Prometheus, flung from wave to wave of terror, pierced by the jagged rocks and overloaded by the pressing weight of mountain ranges, never altered for one moment the fixed resolution of a mind determined to resist. Nor, later, when his mangled body was restored to the upper air, did he weaken beneath the pain as every day the eagle of Zeus came to feed upon his flesh. Every night the flesh was renewed and every day there was reiterated pain. Yet still Prometheus kept his secret and still, in the face of unending persecution, defied the supreme power.

How could this story end except in the fulfillment of the threat which Prometheus had made, or else in some alteration in the character of either Zeus or Prometheus or both? It seems that it was this latter thing that happened. It seems, though this is a hard thing to say of gods, that Zeus, as he grew older in power, grew wiser and more merciful; and it may be too that Prometheus himself, though he lost nothing of his resolution, may have relaxed something of his pride. What is certain is that some form of persuasion was found to intervene between these mighty antagonists. Prometheus was freed and freed by the son of Zeus, Hercules, who climbed the high Caucasus and, after shooting down the eagle with his arrows, released the great Titan from his chains. And Prometheus revealed the secret which he had kept so long and through such sufferings. It was that if Zeus, as he was minded to do, were to marry the sea-goddess, silver-footed Thetis, then she would bear a son stronger than the father. And so Zeus and the other blessed gods betrothed Thetis to a mortal, fearing the event if she were to marry one of them. They chose for her husband the great king of Thessaly, Peleus, and by him, as is well known, she became the mother of the greatest warrior of all men who lived upon the earth, though he died very young, the fleet-footed Achilles.

As for Zeus and for Prometheus, their quarrel was over. Each had, in a manner, submitted to the other, and, though differences still arose among the blessed gods, never again was there to be any struggle in heaven for supreme power.

ION

Where the walls of the citadel of Athens look northwards there is a steep rocky place that is called "the Long Cliffs," and in these cliffs there is a cave. Here, in very ancient times, the god Apollo committed a crime against a mortal woman. The woman, or rather the young girl, was Creusa, daughter of King Erechtheus of Athens. Apollo, with the overpowering strength of a god, surprised her and forced her, in spite of her tears and her unwillingness, to become his mate. So, ravished by the god, she conceived a child and, when the time came for her to give birth, she gave birth secretly so that only one or two of her most trusted servants knew of it. Then, since she was ashamed to have a child and not a husband, she wrapped the baby in swaddling clothes and put him in a cradle made, like a basket, of woven willow twigs. She set by his head golden ornaments in the shape of snakes,—such ornaments as were always worn in those days by members of the royal family of Athens,—and she carried the baby to that very cave in the Long Cliffs where she had been surprised and outraged by Apollo. Here, though with a sad heart, she left the child, not knowing whether he would be found and taken care of by some shepherd or traveller or whether he might become the prey of the wild beasts and the birds. But later she repented of what she had done and went back to the cave. She found it empty. There was no sign either of the baby or of the cradle in which she had laid him. So she went away unhappy and gave him up for lost.

Yet the child had not been devoured by wild beasts nor had he fallen into the hands of strangers. Apollo himself had taken him up in his cradle, just as he lay, and carried him to his own great sanctuary and temple at Delphi. He had set the cradle down inside the court of the temple and he had put it into the heart of the Pythia, his chief prophetess and the one who in her own voice declared his oracles, to find the baby and to bring him up as a servant of the god. So Ion (for this was the name given to the child of Creusa and Apollo) grew up in the temple to be a strong and beautiful young man and delighted in serving the great god who was, though he did not know it, his own father. The tasks which he had to do were tasks which gave him pleasure, for he worshipped Apollo in purity of heart and thought of him as the source of all truth, all splendour and all perfection.

So, with the first light of every day, Ion would rise and see that everything in the temple was in order. He would sprinkle over the floors the holy water taken from the springs of Castalia and with branches of the bay tree he would sweep and clean the whole building. Then, with his bow and arrows in his hand, he would sit in the bright sunlight and would chase away any birds that might come to defile the temple's golden roof or to snatch up some portion of the sacrifices. For from the high cliffs of Mount Parnassus which rise like a great wall to the sky behind the holy place the jackdaws and ravens would come circling out with their harsh cries and, wheeling above them, would be the eagles and the vultures; while, from the river valley below and the silver-green of innumerable olive trees, sometimes the white swans would come flying with outstretched necks towards the gorgeous habitation of the god. All these birds Ion would scare away with his arrows, keeping the temple pure and delighting in the care that he took to do so. He knew nothing of his own parents and, though he sometimes wondered who they could be, he was proud to be known as "the servant of Apollo" and content with the life that he led.

Yet he had a more glorious fate in front of him than he imagined, and he was to learn to know his parents, though the knowledge would give him pain and, in acquiring it, he was to run into danger.

While Ion had been growing up at Delphi, his mother Creusa continued to live in Athens. After the death of her father, King Erechtheus, the Athenians suffered much in war. From the neighbouring island of Euboea great forces came against them, ravaging the countryside and defeating the Athenians themselves in battle. In the end, however, the Athenians found a man who was both a skilful general and a stout warrior, and under his leadership they drove back their enemies and were able once more to enjoy the pleasures of peace and power. This man, whose name was Xuthus, was not an Athenian himself, but an Achaean; yet he served the Athenians so well that they gave him as a reward the hand of Creusa, the King's daughter, in marriage.

So for some time Xuthus and Creusa lived happily together. Only one thing disturbed their happiness and this was that they had no children. At length Xuthus determined to consult the oracle of Apollo at Delphi, and he set out on the road northward from Athens, taking his wife Creusa with him. Creusa herself was glad to go. Not that she loved the god Apollo, who had betrayed her; but she wanted to bear children to rule in Athens and also she hoped, or half-hoped, that the oracle might reveal to her what had been the fate of that one child whom she had borne in the past, though she had little enough hope that he survived anywhere on the earth.

It was Creusa who arrived first at Apollo's shining temple of Delphi; she had come ahead of her husband since he had delayed on the way in order to consult another oracle, the oracle of Trophonius, whose ancient and sacred place is in a rocky gorge at the foot of the great mountain mass of Parnassus up which goes the road to Apollo's sanctuary at Delphi. It was by this road that Creusa travelled, with her women servants and her armed attendants, and, when they came in sight of Delphi itself they were amazed at the statues of gold and marble and bronze that stood there, at the shrines and altars set up by cities or by great men, and most of all, at the sight of Apollo's own temple with its golden roof and the fine carvings in stone of the deeds of heroes and of gods.

But when Creusa saw this temple, so gloriously built to show the greatness of the god, what she remembered was his violence against her and his treachery, and the tears fell from her eyes as she stood gazing at all this magnificence. And now her tears were interrupted by the voice of a young man, the attendant at the gates of the temple, who was indeed her own son Ion, though she did not know this, nor did he know that he was now seeing his mother for the first time. He asked her in surprise why she was weeping, since to him the house of Apollo was a house of joy and peace. Creusa said that she wept because of the misdeeds done by the gods, but this was something which Ion could not imagine or understand. "All goodness comes from the gods," he said. "How can the gods do evil?"

Then Creusa told him of the question which she wished to ask Apollo's oracle. But, since she did not wish her own story to be known, she disguised the facts. She said that she had a friend, one of the women of Athens, who had borne a child to the god Apollo and who had then been deserted by him. This friend of hers, said Creusa, did not even know whether her child was alive or dead, though she feared that he was dead. She wanted the oracle to tell her just this,—was the child still living or had he been devoured by the wild beasts?

Ion was shocked and horrified both by the question and by the story which lay behind it. He could not believe that the great god, whose servant he was and whom he worshipped in such purity of heart, could have done this injury to a mortal woman or allowed his own child to perish. "This story of yours," he said to Creusa, "is not one in which I myself can possibly have any faith, even though it seems that your friend has succeeded in persuading you to believe in it. But I am sure that the gods do not do such things. And, even if there were any truth in the story, would not Apollo see to it that his son was safe and happy, perhaps in some place of his own far away from Athens? However, in any case the question which your friend wishes to ask cannot be asked here. Here we approach the god with reverence."

Creusa saw that Ion would not help her to have her question put to the oracle of Apollo. While the young man had been speaking she had looked at him closely and had admired the beauty of his appearance and the grace and sincerity of his words. Her own son, she thought, if only he had lived would now be of the same age as this young man and might have had just such a noble look. She began to question him as to who his parents were and from what city he came. But when Ion told her his story—that he did not know his parents and that from childhood he had been brought up in the temple of Apollo—it still never entered her thoughts that here in front of her was the very child whom she imagined to be dead and hoped might, by some chance, be alive. Nor, of course, could Ion have guessed that this lady, the Queen of famous Athens, was his mother and that his father was the great god whom he worshipped.

And now, while they were still in conversation, Creusa's husband, the warrior King Xuthus, arrived. He had visited the oracle of Trophonius and had then made haste to follow his wife, since he had good news to tell. The oracle had not given a full reply, since it was known that Xuthus was on his way to the prophetic place of Apollo. Only one sentence had been spoken and it was this: "Neither you, Xuthus, nor your wife Creusa will return childless from Delphi."

Xuthus had been greatly heartened by this sentence and, after he had greeted his wife and told her of his good hopes, he asked to be allowed to go at once into the inner sanctuary so that he might consult the oracle of the god. So Creusa, with her women, retired to her place of lodging; and now she herself felt her heart lightened, for she, just as much as Xuthus, wished to have a child who would rule in Athens after her death. As for Ion, he performed his task, which was to admit Xuthus into the inner sanctuary, and then he took up his usual position in front of the temple gates. But now his spirit was unusually restless, for he had been disturbed by the story which Creusa had told him. Was it possible, he wondered, that it might be true? And, if it were true, what was he to think of the gods? For, if the gods acted no better than sinful men, how could they deserve to be worshipped?

So he sat still in the high mountain air, uneasily thinking to himself, when he was surprised once more by an event which he could scarcely have imagined. For now the temple gates were opened and Xuthus, with every expression of joy upon his face, came out into the bright sunlight and, seeing Ion, hurried towards him with outstretched arms, as though eager to embrace him. Ion, at the sight of the great warrior advancing upon him with such curious signs of affection, started back a pace. His first thought was that Xuthus had somehow lost his wits, and he fitted an arrow to his bow, so that, if necessary, he would be able to defend himself. But Xuthus, still with a most joyful face, merely cried out to him: "Shoot at me, if you will; but, if you do shoot, you will be shooting your own father." At this Ion stood still in astonishment. Again he felt convinced that Xuthus must be out of his mind; but Xuthus hastened to explain that for what he said he had the authority of the god Apollo himself. He had asked the oracle whether he could have children and the oracle had replied that, not only would Apollo grant him children but that the first person he saw on leaving the temple would be his son. It was Ion whom he had seen first and it was Ion therefore who was his son.

Indeed it seemed impossible to doubt the words of the god, but still some mystery remained. "Who then can be my mother?" Ion asked. But Xuthus was so delighted at having discovered a son, that he had not yet even given a thought to the subject of who the child's mother might be. And even now he was most uncertain, as indeed was natural, considering that Ion was not really his son at all. He could remember that in his youth, before he had married Creusa, he had once come to Delphi and had taken part in the nightly revels in honour of Bacchus, the god of wine. At these revels the worshippers are often drunk with wine and it sometimes happens the children are born afterwards without anyone having a very clear idea of how they came to be conceived. So now it seemed to Xuthus that perhaps some woman of Delphi, whose existence he had entirely forgotten, had been the mother of Ion and had se-

cretly placed the child in the temple of Apollo, where he had remained ever since. To Ion also this appeared to be the most likely
explanation and, although he was saddened by the thought that he
would never know who his mother was, he was glad to think that
he was not the son of a slave, since only free-born women were
allowed to take part in the festivals of Bacchus, and he had at least
discovered (or thought he had discovered) a father who was a
great warrior and the ruler of Athens.

As for Xuthus, he was so pleased with what had happened that
he forgot a most important consideration which was that his wife,
Creusa, had also been promised a child. He was so full of his own
joy that he scarcely thought of what her feelings would be when
she discovered that, while he had a child whom he would make
King of Athens, she herself, an Athenian born of the royal house,
was still childless. Ion was more quick than Xuthus to realise the
difficulties that might lie ahead. He saw that not only might
Creusa hate him for taking a place that ought properly to belong to
her own children, but that also the Athenians themselves might
not be willing to accept him, since neither his father nor mother
was of Athenian blood. And so when Xuthus told him with glee of
how he would make him rich and famous at Athens, Ion himself
could not enter into the joy of his supposed father. Indeed he almost wished that this discovery had not been made and that he
might continue to live humbly as he had done, in peace and quiet
at Delphi, serving the god Apollo and innocent of the world outside the temple of the god. But Xuthus would hear nothing of
these misgivings. What he wished to do at once was to hold a great
feast at which he would publicly acknowledge his son and do him
all the honour that a great and powerful king could do.

So he and Ion began immediately to make the preparations for a
banquet. Huge tents and pavilions were pitched upon the level
ground and were so arranged that neither the fierce rays of the sun
at midday nor the slanting light of evening could disturb the feasters. Sheep and oxen were slaughtered and prepared for the tables;
wine, fruit, eggs, olives and all good things were ordered in abundance and all the people of Delphi were invited to join in the festival.

Meanwhile Creusa had been waiting in her own lodging to hear
what had been the reply of the oracle to her husband. At length a
faithful servant of hers, an old man who had known her since her

childhood, came to her with the news; but it was not at all the news that she had expected or desired. The servant also was indignant, for, though he loved King Xuthus, he loved his mistress more. It seemed to him unfair that, while Xuthus should have a son, Creusa should have been left unnoticed by the god. Moreover this son of Xuthus, Ion, was as it seemed an alien, and yet he was to rule in Athens. And so the old man allowed the state of his own mind to influence him as he told the story and, although he did not tell Creusa anything that was untrue, he laid most weight on those things in it that would most displease her.

Creusa herself was made both angry and wretched by what she heard. She loved her husband, but she could not bear the thought of a stepson taking the place that should have belonged to a child of her own. And now too it seemed to her that she had been betrayed a second time by Apollo who had not only taken away his own child from her, but was giving to her husband another child, a stranger, while for her there was nothing left in life which would give her pleasure or hope. She now began to hate the young man Ion, whom, when she had seen him at first, she had so admired; and she was ready to listen to the old servant who suggested that she and all the people of Athens were being tricked. For might it not be, the old man said, that Xuthus had betrayed his wife and had become the father of a son by some slave girl; that he had had the child brought up at Delphi and had then, no doubt with the aid of some corrupt priest of the god, arranged beforehand that when he came to Delphi pretending to be interested in the birth of children to himself and his wife, this child should be declared openly to be his and to be the heir to the throne of Athens? In all this, so the old servant suggested, he had never even thought of his wife and now he was actually making merry in his own good fortune and in her misery.

Creusa, in her anger and her dismay, came to believe that this was in fact what had happened; and now her thoughts began to turn to revenge. Most of all she would have wished to revenge herself on Apollo himself and to have burned down his whole temple and sanctuary. She was angry too with her husband; but when the old servant suggested that she should take his life, she shrank back in horror from the idea; for even though she was angry with Xuthus, she still loved him and respected him. It seemed best to her to take, or attempt to take, the life of the young man, Ion; for,

in so doing, she would both hurt her husband and free herself of
the prospect and of the reality of having to live and see her husband
happy in the presence of a son of his own, while she herself was
childless. So she took this wicked resolution and proceeded to carry
it into effect, little knowing that what she was planning to do was
not only to kill an innocent man, but to kill her own and Apollo's
child.

The old servant was willing enough to help her. He took from
her some poison so deadly that a single drop of it would be suffi-
cient to kill a man instantly. It would be easy for him to make use
of it since he was to be in charge of serving the wine at the feast.
So he went off confidently to carry out the treacherous plot, and
Creusa waited equally confidently for the news of its success and of
the cruel revenge which, she thought, would bring comfort to her
vexed and tortured spirit.

By this time a herald had been through Delphi inviting all who
wished to come to the feast. The tent was thronged with the guests
who came and soon they were sitting down with garlands on their
heads, eating and drinking to their hearts' content. After they had
eaten their fill the old servant of Creusa saw to it that water was
carried round so that they might wash their hands. Then Xuthus
himself retired from the feast, for he wished to make in private the
proper sacrifices to the gods that are made at the birth of a son.
This to him seemed to be his own son's birthday and, as he went,
he left Ion behind as master of the feast. And now the old servant
ordered fresh wine to be brought out together with newer and bigger cups of gold and silver. Into one of these cups he put the
poison and then, filling it with wine, he gave it to Ion, pretending
that he was honouring him as his new master. Ion raised the cup to
his lips and all the other feasters prepared to drink with him and to
wish him happiness. But, just as he was about to take this drink
that would certainly have destroyed him, Ion happened to hear one
of the servants making some remark which he, with his knowledge
of prophecy, thought to be ill-omened. He therefore called out to
the guests not to drink the wine in their cups, but to pour it out on
the ground in honour to the gods and then to have their cups re-
filled. In silence they all did as he said and he himself first poured
on to the ground the wine from his own cup. And now, by the will
of the gods, the plot that had been made against his life was discovered. For there are many doves which live unmolested in the

place sacred to Apollo and some of them had flown into the tent where the feast was being held. One dove, and one only, approached the drink offering that had been made to the gods and she came to that spot of ground where Ion had emptied out his cup. But no sooner had the dove dipped her beak in the spilt wine than she gave a strange cry and began to flap her wings and roll her neck in agony. Everyone wondered at the sight of the bird struggling in its pain; but the pain did not last long; suddenly the pink claws relaxed and the dove fell on her side dead.

And now Ion drew his cloak aside and leapt upon the old man who had given him the cup. "It was you," he shouted, "who tried to murder me. Confess who it was who set you on to do it, or else you die immediately."

As for the old servant, surrounded as he was by the angry guests and threatened with torture unless he spoke the truth, he was so terrified that he told everything. Creusa, it was now known, had not only plotted against Ion's life, but had so contrived her plot that, if it had been successful, the young man would have been killed on ground sacred to Apollo. The penalty for murder or attempted murder in the god's sanctuary was a clear one, and it was at once decreed by the rulers of Delphi that Creusa should be taken to the top of the high rocks above Apollo's temple and from there should be hurled down the precipices to her death. Ion himself, with a band of armed men, hurried away to see that this just sentence should be carried out.

But meanwhile some friend of Creusa who had been present at the feast had warned her of her danger, and Creusa, knowing that this was her only hope of safety, had hastened to the temple of Apollo, to the very altar of that god who had been, or who seemed to have been, of all others most unkind to her. Here she stayed, clinging to the altar in the hope that no one would dare to violate the holy place by dragging her away; and it was here that Ion found her.

So furious was Ion with her because of her attempt on his life that he refused to listen to her prayers for mercy and her appeals to the protection that ought to be afforded to her as a suppliant at the altar. To Ion it seemed that, since she had plotted against him, the servant of Apollo, in Apollo's own sanctuary, she could not possibly seek protection from the very god whom she had so insulted. His rage was so great that he would actually have torn her away from the altar by force, if, at this very moment, he had not been checked by the appearance of the Pythia, the chief prophetess of Apollo, through whose mouth the god himself reveals his mind to mortals. This was the same Pythia who had taken Ion into her arms when he was a baby and who had brought him up in the temple as though he were her own child. She loved Ion both because of the care she had taken of him and for himself, and now she came forward out of the inner sanctuary, partly because she wished to restrain him from the guilt of dragging away a suppliant from the altar and partly because the god had put it into her heart to reveal something which, up to this time, she had kept hidden. First she addressed Ion and said: "My son (since to me you are like a son), I want you to go to Athens unstained by any sin. You must respect the altar of Apollo, in whose temple you have grown up as though he was your father. You must not use violence against one who has taken refuge here."

But Ion, greatly as he respected and loved the Pythia, was still not persuaded by her words. "How can it be wrong," he said, "to kill an enemy who has offended not only against me but against the god himself?"

"Then wait," said the Pythia, "for Apollo has made it known to me that I must show you something which you have never seen before." She then brought out from the inner sanctuary a cradle, made curiously out of woven willow twigs, and told him that this was the cradle in which she had received him when first she found him in the temple. It was a sight which made Ion glad, for, though he thought that he had discovered his father, he longed to know who his mother was, and it now seemed that in this cradle there might be some clue which would enable him to find her out. But when Creusa saw the cradle, her heart seemed to stop still, for she recognised it at once as the one in which she had so sadly laid her baby, when she had left him in the cave on the Acropolis of Athens. For a few moments she listened to the Pythia, who was describing to Ion exactly how he had been found and how, at the command of the god, she had until now revealed nothing about the cradle itself and the ornaments which it contained. And as she listened she became certain that the young man whom she had tried to murder and who was now so intent on killing her was indeed her own son. So she cried out joyfully, "My son, my son!" and left the altar in order to embrace him.

Ion was now more bewildered than ever, but it was not long before Creusa convinced him. She told him of what he would find in the cradle,—of the coverlets which she, as a young girl, had woven and embroidered with the head of a gorgon, and of the golden serpents, the royal ornaments of the house of Erechtheus. And now Ion, with equal joy, embraced his mother; for all his life he had longed to find her. And now too he learned the final secret of his parentage,—that his father was none other than the god Apollo himself, who, though he had been unkind to his mother, had watched over the young life of the child and had now, by making a gift of him to Xuthus, established him as heir to a great Kingdom.

Creusa, for her part, was at last happy, since she had found the child of her own body who had been lost. As for Ion, his heart was full of a number of distinct feelings, some of joy and pride, others of a strange perplexity. Proud indeed he was to know that his mother was a queen and his father a great god; yet how strange to him and how incomprehensible seemed the workings of the divine powers! After so many changes and chances, could he even yet believe in the truth of what he had been told?

Yet before he left the temple his mind was set at rest. A vision of the goddess Athene appeared to him and to Creusa and to the Pythia. Apollo himself, said Athene, would not appear, lest there should be blame for things done in the past; but in his name she declared that Ion was indeed his son and the son of Creusa. Apollo had given Ion to Xuthus as a friend might give to another friend who was childless one of his own sons to be his heir. So Ion was to rule in Athens and his mother would be content in the knowledge that, even though for the time others might think him the child of Xuthus, he was in reality her own child. And soon other children would be born to her and Xuthus, great leaders of men who would establish kingdoms in Achaea and in Doris. As for Ion himself he would have four sons who would give their names to the four tribes of the Athenians and later their descendants would cross the sea in their ships and found great cities on the coasts of Asia and on the islands in the sea. They would be a great people and would be called after Ion "the Ionians," and in years to come would hold their great festival of singing and dancing and athletic games in Apollo's own island of Delos.

So they thanked the goddess for her comforting words and for her assurance of happiness and they prepared joyfully to return to Athens, where everything that the goddess had told them would be fulfilled.

ALCESTIS

There was a time when the god Apollo greatly offended Zeus, his own father and the father of gods and men. Apollo had a child by a mortal woman and this child, Asclepius, when he grew up, became the greatest of all physicians. He had learned from Apollo himself all the arts of healing and so well did he practise them that he was able even to bring back the dead to life. Zeus, thinking that no mortal should possess such power, slew Asclepius with a thunderbolt, and Apollo, in his anger at losing his son, destroyed the giants called "the Cyclopes" who forged the thunderbolts for Zeus. Then Zeus drove Apollo out from the company of the blessed gods and sentenced him to work among mortals on earth.

Now the household in which Apollo was a servant was that of Admetus, the great King of Thessaly. It was a rich and hospitable household and in Admetus Apollo found a master who was generous and considerate to all his servants. Long before Admetus was aware that he was sheltering a great god, the divine power of Apollo made itself felt. For now the wealth of Admetus increased continually; great harvests of golden corn came in from the rolling plains of Thessaly; the fruit trees bore more fruit than they had ever done; all things prospered,—the herds of fine horses, the cattle, the sheep, the olives and the vines. And Apollo himself, who watched the sheep, would play on a shepherd's pipe instead of his own lyre, and at the sound of his sweet music spotted lynxes would come out of the forests and lie down with the sheep to listen, lions too would troop down from the mountains and dappled fawns would come fearlessly with them. Then, when his year's service was over, Apollo wished still further to reward his host. He won for him a gift from the Fates themselves, and this was that, when the day fated for his death should arrive, Admetus might still live, provided that he could find some other person who would die instead of him.

But people are not as a rule willing to sacrifice their lives for others and it was far from easy for Admetus to find any person who would be willing to die, when the time came, in his place. He approached, amongst others, his aged father and pointed out to him that he could not in any case have very much longer to live and that, by foregoing the few years of life which were all that he could expect, he would win honour for himself besides conferring a great benefit on his son; as he was so old already, he could scarcely get much pleasure out of life and it might even be a positive advantage to him to die rather earlier than he might otherwise have done. But Admetus's old father was merely angry at the suggestion. He had already, he said, done a great deal for his son in resigning his kingdom to him while he was still alive; he had no wish at all to gain honour by departing from this life a minute earlier than he could help; he enjoyed it very much indeed. Much the same reply was given to Admetus by his mother and by various other old people, none of whom was prepared to recognise the force of the arguments which he employed.

Indeed there was only one person who was willing to help him and that was his beautiful young wife Alcestis. She had borne children to Admetus and she loved him dearly. She thought that, in any case, life without her husband would not be worth living and so she declared that, when the time came, she would allow Death to take her away so long as her husband was spared and left alive upon the earth.

Admetus accepted the offer, though he still hoped that his friend Apollo might be able to arrange matters in such a way that this sacrifice of the woman whom he so dearly loved might not be necessary.

And so for years Admetus and Alcestis lived undisturbed, but finally the day came which had been fixed by the Fates to be the day of death for Admetus. It was an earlier day than might have been expected, for Admetus's old parents were still alive, and he and his wife were still young. As this day drew near Alcestis began

to feel its approach and to know that now the time had come for her to keep the promise that she had made. She began to grow weak in the body and in the head; she felt the powers of life fading away from her and she called to her husband and to her children to tell them that they must now say their last farewells, since Death himself would soon come to take her into the world of ghosts below the earth.

Now indeed Admetus was heartbroken and he wished that this gift from the gods had never been given to him or that, in any case, he had refused the noble offer which his wife had made. He had grown to love her more and more, and now she was to leave him for ever. He prayed to Apollo to help him, and indeed Apollo did all that he was able to do. When that grim creature Death, a power that is hated by gods and men, came to the palace of Admetus to take away Alcestis, Apollo met him and begged him to relent. But Death insisted upon his rights. He knew that a life was owing to him and he was going to take it. "Nothing," he said to Apollo, "can save her. And there is no champion either on earth or among the blessed gods who can rescue her from my hands." So, having failed to win the goodwill of Death, Apollo went away, though he knew that Death, as will be seen, was boasting of more power than he really had.

Meanwhile inside the palace there was nothing but mourning and lamentation, for now Alcestis was very near the moment of dying. Her servants had thronged round her, kissing her hands for the last time and weeping helplessly for her; for she had been a good and kind mistress to them and there was not one of them who did not love her. Next she said good-bye to her children and to her husband. There were two small children, a boy and a girl, and, though Alcestis loved them both, she was most sad when she thought of the daughter who would be left motherless. The boy would grow up to be a king and, as he grew up, his father would protect him and support him; but the girl would have no mother to dress her as a bride when the time for her marriage came, or to advise her in the new duties which would then be hers. So Alcestis wept as she kissed her children and she begged Admetus not to take a new wife after she had gone, since a new wife might cause him to forget or to neglect the children whom he had already. As for Admetus it was easy for him to give the promise which she asked of him, for he loved her with his whole heart and he could not bear the thought of ever marrying some other woman. Now indeed he wished that it was he, not she, who was to die, since death seemed to him a better thing than life spent in longing for her. His tears fell fast as he promised her not only that he would not marry again but that he would mourn for her throughout his life and would keep her image before his eyes, sleeping and waking, until the time came when he too would have to obey the summons of the Fates and descend into the bloodless world of the dead. Even as he spoke to her, he saw that she was growing weaker and weaker; she smiled at him, but there was a mist in front of her eyes; he cried out to her, begging her, uselessly enough, to stay with him. But the moment fixed unchangeably by the Fates had now been reached. The eyes of Alcestis were closed in death. Admetus and his whole household wept and lamented for her as for one whom they would never see again moving among them in her gracious and loving way.

And now, while the body of Alcestis was being prepared for the tomb in which it was to be laid, while the children were weeping for their mother and while Admetus, distraught with his own grief, was scarcely able to attempt to comfort them, it was suddenly announced to him that a friend of his had arrived at the palace and was asking to receive hospitality. This friend was the hero Hercules who was still, because of the anger of Hera, the wife of Zeus, forced to serve the cowardly King Eurystheus for whom he was performing those great labours which were to make him famous for ever. Just now he was travelling northward to the land of Thrace where he was to fight for and to win the terrible man-eating horses of the Thracian King Diomedes. As his way lay through Thessaly he had been determined to visit Admetus, who had long been his friend and in whose hospitable house he had often eaten and drunk in times past. He knew nothing of the calamity which had now fallen upon this house and, had he known of it, he would never have come at a moment so ill-suited for entertaining guests. As it was he was weary from his journey and, since his appetite was as prodigious as his strength, he was looking forward to a great feast and long draughts of wine and the music and singing which he expected.

Admetus himself knew that Hercules would not easily find elsewhere the hospitality that his own palace could afford. In happier days he himself had enjoyed feasting with the hero and now, when, because of his grief, it was impossible for him to eat meat or drink wine, he still did not wish to turn a friend away from his doors. So, when Hercules came to greet him and noticed on all sides sad faces and the signs of mourning, Admetus disguised the real truth from him and, in order to show kindness to his guest, pretended that, though indeed there had been a death in the house, it was not a death that concerned him dearly. "My dear friend," he said, "as you can see, I have to attend a funeral today and so I cannot join you in the feast. But you must not leave this house without being entertained; and he gave orders to his servants to prepare a room for Hercules in that part of the palace which was reserved for guests and which was at some distance from the rooms where the mourners were gathered together and where the body of Alcestis was being prepared for burial.

At first Hercules objected. "I cannot disturb you," he said, "at a time of mourning. Let me go on my way now and visit you later, when I am coming back from Thrace." But Admetus would hear of no excuse. Even in his own misery he wished to be hospitable to his friends; and so Hercules was taken in the guest chamber and there a large meal was prepared for him. Admetus himself, with his children and those of the servants who were not waiting upon Hercules, retired to another part of the palace and mourned for the dead Alcestis. Later, when the proper rites had been performed, they took up the body and, in a sad procession, carried it out of the palace and set it down in the tomb that had been built for it outside the city.

Meanwhile Hercules, quite ignorant of what was really taking place in the house, was occupied entirely in enjoying himself. He crowned his head with garlands and sat down eagerly to the great banquet that was set before him. He ate plentifully of the meat and drank bowl after bowl of the dark wine. The more he ate and drank the more pleased he felt with himself and soon he began to shout out songs, unmusically enough, since, though he was a great warrior and the strongest man of his time, he had little knowledge of the arts of singing and of playing upon the lyre. The servants who waited upon him looked on with disgust at his drunken revelling and listened with a kind of dismay to his bellowing and howling. All their thoughts were with their dead mistress and, in the general grief, they felt affronted at the sight of this unseasonable and tipsy merriment. They did their best to hide their tears, for

Admetus had strictly ordered them to do so, but it was impossible for them to smile or laugh or look cordially on the uncouth revelling of this insatiable guest.

In the end Hercules himself noticed the sour looks and downcast eyes of those who were waiting on him. He seized hold of one of the servants and dragged him to the table. "Drink, drink, my good fellow!" he shouted, "and get rid of that miserable look of yours. We all know the pains of life, but there are pleasures too. While there is wine to drink and while there are women to love, we can at least be merry from time to time." And he thrust a great bowl of wine into the servant's unwilling hand.

Now the servant could contain his feelings no longer. "Indeed," he said, "I know all this that you say. But we cannot be happy in this house at this moment. Our dear mistress, the wife of Admetus, is dead and is even now being carried to her tomb."

This news made Hercules sober at once. "How terrible it is," he said, "that on such a day as this I should have been revelling and feasting and singing in my friend's house. But why did Admetus hide this from me? Why did he not let me share his sorrow?"

"He wished to give you pleasure," said the servant, "and I have disobeyed him in telling you the true position of this house. My master is a hospitable man and he wanted you to be happy and refreshed even though he himself was miserable."

"Then," said Hercules, "since this noble man has treated me so nobly I shall return him good for good. You must tell me where the tomb is and I shall go to it. Then I shall wait in ambush until Death himself comes to drink the blood-offerings and to carry away his victim to the lower world. When I see him coming, I shall leap out on him and grip him in my strong arms. Let him strain and wrestle as he will, I shall hold him fast and shall never let him go until he gives up Alcestis to me so that I can bring her back to the palace and to her husband. And, if I fail to find Death at the tomb, I shall go down to the world of ghosts, the Kingdom of Pluto and Persephone, and even from there I shall bring Alcestis back."

So Hercules spoke and the servants told him in what direction he might find the tomb. Few of them had any belief in what he had said that he would accomplish, for his words seemed more like the boasting of a drunken man than like a plan that could really be carried out.

Nevertheless Hercules set out on his way to the tomb and, soon after he had gone, Admetus himself and those who had accompanied him came back to the palace from the funeral. They had laid the body in the tomb and had made the proper sacrifices of black cattle and of black sheep to the gods below the earth. Then, with wailing and lamentation, they had returned. And now the grief of Admetus was boundless, for he had looked, he thought, for the last time of all on the face of his wife whom he loved and who had loved him so much that she had died for him. Now every sight in his great palace was painful to him, for everything reminded him of her,—the chair where she used to sit, the bed where she slept, the courtyards and gardens where she had walked and talked with him. Now he cursed the gift which Apollo had won for him from the Fates. Though he was indeed alive himself there was no pleasure left in living without the woman who had given her life for his. Nor could he even live in honour, since he was ashamed to have escaped death himself by having accepted the sacrifice of another's life.

So he sat down in the front of his rich palace, miserable and wretched as he had never been, nor could any words be found to comfort him. All that day he remained there until at sunset it was seen that two figures were approaching. One of them was without doubt the hero Hercules, for there could be no other man with so tall and stout a frame. He was leading by the hand a woman whose body and face were entirely covered in a thick cloak and veil. Soon they stood in front of Admetus and first Hercules reproached his friend for not having let him know of his terrible loss. "I still feel ashamed," he said, "to have feasted and made merry in your house at the very time when you were burying your wife."

"I too," said Admetus, "would have been ashamed if I had turned you away from my doors and let you go on your way without comfort and refreshment."

"Indeed you acted nobly," said Hercules, "and now let me tell you that this grief of yours will not last for ever. Time heals everything."

"Nothing," said Admetus, "can put an end to my sorrow. Time cannot cure it. It can only be healed in death."

"Be that as it may," Hercules replied, "I have one request to make of you before I set out again on my journey. Keep this woman for me in your house and let me see her on my return. To-day I won her in a wrestling match."

But Admetus turned his head away. "Ask me for anything else," he said, "but not this. How can I, who have just lost the best woman in the world, keep another woman in my house? Indeed I could not do it."

"Yet you would be wise to do so," said Hercules, "and I still ask you to do this for me as a favour."

Admetus glanced at the woman and then he looked quickly away. "You are asking me for something impossible," he said, "for her bearing and her stature are like those of my dead wife. Every time I saw her my sorrow would be renewed. I could not bear it for her to be in my palace where, as it is, everything reminds me of Alcestis."

"Then just look once in her face," said Hercules, "and after that I will ask nothing else of you."

So, though reluctantly, Admetus turned his head towards the veiled woman and the woman drew back the veil from her face. What Admetus saw was nothing strange and nothing that he had expected. He saw the face of his own wife Alcestis who had come back to him from the dead. For some moments, while he stared at her in amazement and fixed his eyes upon that smile of hers which he knew so well, he could not believe in his eyes, nor could he form any conception of his own happiness. Then Hercules told him of how he had wrestled with Death himself and how he had won back the noble woman who had been for a short time in Death's strong hand.

So Admetus received his wife back again and now life was happier for both of them than it had ever been before. As for Hercules, he went on his way northward, for he still had other labours to perform.

HIPPOLYTUS

There were many famous deeds done by Theseus, the great King of Athens, when he was a young man. Among them was an expedition which he made with his friend Hercules against the Amazons, a race of warlike women. Theseus carried off the Queen of the Amazons and by her he became the father of a son whom he called Hippolytus.

Some time later he married Phaedra, the daughter of Minos, King of Crete. With her he lived happily and two children were born who were, so Theseus hoped, to become kings of Athens after his death. Meanwhile Hippolytus, his first son, was being brought up not in Athens, but in the town across the water, Troizen, where Theseus himself had been born and where he had spent his childhood. Theseus left Hippolytus in the care of his own grandfather. This was the wise and good King Pittheus of Troizen, whose daughter Aethra had been the mother of Theseus. It was not certain who was the father of Theseus. Some said that it was Aigeus, King of Athens; others that it was the great god of the sea, Poseidon, and that this god had promised Theseus that in the course of his life he could make three prayers to him and each of these prayers would be granted.

Under the care of Pittheus Hippolytus grew up to be a young man of whom any father might be proud. He was strong and handsome; he was wise and moderate in his behaviour; he was a great rider and huntsman, a lover of all athletic sports. More than all things he worshipped the virgin goddess Artemis, herself a great huntress and one who chiefly preferred those men and women who enjoy the green woods and the sport of the chase more than the pleasures of making love. So much did Artemis love Hippolytus that she would go with him on his hunting expeditions and, though she would never let him see her face, she would speak to him and he would hear her voice; she would be at his side, and he could feel her presence. And for the young Hippolytus this was the happiest of all lives, to spend his time in hunting and in manly exercise and every day to converse with the great goddess whom he honoured and adored.

But by living this kind of life he made another goddess jealous of him. This was Aphrodite, the proud goddess of love, through whose power everything that lives on the earth, in the air and in the waters, has its being and perpetuates its own kind. Though he was himself the especial favourite of Artemis and it was in her company that he most delighted, Hippolytus respected the other gods and goddesses and paid them the honours that were due to them. Aphrodite alone he neglected to honour, for nothing in his life had anything to do with the love that exists between men and women; instead all his pleasure was in training horses, in hurling the javelin, and in the company of the huntress Artemis.

The gods, like men, are pleased when they receive praise and angry if they feel themselves insulted. This was the case with Aphrodite. She was angry when she saw the offerings upon the altars of Artemis and no offerings upon her own. She determined to be revenged upon Hippolytus and she thought out a cruel plan by which she would destroy not only him but others as well.

It happened that Theseus, in order to atone for a sin which he had committed, had been ordered by an oracle to leave Athens and spend one year away from his own city. So, with his wife Phaedra, he crossed the water to the nearby kingdom of Troizen where he was made welcome by the old Pittheus and by the young man Hippolytus. It was now that Aphrodite proceeded to carry out her plan of vengeance.

For her it was easy; indeed some of the work had been done already, since, a little time previously, Hippolytus had come to Athens to visit his father and to take part in the holy mysteries of Eleusis, and, while he was there, Phaedra had seen him and, though it was against her will, she had fallen in love with him. How could she help it, when Aphrodite, the goddess of love herself, forced her to do so? And now, when she was actually living in Troizen and seeing Hippolytus every day, the love that Phaedra felt for the young man became greater and greater. She began to waste away in a sickness of which no one knew the cause. And all this was by the will of Aphrodite, who wished Theseus to believe that Hippolytus, though he was entirely guiltless, was conspiring to gain the love of his wife; then, so Aphrodite planned, Theseus

would call down upon his son one of the curses which his father Poseidon was bound to fulfil. Phaedra too would have to die, but to her fate the goddess was indifferent so long as her own revenge was satisfied.

There was a day when Theseus was absent from the palace of Troizen, though before evening he was to return. It was this day that Aphrodite chose to destroy Hippolytus. Her eyes were upon him as he came back on this day from hunting. His friends and his servants were surrounding him as they approached the palace, singing, as they came, a hymn to Artemis. No one, except Aphrodite, knew that this was the last day that ever Hippolytus would go hunting in the forests of Troizen.

Standing in front of the palace were two statues, one of Artemis and one of Aphrodite. Now, as Hippolytus approached the palace, he knelt down, as he always did, before the statue of Artemis. In the green woods he had found a cool meadow, a lonely place where no shepherd had ever fed his flocks nor had the grass ever felt the stroke of iron; only the bees crossed and re-crossed this virgin meadow in the spring. Here he had picked flowers and made them into a wreath, and now he brought the wreath and offered it reverently to the statue of the virgin goddess who was his friend, thanking her for her kindness to him and praying her that his life might for ever be as happy as now it was. After he had made his offering he rose to go into the palace, but first an old servant of his, one who knew him well and loved him, asked permission to give him some advice. Hippolytus gladly gave him this permission.

"Do you not know, then," said the old man, "that when a person is proud and exclusive people dislike him, but they are grateful when a person speaks kindly and politely to them?"

"Of course," Hippolytus replied. "Everyone hates arrogance; and, as for being polite, it is no trouble to one and it gives other people pleasure."

"And do you not think," asked the old man, "that the gods also think as we do about this?"

"No doubt they do," said Hippolytus.

"Then," said the old man, "will you not take my advice and say one word of greeting to that other great goddess at the gate, the goddess Aphrodite?"

But Hippolytus would not. "There are different tastes," he said, "both among gods and men. And as for me, I have no taste for a goddess men worship in the night, away from the race tracks and the bright mountain air where my life is spent so happily."

So, after giving instructions to his servants to rub down the horses and get them ready to be yoked to his chariot in the afternoon, Hippolytus and his young friends went on into the palace where the meal was prepared for them.

The old servant stayed behind and bowed low before the statue of Aphrodite. "O great goddess," he prayed to her, be merciful to a young man who, because of his youth, speaks foolishly. I beg you to have pity on him and to understand him, as I do. For gods ought to be wiser than men and more understanding."

But this prayer had no effect at all upon the angry heart of Aphrodite.

All this time, and for many days past, Phaedra had kept away from company and had remained inside her room restless, fevered and sick because of the passion for Hippolytus which the goddess had put into her heart. She would not touch the food that was offered to her; she did not trouble to dress or to adorn her golden hair; neither music nor conversation gave her any pleasure; for music reminded her of love and in no conversation could she bear to reveal her own guilty thoughts. Sometimes she would be half out of her mind and would speak deliriously. At these times all her talk would be of the beating of horses' hooves, of Thessalian javelins and of the cool glades in the forest where the wild beasts were encircled by baying hounds and by the bands of huntsmen. At other times she would come to herself and then she would wonder in misery what she could have done to make her so unhappy, how this madness could have come over her and which one of the gods it could be who was so persecuting her with desires from which she shrank away. She was attended only by her old nurse, who loved her, but who had no notion of what was the real nature of her disease.

On this morning, restless as ever, Phaedra had asked that her couch should be carried out of the palace into the open air, although wherever she was, whether indoors or out, her suffering found no relief and her tired brain enjoyed no relaxation. Her nurse was with her and, in the light of day, could see how wasted were her mistress's features, how wild was her eye, how desperate the whole manner of her behaviour. And for this terrible distress of mind there seemed to be no reason. Phaedra was a queen and lacked nothing; her husband, Theseus, loved her; she had children who were to be kings. If only she would say what was the matter with her, it would be easier, so her nurse thought, to find some way of helping her. Yet, though she questioned her over and over again, Phaedra would give no answer that could account for her unhappy state. All that she would say was that she was resolved to die and that it would be better for her and for everyone else if indeed she could die. Her nurse attempted to make her see how wrong she was to entertain such an idea.

"If you were to die," she said, "what would happen to your children? Without you they might lose their place in their father's affection. Someone else might be chosen to rule in Athens. Remember that Theseus has another son, Hippolytus."

Now, at the name of Hippolytus, Phaedra could not help crying out aloud. She begged and implored her nurse never again to mention that name in front of her. But the nurse, though still she could not guess why it was that Phaedra had cried out so despairingly at the young man's name, began to question her more closely and, in the end, weak and tired as she was, longing too to free her own heart of the burden of its secret, Phaedra confessed that she had fallen in love with Hippolytus and it was for this reason that her mind and body were being destroyed.

Her nurse was horrified at what she heard. Her mistress, she knew, was wise and good. How could it be that she could even think of betraying her husband and of losing her own good name?

As for Phaedra, now that she had been able to say aloud truthfully what it was that had been torturing her, she became calmer in mind and began to explain exactly what had happened. She hated, she said, those women who are false to their husbands; for they bring shame not only upon themselves but upon their children after them. And so, when first she found that she had fallen in love, she had tried to cover up her feelings and to conquer them by the power of reason. This she had not been able to do, and so now, since there was no help in reason, she was determined to die, for in this way alone she could keep an honourable name for herself and be honoured afterwards by her husband and by her children.

She spoke sadly and she spoke with resolution; but her nurse, who loved her, was resolved above all things to save her mistress's life. So now she began to argue with her. "There is nothing strange," she said, "or unheard of about falling in love. Many people before now have fallen in love with those who were not their wives or their husbands. Even the gods, according to the old stories, have done so. It is not really possible for anyone in this life to be absolutely virtuous. All that one can be expected to do is to look virtuous and to hide one's sins. Certainly it is ridiculous to put an end to your life, just because some god has put it into your heart to fall in love with the wrong person. It would be much better to enjoy your love. Maybe it is wrong, but it is better to enjoy yourself than to kill yourself."

Phaedra was glad to hear such an argument, even though she knew that it was a wicked one and untrue. And now the nurse began to beg her mistress to leave matters to her. There were magic spells, she said, which might be used in such cases; nothing, in fact, was impossible.

Such words as these swayed the weak mind of Phaedra. She began to hope that somehow, though she did not know how this could be, she might escape from her pain and still, again in some way that she could not understand, remain honest. Partly she trusted her nurse and partly she distrusted her. She might say some word to Hippolytus himself. That would be a dreadful thing. Yet, if Hippolytus were to listen to the nurse's words, it might not be so dreadful. So, with a mind divided between hope and fear, between shame and desperation, Phaedra watched her nurse go inside the palace. At the gate of the palace the old nurse paused and made her prayers to Aphrodite. "Lady of the Sea," she said, "help me and let me gain for my mistress the things that she desires." She did not know that Aphrodite was determined to destroy not only Hippolytus but Phaedra as well. She did not remember how often it has happened that love, which can be so gentle, has utterly destroyed those who have felt it in its full and destructive force. For not the thunderbolt itself can be more heavy on men than the arrow of Aphrodite.

Now there was a time of waiting, but soon Phaedra heard from inside the palace the sound of a voice raised in anger. Shame and terror gave her strength. She sprang up from her couch and went to the door of the palace where she could listen to the words that were being spoken inside. She found that everything which she had most feared had taken place. Her nurse had approached Hippolytus, had first made him swear a solemn oath that he would keep secret what she had to say, and had then told him that Phaedra, the wife of his father, was dying for love of him. If the old woman had expected that Hippolytus would feel any sympathy for such a story, she was wholly mistaken. Hippolytus felt outraged by what he had heard, and the words to which Phaedra was now listening were words of hatred and contempt for herself and for all other women in existence. His rage was boundless. "Why," he shouted out, "did the gods ever allow women to exist? Surely there could have been some other way of getting children and then men could have lived happily without wives. For all wives are vain, expensive, treacherous and deceitful." Turning to the nurse he told her that her words were so horrible that he felt unclean simply to have listened to them. If he had not foolishly bound himself by his oath, he would have told Theseus the whole disgraceful story. As it was, so long as Theseus was absent, he also would stay away from home. Nor would he ever cease hating women; for until someone could teach them modesty and self-control, he could never learn to feel anything for them but contempt.

Phaedra had heard enough. Now that her feelings had been betrayed and had been trodden underfoot she knew that there could be no end except death to her unendurable pain. She hurried to her room, determined to take her own life. But before doing this dreadful thing she would secretly revenge herself upon the innocent man who was the cause of her death, and, in revenging herself, she would, or so she thought, preserve her own good name. She wrote a letter in which she told a story that was the opposite of the truth. In this letter she bade farewell to her husband and wrote that the reason for her death was Hippolytus, who had forced his own love upon her against her will. Then she looked her last upon the light of Troizen which had seen her unhappiness. She fastened a rope about her neck and, holding in her hand the letter that was to avenge her, she hanged herself.

It was not long before her death was discovered, and now the whole palace rang with the cries and lamentations of her servants, who knew nothing of what had caused her death, and of her nurse, who knew only too well. It was in the middle of these lamentations that Theseus himself returned. He was amazed to find no one to greet him in front of the palace gates and to hear, instead of words of welcome, the sound of mourning and of grief. Had anything, he wondered, happened to his children or to the old King Pittheus while he had been away? But soon the gates were opened and he saw what had really happened. He saw the dead body of the wife whom he loved, and he saw that it was she herself who had taken her own life. "O my wife," he cried out in his insupportable grief, "you dearest of all things to me and best of all women that the sun shines upon, how could you have left me alone? How could you have left our children motherless?"

For some time his grief was too great to allow him to think. Then he noticed that there was a letter in his wife's dead hand. "Perhaps," he thought, "the poor creature has written in her pain to say good-bye to me and to leave her last wishes for the children. Indeed I shall do everything that she could ask me to do."

But when he took the letter from her hand and read the words that it contained, his mind was overwhelmed with horror and with rage. Now he believed (and how could he help believing it?) that his own son Hippolytus, the son of whom he had been so proud, the son in whose honour and goodness he had had complete faith, was guilty of the deepest ingratitude and of the most unspeakable crime. Theseus raised his hands to heaven and prayed to his father, Poseidon, the god of the sea. "O Poseidon," he cried, "my father, you who gave me the right to pray to you three times and to have my prayers granted, now grant me one of these prayers. Destroy my son Hippolytus. Let him not live to see the sun set on this day."

There were some in Theseus's company who begged him to call back this prayer again, to wait until he was sure that he had found out the truth; but to Theseus the truth seemed sure and certain. No evidence could be more convincing than the letter which he had found in the dead woman's hand.

And now, with no knowledge of what had happened and what was about to happen, Hippolytus himself came to see his father. He had heard a cry of grief and he hastened to see what it could be that had caused it. He stopped still in astonishment when he saw the dead body of Phaedra, but he was more astonished still when he saw his father look so angrily upon him, when he heard his father charge him with a dreadful crime which, as Hippolytus knew well, he could never have committed. What was he to say? He had sworn a great oath by all the gods to the nurse that he would never reveal what she had said to him. And even in his great danger, he would never break his oath. All he could do was to protest his innocence, to remind his father of how pure and blameless his life had always been, of how he had never yet failed in his duty to gods and to men. But to Theseus all this seemed evidence not of innocence, but of a disgusting hypocrisy. Roughly he told his son to leave his presence and never again to set foot in the land of Troizen or in the land of Athens. So, even if Poseidon did not destroy him, he would die miserably in exile, since no good man would receive him into his house.

So Hippolytus prepared to leave the court and to leave the land where he had lived so happily and the forests in which he had hunted in the company of the goddess whom he loved. Bitterly grieved he was at his departure into exile, but more grieved still to find that his father could believe him guilty of something which he had not done and which his noble nature would never have allowed him to do.

Theseus was left alone, mourning for his wife and meditating upon the punishment which, he thought, he had so righteously inflicted on his son. But before the day was over he was to hear of how Poseidon had granted his prayer and of how greatly mistaken he had been in his judgment.

First, after some hours had passed, came one of the servants of Hippolytus with the news that his master was on the point of death. He was still just breathing and still able to speak, but life was ebbing from him fast so that he could not live until the sun set. When he heard this news, Theseus gave thanks to his father Poseidon and asked how this just punishment had fallen upon the young man.

Hippolytus's servant told him the story: after leaving his father's presence, Hippolytus had gone down to the sea shore and with him had gone a company of the young men of Troizen, his friends whom he loved and whom he was sad to leave behind. Hippolytus had mounted his chariot drawn by fine horses which he had trained and bred himself. Then, while his friends wept to see him go, he had taken the reins in his hand and prayed to Zeus, the King of gods, that, whether he lived or died, one day his father would know that he had wronged him. And so he set forward along the road leading northward, the road where in the past Theseus himself had performed great deeds when he was a young man, killing evil men and robbers who had then infested it. With Hippolytus went his servants, running by the side of the chariot.

There was a place where the road ran along the sea shore. When they reached this place they heard a roaring sound, like thunder, rising from the ground. The horses raised their heads, pricked up their ears and began to sweat with terror. And now, looking towards the sea, they saw an enormous wave towering up so high that it hid from their view the rocks and mountains at the further side of the bay. The wave rushed towards the shore where the trembling horses stood, with Hippolytus holding the reins firmly in his experienced hands. It broke with a crash and roar of water, and, out of the white foam and circling eddies where it broke there arose a great bull, a fierce and monstrous shape, which began to bellow aloud, filling all the land with the noise it made. The horses panicked and began to bolt. Hippolytus, seeing that all his strength would be needed, knotted the loose ends of the reins behind his back. Leaning back upon them and tugging with his hands he tried to control the horses, maddened as they were with fear. Yet all his knowledge of horses and all his skill in their management could not help him. If he tried to steer their course on to smoother ground, then the bull would suddenly appear in front of them, and they would swerve away from him in their terror. And then the bull would run silently alongside them, edging them upon the rocks, till, finally, he forced a wheel against a huge stone. The axle broke; the chariot was overturned; and now the maddened horses dragged the body of their master, still entangled in the reins, hither and thither over the pointed rocks that cut into his flesh. Still Hippolytus cried out to them, but the horses would not listen to the well-known voice that so often they had obeyed. Somehow or other, in the end, Hippolytus managed to free himself from the reins. His servants hurried up to him where he lay alone and broken upon the shore. The horses and that fearful monster of a bull had disappeared out of sight. As for Hippolytus, there was little life left in him.

So his servant, sad and angry at his master's fate, told the story to Theseus, and, though he was a servant speaking to a King, he dared to say that he would never believe that Hippolytus was a wicked man, no not if all the women in the world were to hang themselves and to leave messages behind them after their deaths.

Theseus was unmoved. "Bring the young man before me," he said. "He will recognise now that the gods themselves have shown him to be guilty."

Yet the gods, or at least one of them, now showed Theseus that his son had been innocent. Hardly had he finished speaking to the servant who had told him of how his curse had been fulfilled, when he heard another voice in the air above him and looking upwards, he saw, with reverence and with fear, the great goddess Artemis herself, the friend of Hippolytus. In calm words she told to Theseus the whole story of his wife's unhappy passion, of how his son, because he would never break a promise, had been unable to defend himself, and had therefore been wrongfully done to death by Poseidon, who was bound to answer the prayer that Theseus had made to him. All these things had come about through the anger and jealousy of Aphrodite. There was no help for them, nor could Artemis herself have done anything to save the mortal who was her servant and whom she loved.

And now, when Theseus realised the terrible mistake of which he had been guilty, his heart was broken within him. How could he ever be forgiven for the wrong which he had done to his own son? How could he ever forgive himself? As he thought with agony of what the goddess was telling him, Hippolytus himself, now near the moment of his death, was carried into the palace. His beautiful body was bruised and torn and bleeding. Pain leapt along his limbs at every movement of his friends and servants who were bearing him as gently as they could. But he felt immediately the presence in that place of the goddess Artemis and he listened to her as she told him of how Aphrodite had plotted against him and of how his father had been deceived. She told him to forgive his father for what he had done, since his mind had been led astray, and then she said good-bye to him, since no god or goddess can look on dying men and now Hippolytus was very near to death. She promised him that his name would live for ever and that for ever afterwards the maidens of the land of Troizen would make offerings of the tresses of their hair at his tomb before they wedded their husbands. Then, since she could do no more for him, she left him to die. But, before he died, his father Theseus begged him for his forgiveness, and Hippolytus gladly gave his forgiveness to him. For both father and son had been powerless to fight against the power of the goddess Aphrodite who had been determined to destroy the one of them and to leave the other desolate.

IPHIGENEIA

The army and navy that sailed from Greece against Troy to sack
the city and to bring back Helen, whom Paris had treacherously
stolen from her husband, was the greatest force that had ever been
gathered together for war. It was commanded by Agamemnon,
King of golden Mycenae, with his brother Menelaus, the husband
of Helen and the King of Sparta. Ships in their hundreds and warriors in their thousands assembled in the harbour of Aulis, off the
east coast of Greece. From there they were to cross the Aegean sea,
force a landing on the coast of Troy and, they hoped, soon bring
down that proud city and its defenders to the dust.

But the gods willed otherwise. More than ten years were to pass
and many of the greatest of the Greeks were to lose their lives
before their purpose would be accomplished and before the flames
would spread along the long walls and surge above the high towers
of Troy.

Even the very outset of the expedition was unpropitious and, for
a time, seemed impossible. For when the great host had gathered together at Aulis and each man in it was ready and eager to cross the
sea and win glory and booty in the fighting that lay ahead, long and
valuable months went by while the ships lay motionless in the harbour and the army remained inactive on the land. Instead of the
winds that would have taken them over the sea and which were to
be expected at that time of year, the winds that blew were mostly
contrary or else there was no wind at all. And so the ship's hawsers,
sagging in the water, began to rot away. As for the warriors in the
army, they amused themselves as best they could in games and
exercises. You might have seen there great Ajax, the biggest man of
them all, sitting on the ground playing draughts, with his huge
shield and spear at his side; or that fierce fighter Diomedes hurling
the discus from his strong arm. Achilles, the fleet-footed and the
greatest warrior of them all, would race in full armour against a
four horse chariot team, matching his own strength against the

strength of finely bred horses and outdistancing them as he sped over the sand and shingle of the shore.

So the warriors diverted themselves; but the men in the army and soon even the great champions themselves grew tired of the delay and of the purposelessness of this empty waiting for a wind that never came. Food became more difficult to obtain. Inactivity in a great army usually breeds unrest and there were many who now began to wish that they had never left their homes to sail on an expedition to recover another man's wife. It was even suggested that the whole great armament should break up and return, since it seemed that the gods were averse to its ever setting out to its destination.

It was natural that this mood in the army should worry and perplex the leaders, and particularly the two sons of Atreus, Agamemnon and Menelaus. For it was for the sake of Menelaus that this force had been gathered together and Menelaus himself was resolved to recover his wife and to avenge himself upon Paris who had stolen her away from him. As for Agamemnon, he loved his brother and was himself a proud and ambitious man. It was he who was in supreme command of this great army and navy of the Greeks. He could not bear to see such a force disbanded before something noteworthy and glorious had been achieved.

And so, in their anxiety, the sons of Atreus consulted the prophet Calchas, a man who, from dreams, from the flight of birds and from examining the entrails of animals that had been sacrificed, was able to know the will of the gods and to declare it to men. When Calchas was asked for his opinion, he refused at first to give it, saying that he feared that his words would give offence. But the sons of Atreus pressed him hard and in the end the prophet spoke. He said that the goddess Artemis, who was worshipped in Aulis, was angry with the Greeks. It was she who prevented the winds from blowing and her anger would never be appeased until she had received the sacrifice that she demanded. Nor was this sacrifice a goat or an ox; it was something far different. What the goddess desired (nor would she be contented with anything less) was that Agamemnon's own daughter, Iphigeneia, should be brought to Aulis and should there be struck down with the knife, like an animal, at her altar.

When Agamemnon heard the words of Calchas he wished that he had never made any enquiry into the will of heaven. For how could a father kill his own daughter, and a daughter, moreover, whom he loved more than all his other children? In his palace at Mycenae it had always been Iphigeneia who was the first to welcome him and to throw her arms about his neck when he returned from hunting or from travel. She had always been the one to lead the singing and the dancing at his feasts and it was her sweet voice and her graceful movements that delighted him more than all the joys that he had known at home. He had found it difficult to bear the thought that one day his favourite child would have to leave him to marry some great king among the Greeks. But this was nothing compared to what Calchas had ordained. For, if he were to obey the will of the gods declared by the prophet, she would leave him finally and for ever, and he, who loved her most, would be her murderer. He shrank from a thought so dreadful and from a deed so wicked.

Menelaus could well understand his brother's feelings since he also had a daughter, Hermione, whom he had left at home when he set out from Sparta. Yet such was his rage against Paris and his determination to avenge himself upon the Trojans that he was willing to accept the words which Calchas had spoken and he urged his brother to carry out, however painful it might be, the will of Artemis. For, he said, unless this sacrifice were made, Troy would never be conquered and the great expedition of all the Greeks would become a mockery. Trojans in future, emboldened by the success of Paris, would be free to sail the seas and to carry off the wives of the leaders of the Greeks. And then there was the army itself. The soldiers were willing to risk their lives for Greece; but they expected that their generals also should be willing to sacrifice for the sake of the army anything, however near or dear.

In this way Menelaus and Calchas tried to turn the mind of Agamemnon away from the horror which he felt at the deed which he was called upon to do, and in the end they were successful in their endeavours. Agamemnon bowed to the will of the goddess, to the needs of the army and to his brother's prayers. He consented to send for his loved daughter from his house and to sacrifice her in Aulis on the altar of Artemis.

Yet it would be impossible for him to send a message to his wife Clytemnestra, telling her the sad truth. No mother would consent to let her daughter go from home to her death. Nor would Clytemnestra be at all swayed by the misfortunes of the army or by the desires of her brother-in-law, Menelaus. For Clytemnestra regarded her sister Helen as a wicked and dishonest wife who had brought shame upon her family. She would certainly not be willing to sacrifice her own daughter in order to bring Helen home again. And so Agamemnon deceived his wife by sending her a letter in which he asked her to bring Iphigeneia to Aulis, not for the real and dreadful purpose which he had in mind, but in order that she might be married to Achilles, the best of all the Greeks. He did not tell Achilles that he had used his name in order to entice his daughter from the shelter of her home; for Achilles was a proud and honourable man. He might agree that the sacrifice was necessary for the good of the army, but he would never himself take part in a plot to deceive others.

When Clytemnestra received her husband's letter she was full of joy. She had expected that by this time he would have crossed the sea to Troy and she was glad that she would see him again before he was plunged into the dangers of the war. She was happy too that her daughter was to be married to so great a man as Achilles, for of all the Greeks he was the one whom she would have chosen to be her son-in-law. And so, as soon as she had received the letter, she made all the haste she could. Fine horses were brought from the stables and harnessed to the chariot that would carry her and Iphigeneia to Aulis. Few soldiers had been left behind at Mycenae, but these too accompanied the great ladies as an escort. The dresses for the wedding were carefully packed, and so the two women took the road northwards to the camp of the Greeks, expecting to find there not death, but happiness. They travelled fast and arrived, as will be seen, even earlier than Agamemnon had expected them.

Agamemnon, when he had sent the letter to his wife and had taken the dreadful decision to become the murderer of his daughter, almost at once began to repent of what he had done. His nights were vexed with fearful dreams and in the daytime his daughter's face and her noble nature were always present to his mind's eye. He could not bear to follow to the end the course which he had taken, and yet he was too cowardly to say so openly, since he was afraid of Menelaus and of Calchas and of Odysseus, the King of Ithaca, a great warrior and the man of most resource among the Greeks. These three were, so far, the only ones who knew of the intended sacrifice, but Agamemnon was afraid to stand out against them, for, though he was a great king, he was a weak man. So, instead of refusing openly to do what Calchas had required him to do, he acted secretly. He wrote another letter to his wife, telling her that, for reasons which he did not give, the marriage of their daughter could not take place at this time and instructing her to go back again to Mycenae without visiting the Greek camp. He gave the letter to an old servant, a man who was devoted to his family and to Clytemnestra herself, and, to make sure that this old servant would hurry on his way and do all in his power to prevent Iphigeneia ever coming to Aulis, he took him into his confidence and told him the true reason why this innocent girl was being lured from her home. The good old servant was horrified at what he heard and promised to make all the speed he could upon the road; for he loved both his master and his mistress and he would gladly have laid down his life to prevent the dreadful deed which was now so close at hand.

But the letter was never to reach the hand to which it was addressed. As the servant was leaving Agamemnon's tent he was accosted by Menelaus, who knew his brother's mind and was suspicious of it. Menelaus seized upon the old man, snatched the letter from him and tore it open. He saw that Agamemnon was intending to go back upon his promise and he rushed inside the tent in order to reproach him for what he regarded as his treachery. Angry words were spoken between the brothers, neither being willing to give way to the other, but their quarrel was interrupted by the arrival of a messenger who brought the news that Clytemnestra and Iphigeneia, bringing with them Agamemnon's little son, Orestes, had already reached the Greek camp. The soldiers, who did not know yet for what reason the royal ladies had been summoned, imagined at once that they must have come for a wedding and were thronging around the chariot with shouts of joy and of congratulation.

Menelaus himself was moved when he listened to the messenger's account of how this beautiful and noble girl had come thinking that she was about to be married, when in reality she was being carried to her death. Though he, more than anyone, longed to be on the way to Troy, he had a generous heart and, forgetting the angry words that he had just been speaking to his brother, he grasped him by the hand and promised to do all he could to help him in saving Iphigeneia from the dreadful fate ordained for her by the prophet Calchas and the goddess Artemis. "Let the army go home," he said, "and let us forget all our thoughts of glory and of vengeance! I would rather leave Helen where she is in Troy and find myself another wife than win her back at the cost of the life of your innocent daughter and your broken heart."

Agamemnon was grateful to his brother for the generous affection which he showed. Yet now his own mind was overcome by cowardice. He feared that when Calchas and Odysseus told the army of the will of Artemis, the army would certainly demand that the sacrifice should be carried out. His daughter was now already in their camp and, if he should refuse to sacrifice her, the army would, he thought, turn upon him. Instead of being the commander-in-chief he would become a fugitive; nor would he in any case be able to save his daughter from her fate. It seemed to him that there was nothing now to be done except to perform the commands of Artemis. But, though he was chiefly frightened of the army, he was also frightened of his wife Clytemnestra, and he asked Menelaus to let her know nothing of the truth until the sacrifice had been made and the dreadful deed, for good or evil, was over and finished.

And now, in the middle of their words, Clytemnestra and Iphigeneia arrived. They had brought with them Agamemnon's little son, Orestes, a boy who was still an infant, too young to understand the happiness that had been promised to his sister and the very different fate which was, in fact, to overtake her. Iphigeneia herself, beautiful and affectionate, threw herself into her father's arms, weeping in her joy at seeing him again, and Agamemnon, as he felt the warm embrace and looked into the innocent eyes of his favourite child, wept too and turned his head away so that she should not see his tears. But she was quick to notice his mood and begged him to be cheerful, asking him whether she had done anything to offend him and whether she could do anything to relieve the anxiety which seemed to weigh upon him. Agamemnon, in his misery, told her that indeed she had done nothing to offend him; she was always the delight of his eyes, and what weighed upon him was the responsibility and cares of a general in the field; moreover he had an important sacrifice to attend to before the day was over.

"Can I take part in the sacrifice," Iphigeneia asked, "and lead the dances round the altar, as I used to do at home?"

To this question Agamemnon could not bear to make a reply. He kissed his daughter and again he wept tears. "These tears," he said, "are because of the long farewell that I must soon take of you.

And now go inside the tent and rest. I myself must make the preparations for the sacrifice."

So Iphigeneia withdrew and, as she went, she smiled kindly upon the father who was planning to take her life.

And now Clytemnestra began to question her husband about the arrangements that had been made for the wedding and about the birth and the qualities of Achilles whom she fancied was to become her son-in-law. Agamemnon gave evasive replies to her questions. What he wanted most was for her to leave the camp before the sacrifice took place, but, when he suggested that she should return home to Mycenae and leave the whole matter of the wedding in his hands, she was, as might have been expected, both angry with him for making such a request and determined not to grant it. She had a right, she said, to be present at her own daughter's wedding, and nothing would make her forego that right. Once again, then, Agamemnon found his plans miscarrying. Yet, though he could not persuade his wife to leave the camp, he was determined to conceal the truth from her for as long as possible.

Even in this, however, he was disappointed. For now he went away in order to consult with Calchas how the army should be told of what Artemis had demanded and of how the sacrifice should be performed. While he was away Achilles himself came to his tent. He was finding that his own troops, the famous Myrmidons, were becoming restive because of the delay in sailing and he had come to consult with Agamemnon as to the best means of keeping the men quiet.

The camp of Achilles was some way from that of Agamemnon and so he knew nothing of the arrival of Clytemnestra and of Iphigeneia. He was surprised when Clytemnestra welcomed him outside her husband's tent, and he was still more surprised when she addressed him affectionately as one who was about to become her son-in-law. "I have never wooed your daughter," he said to her, "nor have I ever till this moment heard any mention of a marriage."

At these words Clytemnestra was filled with shame and astonishment. It appeared plainly that some trick had been played on both Achilles and herself, but neither of them could imagine what could be the purpose of so cruel a deception. They were soon to find out the truth, for the old servant to whom Agamemnon had entrusted the letter that was never delivered, now that he found Clytemnes-

tra alone with Achilles, came forward and revealed to them the
terrible message of Calchas and the terrible danger in which Iphigeneia stood. It was for death, he told them, and not for marriage
that Iphigeneia had been summoned from her home, and now he
begged Achilles, whose name had been used in vain, to protect the
girl who, in her innocence, imagined that she was betrothed to
him. For this old servant was above all loyal to Clytemnestra and
her family, since he had been in her service before ever she married
Agamemnon.

Clytemnestra, horrified and distraught by the dreadful story she
had heard, also implored Achilles to help her, if he could. As for
Achilles, whose chief thoughts were always of war and of honour,
he was furious that his name had been used when he himself had
never been consulted. He was as eager as anyone for the fleet to be
able to sail, and, had he been told that Agamemnon's daughter
must die for the whole of Greece, it is probable that he would have
agreed to the sacrifice. What vexed him most was that he had not
been told. He had been rated below Menelaus and below Odysseus, whereas he regarded himself as being second to none in the
army. Thus he was enraged against Agamemnon and swore that he
would defend Iphigeneia in his own person and would, if need be,
die for her rather than let the others so much as touch the hem of
her robe.

Clytemnestra was grateful to him for the help he offered, but she
saw clearly that, against the will of all the Greeks, not even Achilles
could prevail. She told him that she herself would make one last
appeal to her husband not to do this terrible thing and she urged
him, when the assembly of the Greeks was held at which the words
of Calchas would be made known to the army, to oppose the
wicked resolution with all his force and all his influence. This
Achilles promised to do and he promised also that, should he fail
in this, he would still be willing to fight to the death in order to
preserve Iphigeneia's life.

So Achilles went away to consult with his own troops and it was
not long before Agamemnon returned to find his wife in a very
different frame of mind from that in which he had left her. Most
bitterly she reproached him with his treachery to her, his cruelty to
their daughter and his cowardice in face of the army. And, as she
saw that her complaints and her tears were having no effect, she
brought forward Iphigeneia herself in front of her father and asked

him, in her presence, how he could contemplate becoming the murderer of such a daughter. Iphigeneia joined her tears with those of her mother. She could scarcely believe it to be possible that a father whom she loved so dearly and who, she thought, loved her too, could consent to be her executioner. She loved the light of day and shrank from the darkness of death which threatened her. She had expected a joyful marriage and had looked forward in the future to welcoming her father in her own home and to seeing his pride in the grandchildren she would bear. But now, young and unmarried, with no dances and no happy songs, she was to be led, like some animal, to the altar of sacrifice.

Now indeed Agamemnon wished that he had never consented to the cruel demand of Calchas; but now it seemed to him that the decision was irrevocable and that nothing could alter it. He knew that at this very moment the Greeks were meeting in an assembly and that Calchas was telling them what the will of the goddess was; he knew that they would be told that, unless Iphigeneia was sacrificed, Troy would never fall, nor would the expedition ever sail from Aulis; and he knew that such was the temper of the army that, however much they might pity the fate of an innocent girl, they would not let her life stand in the way of the great ambitions and their desire for war. And so, though he did not hide the grief he felt, he remained inflexible to the prayers of his daughter and of his wife. Partly to calm his own conscience he began to minimise his own responsibility for what was to take place and, as he left the two women and went away to hear what was happening at the assembly, he said to Iphigeneia, "It is not I and it is not Menelaus who wish this thing to be. It is not Calchas or Odysseus. No, it is something more important than any of us. Your blood is to be shed for the freedom and the greatness of Greece herself."

These words, whether sincerely spoken or not, had their effect upon the noble nature of the girl, and, even in her tears, she began to recover her courage and to reflect that the death she shrank from was a death which would bring her undying honour. For on her alone depended the success and safety of the army and navy of the Greeks. The great warriors, each one of them, were prepared if need be to die in battle. Should not she, though only a young woman, also be ready to lay down her life for the good and greatness of her country?

Soon, indeed, came the time for her to do so. For now Achilles came hurrying to the tent straight from the assembly of the army. He had no good news to tell. The words of Calchas had been received with joy and with relief; in the whole host there was one overmastering desire, which was to man the ships as soon as the promised winds blew and to be upon the sea on the way to Troy. Only Achilles himself had ventured to stand up and to oppose the sacrifice, and, so furious had the army been at his opposition, that in spite of his great name and his brilliant qualities, even his own troops had threatened to stone him to death unless he ceased to interfere in what the whole expedition was resolved to do. Even now troops were on the way to escort Iphigeneia to the place of sacrifice. Achilles himself had come, as he had promised, fully armed and ready to die in her defence. Not that he had any hope of saving her, but he was determined not to break his word.

But now Iphigeneia gently declined to accept the help that he offered. "Why should so many," she said, "be prepared to risk their lives for their country and I alone cling to my poor life, when my death is able to do such good? It is better to do the will of the gods without complaint and to help my fellow countrymen in whatever way I can do so. Indeed I am proud to die, since ever afterwards men will honour me for my death."

As Achilles looked at the girl and saw the beauty and the resolution in her face, he wondered at her. Now he wished that the lying message of Agamemnon had been true and that this noble creature could become his wife instead of being led to the slaughter for the good of the army. And Iphigeneia, as she looked upon Achilles in all the beauty and strength of his youth, might herself have been glad to find such a husband; but now her mind was set on something very different from a wedding and, though Achilles still urged her to allow him to stand in front of her and shield her from the approaching guards, she would have none of his help. So Achilles departed, since it was his duty to be present at the sacrifice.

And now Iphigeneia said farewell to her mother, begging her not to be angry with her husband Agamemnon and to welcome him with love when he returned victorious from Troy. But Clytemnestra's heart was bitter within her: she would never forgive her husband for the part which he had played. Now, however, she could think of nothing but her daughter and she clung to her despairingly as she saw the guards approach who were to take her to be sacrificed.

Iphigeneia's own purpose never wavered. She freed herself from her mother's embrace. No violence was required to bring her to the appointed place. Instead she walked between the guards like a princess in some triumphal procession, calm and noble, holding her head high, and it seemed to her, as she went, that she was filled with some divine power and strength which was leading her on in a direction different from anything that she had imagined, towards something new and strange and glorious.

So she came to the place of sacrifice where all the army was assembled, and, as the men looked at her, they felt a holy awe and a deep compassion for her fate. Then the herald proclaimed silence; they crowned the maiden's head with garlands, and Calchas, the priest, took from the altar the keen knife which he was to plunge into her throat. But first, in the name of all the Greeks, Achilles prayed. "O lady Artemis," he said, "accept this sacrifice that we offer, the innocent blood of a pure maiden; and grant to us in return favourable winds and that with our long spears we may overthrow the proud towers of Troy."

And now the moment for the sacrifice had come. No hand was laid upon Iphigeneia and she unflinchingly bared her white neck to receive the blow of the knife which Calchas held. Meanwhile the leaders of the Greeks and indeed most men in the army stood with bowed heads, for, though they had approved the sacrifice themselves, they could not bear to see it carried out. And so Calchas raised the knife and struck and, as he struck, a great sigh went up from the whole army like the sound of a sudden wind through dry grasses. Yet in an instant the sighing changed to cries and exclamations of astonishment. For a miracle had taken place. At the very instant when Calchas had thrust the knife firmly at the girl's throat, the noble girl herself had changed or been dissolved into the air. Now, in the place where she had been, they saw a great stag gasping out its life upon the ground as the streams of blood issued from a great cut in its neck.

The army cried aloud in joy, for it was plain to all that the goddess Artemis herself had refused the human sacrifice and had, in her divine power, given the great stag to take the place of the noble daughter of Agamemnon. Iphigeneia herself had been carried away by the goddess, far from the haunts of men, to be her servant and companion. The greatness and generosity of her soul had been rewarded.

And now the winds began to blow from the shore. In joy and gladness the Greeks trooped down to the sea and began to man their ships. At long last the great expedition was to sail upon its way. Among the shouts of seamen and the clash of arms, Agamemnon said good-bye to his wife and told her that their daughter, so far from meeting death, had found honour with the blessed gods. But Clytemnestra's heart remained unchanged within her.

AGAMEMNON

While King Agamemnon was leading the Greek forces in their long war against Troy, his wife, Clytemnestra, was betraying him at home. She, during his absence, ruled in the rocky citadel of golden Mycenae and she ruled without check or hindrance, since all the great warriors had gone to Troy and only the women, the children and the old men were left behind.

Years passed and from the battle front, far away across the sea, news came infrequently and when it came it was bad news. The fighting seemed to have no end; more and more of those young men who had set out confidently to win glory and riches in the great war were reported as dead or missing somewhere in the plains of Troy, and those whose hearts ached for them,—fathers, sisters and wives—had nothing to console them, unless it were the dust and ashes of the dead sent home in a funeral urn. It was no wonder that, as the long time went by, there were some who cursed Agamemnon and his interminable war in which was perishing so much of the youth and strength of Greece; yet on the whole the people remained loyal to their King, praying for victory and for his return.

But these were never the prayers of Clytemnestra. If she had received the news of her husband's death, she would have laughed for joy at the hearing of it; for she hated her husband and she loved her husband's most bitter enemy. She had, or thought she had, good reason to hate Agamemnon; for, at the time when the great expedition was ready to set sail for Troy but was delayed by contrary winds, Agamemnon had listened to the words of the priests and prophets in his army and had been ready to sacrifice to the goddess Artemis his own daughter, Iphigeneia, so as to secure fair sailing weather for the fleet. It was after this that there had come to Mycenae one who, if Agamemnon had been there, would never have dared to set his foot across the frontier. This was Aegisthus, a man who was in no way the equal of Agamemnon, but who won the affection of Agamemnon's wife. Their guilty love was as a link in the chain of evil—evil which had been done before and evil which was to follow after. For Aegisthus' father, Thyestes, was the brother of Atreus, who was the father of the Kings Agamemnon and Menelaus. After the birth of these two princes Thyestes had secretly become the lover of Atreus' wife and by her had had children. In the end Atreus had discovered the shameful fact and he had taken a terrible vengeance upon his brother. He had invited Thyestes to a feast and had set before him to eat the flesh of his own children. Not till Thyestes had eaten of this flesh did Atreus reveal what he had done, and then Thyestes, with a great cry, had overturned the table with his foot and had, though guilty himself, called down a great curse on the house of Atreus. He had then left Mycenae for ever, but, before he died, he became the father of Aegisthus, who was to do evil himself and to bring evil upon others.

Now, while all the best of the Greeks were fighting before Troy, Aegisthus came to Mycenae and was the lover of Agamemnon's wife. He and Clytemnestra did not live openly together in the splendid palace that stood on the height of the great fortress that looks out over the mountains and the wide plains of Argos to the sea. For they feared the people who, though many of them might grumble at the long war, still were loyal to their King and would never, so long as Agamemnon was alive, accept as their master one who, like a jackal, was sleeping in the bed where the lion had lain. Yet the love between Clytemnestra and Aegisthus did not go unnoticed. The old men, loyal counsellors of Agamemnon and of his father before him, longed for the day when the King would return and would set his house in order; but there were others who began to rest their hopes upon Clytemnestra and upon Aegisthus, as the

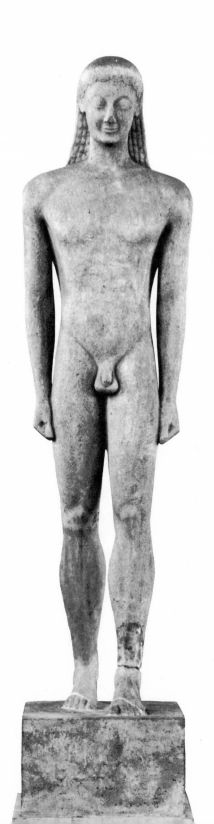

war dragged on and on and as the King, with all the flower of Greece, still tarried overseas.

Suddenly came the news for which all had so long been waiting. One night the watchman on the roof of Clytemnestra's palace saw in the northern sky, outshining the gleam of star-light, the distant blaze of fire. As the flames grew and mounted he knew their meaning. He was watching the light of a beacon which carried the message that Troy had fallen. From mountain top to mountain top, from island to island, across the seas, the rivers and the plains this signal of fire had come from Asia into Europe, from the conquered walls of Troy to the citadel of Mycenae. As the watchman gazed upon the distant light he cried aloud in joy because he knew that the long war was over and that his master would return. But, knowing how matters were in Mycenae itself, he prayed to the gods that the Greeks, in their hour of victory, might be restrained from outrageous conduct and impiety and might return home safely and with the blessing of heaven. Then he gave the news to his mistress, and Clytemnestra, though no news could have pleased her less than that of her husband's return, had still to pretend that she was glad of it. She gave orders for sacrifices of thanksgiving to be made at all the altars of the gods; she joined in the singing and the dancing; she joined too in the prayers, though secretly her own were different from those of the others who longed to welcome back their dear ones; for already she and Aegisthus were making their own plans.

Meanwhile at Troy the Greeks had done just what the old watchman had prayed that they would be prevented from doing. After the long ten years of hardship, of wounds and of dangers, they had, in the moment of victory, lost all control over themselves. Old and young had been butchered in the streets of Troy without thought or mercy; oaths had been broken and the temples of the gods had been profaned. Thus the gods were angry with the Greeks and made their homecoming more difficult than their setting out. Many of them were to wander for years, driven by storms over the face of the ocean, before ever they were to return; others were to find in their own homes not peace and quiet but peril and even death.

Agamemnon was not of those who had to wander for long over the sea before he reached his home. It was not many days after the message of fire had been received that he and his ships sailed into the harbour of Nauplia in the bay below the palace and fortress of Mycenae. Messengers soon brought to Clytemnestra the news of his coming. He came rich with the spoils of war and proud in his victory, but the men who accompanied him were few indeed compared with the number who, ten years previously, had set out on the great expedition; so great had been the slaughter beneath the walls of Troy. Among the slaves taken from the captured city Agamemnon was bringing with him Cassandra, the beautiful daughter of King Priam of Troy, to be his own handmaid. This princess, who was now a slave and chattel, had been in every way unfortunate. For the god Apollo himself had loved her and had given to her the gift of knowing the future; but then, either from fear or from modesty, she had rejected the god, and Apollo, though he could not take back the gift he had given, made this gift worthless. For he brought it about that, while Cassandra knew the future and could reveal it to others, no one would believe what she said. Thus she had known that Troy would fall and that she and her sisters and her old mother would be made slaves; she had urged King Priam and her brother Hector to make peace with the Greeks while peace could still be made and while still great Hector lived. But her true words were taken to be the idle ravings of a crazed woman. Now she went as a slave in the company of Agamemnon and, as she landed on this foreign shore, her prophetic heart began to stir within her. She dreaded the mountains in front of her and she half seemed to see already, what was still out of sight, the great palace of Atreus and his sons, a home of blood, towards which they were going.

And so, while Agamemnon, with the remnants of his army, with his slaves and his booty, made his way up from the coast to the fortress which was the capital of his kingdom, in Mycenae Clytemnestra prepared to welcome him, and, as she saw in the distance the band of veterans from Troy winding its way up the rocky paths, she prayed to Zeus that her own deeply laid and treacherous plans might be successful. She knew that, if she were to act at all, she must act at once, before Agamemnon could re-establish his authority or discover the extent to which already she had betrayed him. Meanwhile Aegisthus and his bodyguard were waiting in hiding nearby.

So at the gateway of the palace Clytemnestra met the great King who was her husband. She looked at him closely and saw that the

ten long years of war had left their mark upon him. There was a
majesty and a strength in his bearing as he stood there, looking
steadily in her face, and she, with all her resolution, trembled at
the thought that he might already have been told something of her
conduct. She spoke hurriedly and, had he indeed been suspicious,
he would have noticed in her words a kind of exaggeration which
would have shown that they were not sincere. She told him that all
the time that he had been away she had wept for him continually;
day and night she had been in tears at the thought of the dangers
that might be threatening him; and for herself there had been not
a single moment of joy or pleasure until this glad moment of her
husband's return. And now, she said, she felt as she saw him like
the shipwrecked sailor who suddenly comes in sight of land; to her
his coming was like the sweet light in the sky that follows the tem-
pest, like a cool spring of water which refreshes the weary traveller.

As she spoke, Agamemnon remained standing in his chariot,
looking now at her, now at the people assembled about her. He
was seeing his home and his people for the first time in ten years.
And now Clytemnestra ordered her slaves to spread on the ground
a great purple carpet. "Let not my lord, the King," she said, "set
his conquering foot upon the ground. Instead let him tread on
purple, and let Justice lead him to his home!"

So saying, she bowed before him and all her slaves and attendants also prostrated themselves. But Agamemnon looked at her
coldly. It seemed to him that she had protested too much; moreover he was a soldier and a Greek; it was not to his taste to be
welcomed with this extravagance of bowing and of purple carpets
as though he were some barbarian monarch. "Give me," he said,
"only the honour that is due to a man, and keep such ceremonies
as these for the service of the gods."

But Clytemnestra continued to beg and plead with him to do
what she wished and in the end Agamemnon, though he made no
secret of his displeasure, allowed himself to be persuaded to set his
foot upon the costly glowing colours of the royal carpet. First,
however, he removed his sandals, for he wished to behave with
humility and not to invite the jealousy of any god as he went into
his home. He turned also to Cassandra and told his wife to look
after her well. Clytemnestra glanced at the strange foreign girl who
had come with Agamemnon from Troy. She saw how her eyes were
staring wide in terror at the great walls and battlements of this

palace to which she had been brought. For, though Clytemnestra did not know it, the prophetic spirit in Cassandra was stirring. She knew that she was in a place of blood. As for Clytemnestra, she looked coldly at the poor slave who had been loved by Apollo and who was Priam's daughter, since it was her purpose to kill Cassandra also, when the time came.

Meanwhile great Agamemnon strode along the purple into his home and did not know that, in what seemed a moment of perfect triumph, he was in fact going like a sacrificial beast to his own slaughter. Clytemnestra watched him go and then prepared to follow him so that she might carry out her own evil and cruel plan. First, however, she spoke to Cassandra, telling her roughly to get down from the chariot in which she stood and to go indoors with the other slaves. But Cassandra still stared fixedly in front of her, seeming not to hear the Queen's words; and not even when Clytemnestra raised her voice in anger did the prophetess pay her any attention. So, since she did not wish yet to show openly the violence that she planned, Clytemnestra left her standing at the gate, while she herself followed Agamemnon into the palace.

And now the troops who had for so long and so faithfully guarded their King in the perils of war dispersed to their own homes, believing that they had brought their master back to a place of peace. There were left outside the palace only Cassandra and some of the old counsellors of Agamemnon who remained to discuss among themselves what they knew of the past and what they feared or hoped for the future. They could never have feared anything so dreadful as what was just about to take place; for who could have imagined that a wife, unaided and with her own hand, would destroy her own husband, the greatest King among the Greeks, in the moment of his homecoming? Only to Cassandra, with the god's gift of prophetic insight, the whole evil of the past, of the present, and of the future was visible and alive. As she stared at the gigantic walls of Agamemnon's palace it seemed to her that the walls were running with blood and that stains of blood were spreading over the floors. Though she had never heard the story of the cruel feast that Atreus had placed before his brother Thyestes, in her mind's eye she seemed to see the figures of children holding in their hands cooked portions of their own flesh. She cried out in horror and now the great power of the god of prophecy, Apollo himself, descended upon her and overmastered her. She spoke in a voice that was no longer her own voice; her head and her limbs were tossed like leaves in a wind; her breathing was heavy and laboured as she tried to tell what she still saw through a kind of mist—the evil that was being done or that was about to be done. And, as the old men questioned her, they were both astonished and alarmed by what she said; for she told them what the god showed to her, all the past history of the crimes that had been committed in that place; she told them of what they either knew or suspected, that Aegisthus, while the King was away, had stolen into the heart and into the bed of the King's wife; and she told them that even now, at this instant, a web or net of death was being spread for Agamemnon himself. And now gradually the prophetic frenzy began to leave her. Her voice and manner became quiet and calm; her eyes lost their fixed and fearful stare; she seemed like a princess, though pitiful in her slavery, as she went herself into the palace, knowing that she was going to her own death.

Once more she had spoken the truth and once more it was not believed. For, though the old counsellors to whom she had been speaking were indeed frightened by her words, they still could not bring themselves to imagine that those words were strictly true. Yet so it was. Inside the palace Clytemnestra had prepared a bath for her husband, knowing that he would wish to refresh himself after his journey. She had also cunningly prepared a robe, a wicked and treacherous instrument of death which, like a strait jacket, locked the arms of anyone who wore it, making even the strongest man impotent to defend himself. And so, in the bathroom of his palace, fettered in this robe, Agamemnon was slaughtered like an ox in a stall, slaughtered by the hand of his own wife who struck at him, defenceless as he was, with a heavy axe. Twice Agamemnon cried aloud before he fell to the ground in the streams of his own blood; but there was no one to help him.

Next Clytemnestra gave orders for Cassandra to be put to death. She had been the property of Agamemnon, and nothing of Agamemnon's was to be left. And now, as had been arranged, Aegisthus came with his band of armed men. He had taken no part in the murder himself, but he was ready to share in its fruits and to make himself King of Mycenae and of Argos, ruling there with Clytemnestra as his Queen. So suddenly had the dreadful deed been done that those who were still loyal to Agamemnon were left confused, weak and incapable. The few troops that had returned from Troy were scattered about the city; the old counsellors who had heard the prophecies of Cassandra and who, to confirm these prophecies, had heard Agamemnon himself cry aloud in his death agony, were overawed and helpless when they found themselves confronted by Clytemnestra, exultant in the murder that she had done, and by Aegisthus with his armed men.

So Clytemnestra and Aegisthus reigned, and it seemed that they reigned securely. Yet there was an old servant in the palace who loved his master and his master's family. Directly after the murder this servant had hurriedly taken away Agamemnon's young son, Orestes. He and the young boy had ridden fast through the mountain passes to the north and had made their escape from Aegisthus, who, with or without the will of Clytemnestra, would certainly have destroyed any male child of Agamemnon. So Orestes lived and the curse still lived on that had haunted and was still to haunt the House of Atreus.

ORESTES

After Clytemnestra had killed her husband Agamemnon, she ruled in golden Mycenae and her lover Aegisthus ruled with her. Into their hands passed all the wealth of Troy which Agamemnon had brought back home with him—the gold and the slaves and the rich garments—so that their court was more splendid than it had ever been. Yet no one who has an unquiet mind can live happily, and, in the midst of all this wealth and power, both Clytemnestra and Aegisthus were vexed by the knowledge of the evil that they had done and by the fear that one day this evil would be avenged. They were flattered by their servants and their courtiers, but they were neither loved nor respected; nor could their soldiers or the strong walls of their citadel protect them from haunting thoughts in the daytime or from dreams in the night.

As for Clytemnestra, she had tried to quiet her own conscience by the plea that Agamemnon had deserved to die because he had been willing to take away from her one of her own children, Iphigeneia, to be sacrificed for the good of the army and the fleet. Yet now, by killing her husband, she had lost her other children as well. Her son Orestes, who had been a mere boy at the time of the murder, had been carried away into safety by an old servant of Agamemnon's. He was being brought up far away in northern Greece and little news of him ever reached Mycenae, though it was clear enough that he must be growing up in hatred of his mother for what she had done and that, at some time or other, he might attempt to regain the kingdom which was his by right. As for the other child, Electra, she was a little older than Orestes and she, even better than he, had been able to realise at the time the meaning of the dreadful crime of which her mother had been guilty. She had remained in the palace and had seen day after day the proud lovemaking of the woman who had murdered her father and of the man who had not dared to look her father in the face. No words of self-excuse that Clytemnestra could address to her daughter had any effect upon the girl's hard embittered heart; for Electra could think only of one great fact, that her father Agamemnon, leader of all the Greeks, had been treacherously murdered by his own wife at the moment of his homecoming. As for Aegisthus, she thought of him with horror and with hatred; for how, she wondered, could her mother have preferred to her own great husband a man who had the good looks of a woman, but, though his nature was savage enough, none of the courage of a man. And so Electra passed her days and nights in bitterness and humiliation, giving her mother no love and receiving none from her. She prayed only that Orestes would return and would avenge their father's death, though, as the years went by and for long periods of time she had no knowledge of whether Orestes were alive or dead, even this hope would sometimes fail her and she would seem to see no end to her own sufferings and to the triumph of those who had destroyed her father.

It was to be expected that, as Electra remained constantly faithful to her father's memory, she would become more and more hated by Clytemnestra and by Aegisthus. Moreover she was not only hated, but feared. For, if she were to marry a man who was suited to her by birth, she might bear children who would be princes and powerful and who would certainly be taught that they should avenge their grandfather's death. And so, when Electra reached the age at which she might be married and when offers for her hand came from great men among the Greeks, Aegisthus and Clytemnestra, though they had no wish to keep Electra with them at home, still refused such offers. Instead they forced her into a marriage which, they thought, would humiliate her still further and would also serve their own interests. They gave her as wife to a poor peasant who lived in a rough cottage in the fields some way away from the great palace of the sons of Atreus. Thus they hoped to get rid of Electra for ever, for no one in future would want to marry her and she herself, with fresh hardships and sufferings in addition to the sorrow she had already, would soon wear out in poverty her miserable life and would cease to be a trouble and a reproach to those who ruled in her father's palace.

Yet things did not turn out as Aegisthus and Clytemnestra had planned. It was true that Electra's life was miserable, but the man to whom she had been given in marriage, though he was poor enough, had a heart and spirit much more noble than were those of the usurping King and Queen. He pitied Electra for herself and he revered her as the daughter of Agamemnon, whose faithful subject he had been in the past. So, though he was forced to keep her in his poor cottage, he kept her with him not as a wife, but as an honoured guest; for he hoped that one day the murder of Agamemnon would be avenged and, if ever that day came, he wanted Electra to be free to marry some great man among the Greeks, as she should do, since she was the daughter of a King. For this kindness and consideration of his Electra honoured the good man who was, though only in name, her husband. She was forced to share his life of poverty, but she tried to lighten it for him by her care for his comfort and her diligence in the household tasks. Her sorrows remained,—her grief for her father, her longing and anxiety for her brother's return—but in this poor cottage to which she had been condemned she found more real kindness and more solid worth than she had ever known in the great palace where her mother and Aegisthus ruled.

Now all this time Orestes was growing to manhood under the protection of King Strophius of Phocis, whose kingdom was in the mountains beyond the Isthmus of Corinth. He had been brought up with the King's son, Pylades, and the two young princes became inseparable companions, sharing in each other's thoughts and actions, and so faithful to each other's interests that they became to later ages an example of what friendship could be. Both young men were strong and brave, but, while Pylades lived as a prince in his father's kingdom, respected and loved by all, Orestes knew himself to be an exile, cut off from his rights and deprived of his father because of his mother's wickedness. He grew up, in spite of his beauty and strength, with bitter thoughts in his heart and, when he reached manhood, he went with Pylades to the great temple of Apollo at Delphi to consult the oracle of the god. Here, among the towering mountains where eagles circle outwards from the heights and where the air is clear and bright as crystal, the god through the mouth of his prophetess gave the young man no uncertain answer. Orestes was told that he must go back to Mycenae and must there avenge his father's death by killing Aegisthus and by killing his own mother. This was the clear command of Apollo himself and dreadful punishments would fall upon the young man if he failed to carry out the task that was set before him.

So Apollo revealed his will to Orestes, but he did not reveal everything. He did not say that there exist terrible avengers for a mother's blood, the savage Erinyes, and that, by obeying the commands of one divine power, Orestes would be bringing upon himself the full wrath of another. As it was, everything seemed, in that high mountain air, clear and distinct. Though Orestes might shrink, as any son would shrink, from the thought of shedding his mother's blood, he knew his mother's crime, he respected his father's memory and he was supported by the certain authority and definite command of Apollo.

He set out therefore for Mycenae, determined to carry out the dreadful and dangerous enterprise, and his friend Pylades went with him, ready to share his perils and, if necessary, to die with him in the daring attempt. For it was a daring thing indeed for two young men to challenge the force and power of the rulers of Mycenae. They knew of no friends or allies in that country; all that was certain was that if it were once discovered who they were, they would instantly be put to death. However, they put their trust in the guidance of Apollo and set out for the land from which Orestes had fled so many years ago, when he was only a little boy. At that time even his sister Electra had been so young that she would now scarcely remember even what her brother looked like then; no one else, certainly, would recognise him, unless indeed that old man, the faithful servant of Agamemnon, who had carried Orestes to safety after his father's murder, still lived.

When they drew near to Mycenae they travelled secretly and by night. Before dawn they came to the great fortifications behind which was the palace of the sons of Atreus and now, standing in his own country, the first act of Orestes was to do honour to his father's tomb. The tomb was outside the city walls and had lacked the reverence that was due to it. Sometimes Clytemnestra, when she had been vexed with terrible dreams, would send offerings to the spirit of the man whom she had murdered; though no sacrifice that she could make would quiet her own spirit. Sometimes Aegisthus, in his wicked pride, would insult the tomb, pelting it with stones and mocking at the great man who lay within it. The people feared his rage and even those who were still loyal to the memory of Agamemnon did not venture to show their loyalty openly and would only dare to bring any offering to his tomb under the cover of darkness. So Orestes found his father's monument neglected and overgrown with weeds.

Here he knelt on the ground and prayed to his father's spirit, renewing the oath that he had made to the god Apollo, that he would not shrink from taking full vengeance for the murder that had been done. Then he and Pylades sacrificed a black sheep (since black is the colour which is proper in animals offered to the dead); and Orestes cut from his own head a long lock of hair and left it on the tomb as a pledge of honour to his father.

Now the sun was rising and they turned in the direction of the huts and cottages of the peasants who lived scattered along the slopes of the valley and in the plain below. They wished to enquire first where they could find Electra; they would not reveal themselves to her at once, for they did not know in what state she might be found or whether they could depend on her to help them. And so, by chance or by the guidance of the god, they came first to the poor cottage where Electra herself lived. The good man who was assumed to be her husband had already left his home for the fields, and Electra herself was frightened when she came out to draw water from the well and found herself confronted by two strangers, tall young men, with spears in their hands and with something fierce and hungry in the expression of their faces. But they spoke to her kindly and, when they began to ask her "where does Electra live?", her first hope was that they might be messengers from the north who could tell her whether her brother Orestes was still alive. Orestes at once pretended that this was what, in fact, they were, for he did not yet know enough of his sister to know whether he could count on her for help in the dreadful deeds that lay ahead. Also he was surprised and horrified to find that she, the daughter of a King, was living in so poor a dwelling, so destitute of all good things. He told her that he was indeed a messenger from her brother and that he had been sent to find out what was the state of affairs in the kingdom of Mycenae.

At the news that her brother was alive Electra was full of joy, and now she told the strangers, not knowing that one of them was Orestes himself, the story of her own life,—how she had been driven out of her father's palace and forced to marry a poor peasant, how this good man had respected her and shown her more kindness than she had ever known from her mother, how she prayed and longed for the day when her brother Orestes would return and would put an end to the guilty loves and lives of Clytemnestra and Aegisthus.

Orestes, as he listened, felt in his own heart joy and pride and love for a sister who, like himself, had never forgotten the wrong that had been done to their father, Agamemnon. He pitied her for the sufferings which she had undergone and, as she told her story, he could scarcely keep back his tears. Pylades also was moved with pity and with love as he looked at this young girl, so beautiful in face and figure, so gracious in her bearing, who had known in her short life so little happiness and so much misery and humiliation.

And now, when they were in the middle of their talk and before Orestes had been able to decide whether or not to reveal himself to his sister, the good farmer who was in name her husband returned to his house and was, as Electra had been, surprised and frightened to see strangers standing in front of it. But no sooner did Electra tell him that these were messengers from Orestes than he hastened to offer them all the hospitality that he was able to provide. He urged them to enter his house and to share with him the little food and wine that he possessed. Orestes thankfully accepted the generous invitation, but Electra, who knew how very little there was within the house, was glad to see that there was now approaching them an old man, a shepherd, who was their friend and who had been her servant. He was indeed that faithful follower of Agamemnon who, on the terrible day of his master's murder, had rescued the young Orestes and taken him to safety beyond the mountains. Ever since then he had lived with his few sheep and goats in the country far away from the palace where he had looked after the children of his king. So he had escaped the notice of Aegisthus and Clytemnestra; but from time to time he would visit Electra and the poor farmer with whom she lived. He would give them a lamb or a goat or whatever else he could afford to relieve their poverty and he, like they, would pray for the safety and for the return of Orestes.

Now, when Electra saw him approaching she was glad, since she knew that he also would welcome the news that had been brought and also that with his aid she would be able to give these strangers something better to eat than the few crusts of bread which was all her house contained. She quickly told Orestes who this man was and Orestes looked at him with affection, since it was indeed to him that he owed his own life.

As for the old shepherd, he scarcely noticed the strangers at first, so excited was he with the news he brought. He enquired only whether he could speak freely and, when he was told that he could do so, he said what he had come to say. That morning he had been to visit the tomb of Agamemnon and, when he came to it, he had been amazed to find that someone had been there before him, had made a rich sacrifice and had left behind him a lock of hair. Who could this be? According to the old man it could be none other than Orestes himself, and he had looked closely at the lock of hair and found it to be of exactly the same colour and texture as Electra's own hair.

To Electra it seemed that the old man was saying what he wished to be true rather than what was true in fact. "How I long myself," she said to him, "for Orestes to be here, but alas! he is still far away. I have good reason to know this, since these strangers have come from him and are his messengers."

Now the old man looked at Orestes and Pylades, but soon he gave all his attention to Orestes himself, scanning every feature of his face with his keen eyes, trying, it seemed, to trace something there which was known to him alone. And at last he cried out: "Here, Electra, is the man himself. Here is your brother whom you have awaited for so long. Here, grown to manhood, is the boy whom I took to safety beyond the mountains. I know him by his royal bearing and by the scar above his eye. He got it when you and he were children and he fell down when the two of you were chasing a pet fawn in the palace of your father."

So brother and sister were united again, and great was the joy they had in each other. Great too was the joy of the old servant who had lived to see the prince whom he had saved return again to Mycenae, and of the good man who had sheltered Electra beneath his poor roof. Now they all met together like friends long lost, with tears and with laughter.

Yet now, as they all knew, was not yet the time for rejoicing. In front of Orestes stood the great task of vengeance, a dreadful deed in itself and one that must prove difficult to accomplish. So they began to lay their plans, and what seemed to them best was this:

It was known that on this day Aegisthus would leave his palace and go into the country where, in a plot of his own ground, he was to make a sacrifice to the nymphs. No one would be with him who could possibly recognise Orestes and it seemed that, if Orestes and Pylades, pretending to be strangers, were to attend the sacrifice, and if the gods helped and guided them, some chance might occur of cutting down the tyrant in a moment when he had no suspicion of danger threatening him. And as for Clytemnestra, she also might be drawn out of the shelter of her palace and her guards. In order to do this Electra proposed that a message should be sent to her mother to say that she had just borne a male child and that she needed her mother's help in the proper ceremonies of purification which take place after childbirth. Clytemnestra would, in all probability, consent to come, not because of any love for her daughter but in order to see that she had in fact borne a child to a poor farmer,—partly out of curiosity and partly to insult one who had never yielded to her in her spirit. And once Clytemnestra had entered the poor cottage to which she had condemned her daughter. she would find that she herself was condemned to die there.

So they proceeded to carry out their plan. Orestes and Pylades went to the fields and orchards where Aegisthus was holding his feast and making his sacrifice to the nymphs. Aegisthus himself noticed the two young men and asked them who they were and from what country they came. They told him that they were men of Thessaly, from the far north, who were on their way to sacrifice to Zeus in Olympia. Then Aegisthus invited them to his feast. "You men of Thessaly," he said, "are known to be good at taming horses and at severing the joints of animals prepared for sacrifice. You must join us at the feast which we make this day."

Then Orestes and Pylades went in with the others over the green grass to the place chosen for the sacrifice. First a calf was sacrificed and, after he had cut the beast's throat, Aegisthus said: "Come, my Thessalian guests; take the knives and the axes and let us see your skill in cutting up the body." So Orestes took an axe and Pylades took a knife. Quickly they flayed and dismembered the carcase and cleft it open so that Aegisthus could look inside it and see by inspecting the warm entrails what, by the rules of prophecy, might be his fortune. As he bent his head to look, he saw that the liver of the slaughtered animal was misshapen and he saw other signs, all of which portended evil. For a moment Aegisthus shrank back. "What can this be?" he said. "One thing I fear, and that is the son of Agamemnon. Yet he is nowhere near me." And so he peered down again into the body of the animal, seeking to find some more propitious sign. Then Orestes raised the axe high and, with the full strength of his arms and shoulders, brought it down upon the neck of Aegisthus, severing the head from the trunk, slaughtering him there like an ox, and like great Agamemnon himself had been slaughtered.

At once there was a cry of anger and dismay from the assembled guests and from the bodyguard of Aegisthus. Orestes and Pylades grasped their weapons and stood still. Before any move could be made Orestes cried out: "I, who have killed the tyrant, am no stranger, as you supposed. I am your rightful King, Orestes, the son of Agamemnon."

The old servant was there to prove the truth of what he said and soon, among all the soldiers and servants of King Aegisthus, the cries of anger and of violence changed to shouts of joy. They laid their spears down upon the ground and crowned the head of Orestes with garlands.

Thus the first part of his task was done, but the second remained. The body of Aegisthus was carried back to the cottage where Electra was waiting anxiously to hear what had been the success of the attempt of her brother and his friend. She rejoiced at the sight of it and at the full vengeance that had been taken on the man who had betrayed her father. But the time for words was short, for now over the plain could be seen approaching the proud chariot of Clytemnestra. The message sent to her from Electra had had its effect and the Queen, with slaves and attendants at her side, knowing nothing of her lover's death or of her son's return, was coming to visit the daughter whom she had rejected.

And now, as he saw the bright chariots in the distance and knew that his mother was in one of them, for the first time the heart of Orestes shrank within him. How could he kill the mother who had given him birth? How could Apollo be good or wise, if he gave him so terrible a task to do?

Electra saw her brother's distress and was quick to urge him on to the final act. By killing their mother, she said, they would be righteously avenging their father; and the commands of the god of Delphi were too clear to be disobeyed. So Orestes and Pylades went inside the house and waited there for the deed which they had to do.

It was not long before Clytemnestra was at the door where Electra stood to greet her. Except that they were both beautiful, mother and daughter were different indeed to look at; for Electra was dressed in the mean black clothes of a poor woman, while Clytemnestra wore rich soft garments, brilliantly dyed. These were part of the spoils of Troy, and Trojan women slaves, won in battle by Agamemnon, were at her side to help her dismount from her chariot and to attend on her. Yet with all the pride of her bearing, Clytemnestra was secretly afraid of this daughter who had always opposed her and always remained faithful to the memory of her murdered father. There was no pity or love in Clytemnestra's heart even now when she saw the wretched dwelling to which Electra had been banished and believed that inside it was a child newly-born. She wished only to see the child, to take her part in the ceremonies of purification and to depart again quickly; and so, with few words and drawing her clothes about her so as to avoid dirtying them on the smoky walls of the cottage, she went inside the door, as unsuspicious of what was to befall her as Agamemnon himself had been of her own plots on the day that he came back from Troy.

Now her fate came upon her quickly. As soon as her eyes grew accustomed to the dim light inside the hut she saw on the ground a dead body with the head severed from the neck and she saw that the head and body were those of Aegisthus. She turned to flee, but was prevented by strong arms and, as she looked in the faces of the two young men who held her, she knew that the one of them who held the sword was the man whom she most feared, her own son, Orestes. She cried out for mercy, but no mercy was given to her. Orestes had steeled his heart and there, obeying the commands of the god, he slew his mother to avenge his father's death.

He had done as the god in Delphi had commanded, but obedience did not bring content. Now he looked with fear and horror at the work of his hands. Terrible shapes rose up before his eyes, dreadful creatures who would not let him rest or sleep and which followed him like hounds, seeking satisfaction for his mother's blood. These beings were the Erinyes, implacable divine powers, and by them Orestes was haunted night and day, driven mad by their unceasing persecution. Neither his sister Electra nor his friend Pylades could comfort him, nor could his heart find rest in the thought that he had only done the bidding of a god. Though he travelled far and wide, he failed to shake off his pitiless pursuers. Not until, after many wanderings, he reached Athens and put himself under the protection of Athene herself did he know any hope or any respite from his sufferings. In Athens was given the final judgment between Apollo, who had commanded Orestes to kill the murderers of his father, and the savage Erinyes, who would never rest till they had extracted the full price for a mother's blood. Under the guidance and power of Athene these dreadful goddesses now relaxed their claims and ever afterwards were worshipped under a different name—"The Kindly Ones"—in the city of Athens. Orestes, having done much and suffered much, was freed from guilt and the long tale of evil after evil which had fallen upon the house of Atreus now ended. Orestes reigned in the palace of his father. His sister Electra was given in marriage to his faithful friend Pylades; nor did the new King forget to honour the good man who had sheltered her in her misfortunes or that old servant to whom he owed his own life.

THE RESCUE OF IPHIGENEIA

This is another story told of what happened to Orestes when he was haunted by the Erinyes; and this story concerns also his long-lost sister, Iphigeneia.

It is said that even after Orestes had come to Athens to be purified from the guilt of having killed his mother and after he had received the protection of the goddess Athene, there were still some of those pursuing furies, the Erinyes, who would not leave him in peace, but continued to haunt him, so that from time to time he was driven mad by their persecution. So he went once more to the temple of Apollo at Delphi and asked for help, and indeed for simple justice from the god, since all his sufferings had come to him only because he had obeyed the god's commands. Apollo replied to him through his oracle and told him that one more task remained for him to do; once this had been carried out, he would be freed from his guilt and from the dreadful visions that would drive him mad. He was to make a voyage into the far north, through those blue and clashing rocks past which Jason had once sailed in the Argo. Beyond these rocks opened out the Black Sea and on the northern coasts of the sea was a land of barbarians, the land of Tauris, where there stood a temple to Apollo's sister, Artemis. But here, in this barbarous country, the goddess was worshipped with cruel rites and with human sacrifices. All Greeks who were caught on this coast were taken to the temple and slaughtered at the altar in front of an image of Artemis, a holy statue that had fallen from the skies. And now Apollo commanded Orestes to go to this savage and desolate land, to steal the statue from the temple and to bring it back to Athens.

To Orestes this seemed a task which, though not so dreadful, was at least as difficult and dangerous as had been the carrying out of vengeance upon Aegisthus and Clytemnestra; yet, unless he undertook the dangers and the difficulty, he knew that he was doomed to a whole lifetime of misery and shame. His faithful friend Pylades had just married Electra, the sister of Orestes, but he would not allow anything to prevent him from sharing in the perils which Orestes had to face and he was determined to go with him. So he left his newly-married wife and prepared for the long voyage northwards to Tauris.

What neither Orestes nor Pylades knew was that the priestess of Artemis in Tauris was none other than Orestes' sister, Iphigeneia. She, it will be remembered, had suffered a most cruel fate at the hands of the Greeks. When the great expedition had been about to set sail for Troy under the command of her father Agamemnon, she had been brought to the seaport of Aulis, where the army and fleet were delayed by contrary winds, and there, by the commands of the priests and with the consent of her own father, she had been offered up, like an animal, for sacrifice to Artemis in order that the fleet might have fine and lucky weather for its sailing. At the very last moment, when the knife of sacrifice was being plunged into her heart, she had vanished into thin air and in her place a great stag was seen on the altar, drenched in blood that might have been hers. As for Iphigeneia herself, no one knew what had become of her or whether she was alive or dead.

In fact the goddess Artemis had preserved her life, had taken her up by divine power from the sight of the army at Aulis and had set her down in the barbarian kingdom of the swift-footed King Thoas in distant Tauris. Here ever since that time Iphigeneia had remained as priestess of Artemis, a Greek living among barbarians. It was her duty to follow the savage custom of the place, and so, whenever any Greek was captured on shore or sailing along the coast, it was she who had to consecrate him for sacrifice. Not that she herself ever stained her hands with human blood; what she had to do was to sprinkle water over the heads of those who were to be slain, and after that they were taken by the guards inside the temple, where they were slaughtered and their bodies burnt by fire. Thus Iphigeneia, who had, when she was only a young girl, been so nearly sacrificed by the Greeks, now became the priestess under whose authority many Greeks were themselves sacrificed. But it was from necessity, not from any wish for vengeance, that she performed this cruel duty and lived in this savage place. All the time she thought with longing of her distant home in Argos and in golden Mycenae. Sometimes rumours reached her of the great war that was fought at Troy and in the end she heard the news that

Troy had fallen. But she knew nothing of the fortunes of her own family, nothing of her mother's treachery or of her father's murder. Most of all she longed to see her brother Orestes, whom she could remember only as a very small boy. She could never have imagined that he was now close to the wild country where she lived, fleeing from the avenging spirits whom he had roused against himself by obeying the dreadful orders of Apollo.

Nevertheless, since she was a priestess and one whose mind could be inspired by divine knowledge, she did have warning of what was to come, in a dream; yet, so unlikely did the truth seem to her, that she failed to understand it. She dreamed that she was again in her own room in the palace of Mycenae and that, while she slept, there was an earthquake. In her dream she hurried out of the house and saw all the roof falling in; only one pillar, the central pillar, remained standing and from the head of this pillar there seemed to come streams of yellow hair, while the pillar itself spoke with a human voice. She herself then sprinkled the hair with drops of water, as she used always to do over the heads of those who were to be sacrificed to Artemis, and while she sprinkled the water she wept and she woke weeping. When she was awake she tried to think what the dream could mean, and she rightly saw that by the destruction of her father's house was meant the death of her father and of her mother; the one pillar that still stood must mean Orestes, since sons are the pillars of their father's houses, and Orestes was Agamemnon's only son. But she could not imagine that Orestes would ever come to Tauris or that, if he did so, she could ever consecrate him for sacrifice; and so she failed to understand the last part of her dream. She thought that it must mean simply that Orestes was dead, and so she mourned all the more bitterly, being quite ignorant that Orestes was now near at hand and that with him she might herself be either saved or destroyed.

For, in the very night when Iphigeneia had dreamed this dream, Orestes and Pylades, with a ship of fifty oars, had put in to a creek on this wild coast, not far from the place where the temple of Artemis stood. They left their ship at anchor in the water near the shore, so that, if necessary, the crew would be able to escape, and they themselves landed and made their way along the coast till they came to the high walls of the castle where King Thoas lived and the temple, set back from the sea, where, as they had been informed, all Greeks who were found in this country were put to death. Neither of them knew that at this moment, inside the temple, Orestes' sister was thinking of her brother as of one who was lost to her for ever, or that, if indeed they were discovered, it was this sister of his who would have the duty of preparing them as victims for the sacrifice.

One glance at the firmly bolted gates of the temple and at the guards patrolling the battlements of the castle was enough to show them that they would have to wait for nightfall if they hoped to make their way unnoticed into the holy place and steal the statue for which they had come. So they withdrew to a sheltered bay where they hoped to remain unseen for the hours of daylight. However it happened that the bay to which they went, though it looked a desolate enough place, was visited from time to time by the herdsmen of the district, who used to go there to wash their cattle in the salt water of the sea. Some of these herdsmen from the slopes of the hills that surrounded the bay observed the two young men sitting by the edge of the surf, polishing their weapons and talking together. At first, when they saw their long golden hair, their strong limbs and noble bearing, they thought that these must be gods; but there were others among the herdsmen who were not so reverent, or not so superstitious, and who maintained that the two men were shipwrecked Greeks who were hiding because they knew of the custom of the land.

Meanwhile the herds of cattle had begun to make their way down to the beach, and now there came upon Orestes one of those fits of sudden madness which still afflicted him. He seemed to see in front of him those terrible avenging goddesses, the Erinyes, who had pursued him ever since his mother's death. Some had snakes twined in their hair; some waved flaming brands of fire, and one of them carried in her arms the dead body of Clytemnestra. With a great cry Orestes sprang to his feet, shaking off the restraining hand of Pylades, who tried in vain to comfort him. Raising his sword high he rushed upon the cattle and began to cut them down, for in these harmless beasts he seemed to see the terrible shapes of his pursuers.

So the sea was stained red with the blood of the slaughtered animals, and now the herdsmen gathered together in a body, blowing on horns and trumpets to summon aid from all in the neighbourhood, and began to hurl stones at the two young men surrounded on the shore. Soon the fit of madness that had overcome

Orestes ended and Orestes himself fell to the ground in a faint. Seeing him in this defenceless state, the herdsmen pressed on, doubling their volleys of stones; but Pylades stood firm, sheltering his friend's body with his own body and behind the screen of his thick cloak which he held over him like a shield. And before long Orestes came to himself. He looked up and saw the mass of men surrounding them. "O Pylades," he said, "it seems that Apollo has sent us here to meet our deaths; but, if we must die, let us at least die with honour!" Then, shouting out his battle cry, he bore down upon the great numbers of his enemies, and Pylades went with him. Neither the herdsmen, for all their numbers, nor the soldiers who had come out to join them dared to stand their ground. Instead they fell back and from a safe distance shot arrows and hurled stones at the two Greeks. So they wearied them out and in the end with their stones they knocked the weapons from their hands.

In this way Orestes and Pylades were overpowered and were brought to King Thoas. When the King had heard what the herdsmen had to say he told them to take the prisoners immediately to the temple and to the priestess so that they might be sacrificed at once. "These men," he said, "are without doubt great warriors among the Greeks. In sacrificing such men our priestess must feel joy, since she is avenging herself for what the Greeks would have done to her."

So Orestes and Pylades, with their hands bound, were brought into the presence of Iphigeneia, whose duty it was to sprinkle their heads with water and to say over them the proper prayers. Meanwhile within the temple the attendants were making ready bowls to receive their blood and a fire in which their bodies were to be burned. This was the moment in which, after so many years, Orestes again saw his sister and Iphigeneia her brother.

As she looked at the young men in all their strength and beauty her heart was stirred to pity them. She could imagine the grief which must be felt by a mother or a sister at losing such sons or brothers as these. She was bound, she knew, to take her part in the bloody sacrifice, yet she wished to delay it, at least for a short time, and she questioned the two strangers, asking them their names and where they had come from. But Orestes would not tell her his name. He had no wish that it should be known that he, the last of the great house of Atreus, had died miserably in a barbarian country. Yet, since her manner was so gentle to him, he did not refuse to speak altogether. He told her that he and Pylades, though not brothers, were bound together by their friendship more firmly than any brothers could be, and he told her also that he came from Argos and from Mycenae.

When she heard these words, the names of the great cities of Agamemnon where she had spent her childhood, Iphigeneia sighed and she began again to question him. He told her the whole terrible story of which she had never heard—of how Agamemnon had returned in triumph from Troy and had been murdered by his own wife at the moment of his homecoming, and of how the murder had been avenged by Agamemnon's son. Iphigeneia listened with amazement and with horror. "And where is Orestes now?" she asked. "Is he alive or dead?"

"Just now," was the reply, "he is alive. But wherever he is, he is unfortunate."

At the news that he was alive at all Iphigeneia was strangely moved. It seemed to her that the dream which she had had must have been a deceitful dream; for even now she could not see its true meaning. Above all now she longed to send a message to her brother to let him know that she was still alive. It might be that at some time he might find means to rescue her from her exile on this barbarous coast and bring her back to golden Mycenae; and, even if this were too much to be hoped for, at least it would do her heart good only to hold some communication with him. So she spoke again to Orestes and said: "Stranger, you say that you come from the land of Argos and of Mycenae, and you look as if you came from some noble family. Now there is someone in that land to whom I wish to send a letter. If you will swear to carry this letter for me, I will spare your life and let you go free. I cannot spare your friend's life too, for neither the King nor the people of this land would allow it. But one of you I may spare."

"Then," said Orestes, "it is my friend who must take the letter while I remain here to die. Love for me, and no other reason, brought him with me on this adventure. Indeed it would be shameful if I allowed him to suffer death and went away safe myself. And in any case his life is as dear to me as my own."

As Iphigeneia looked at the young man she admired him. "Even though you will not tell me your name," she said, "I feel sure that you must come from some noble family. I pray that my own brother, who is far away from me, may be one like you, loyal and true to his friends."

So she went inside the temple to write the letter that was to be carried back to Argos. But now Pylades in his turn protested that he would not save his own life, while Orestes was left to die. They were comrades together, he said, and as comrades they should live or die together.

Orestes begged his friend to take the letter and to live. He urged him to go back and comfort his sister Electra and to take not only his own kingdom but the kingdom of Mycenae as well. "For myself," he said, "life cannot in any way be happy, since I shall still be pursued by the avenging spirits of my mother's blood; but you, Pylades, can live a noble and a fortunate life. In being kind to my sister and in honouring my memory you can give me pleasure even in the tomb. It seems certain that Apollo has cheated me, but you have never deceived me. Your friendship has been always the best thing in life that I have known. Now in the name of this friendship I beg you to live. Tell them in Argos that I died bravely and that I was only destroyed because I obeyed the commandments of a god. I killed my mother and now I must die myself."

"As for me," said Pylades, "I shall keep my love for you whether you are alive or dead. Yet still we are both alive. It may still be that the gods will not cheat us—that some mercy may be shown."

So they talked until Iphigeneia, with the letter in her hands, came out again from the temple. First she put the letter into Pylades' hands and then she asked him to swear an oath that he would deliver it safely if she saved his life by interceding for him with King Thoas so as to let him go free.

"But," said Pylades, "supposing that I were to be shipwrecked and the letter was washed from my hands by the waves of the sea. Then I could not keep my oath. It would be better for you to let me learn the words of the letter by heart; then, so long as my life is saved, the words will also be preserved."

Iphigeneia agreed to this and she began to read to him the letter that she had written. "My words," she began, "are for Orestes, the son of Agamemnon, and they come to him from his sister Iphigeneia."

When they heard this, both Orestes and Pylades stood dumbfounded. Indeed they could not believe their ears, for both of them thought that long before this time Iphigeneia had perished at the hands of the gods.

Iphigeneia herself did not notice their confusion. She continued to read aloud the words that she had written: "I who was sacrificed, they say, at Aulis, am still alive, though I am dead to those who love me. The goddess Artemis saved my life and brought me to this savage place where all my youth has been spent. Now, my brother Orestes, I beg you to come here and rescue me, so that I may see once again my own country and my own people."

When she had finished reading she handed the letter to Pylades and, as she turned her eyes upon him and upon Orestes, she was astonished to see the expression in their faces.

"What you would have me do," said Pylades, "is done easily enough," and he took the letter from her hand and gave it to Orestes. "Here," he said, "is your own brother, Orestes himself."

Orestes clasped her in his arms, but she shrank back from him, for she could not even yet believe that this young man, whom she had been on the point of consecrating for sacrifice, was indeed the brother whom she had longed to see. It was not long, however, before Orestes convinced her that this was the truth, and then, with happy tears, she flung herself into his arms. Now, in this moment of joy, it seemed possible to forget the long tale of the sufferings of Agamemnon's house, all the treachery and crime and bloodshed that had taken place since that distant day in Aulis when an innocent girl had been brought forward as an offering for the success of the expedition against Troy. Now, in the dark recesses of his own mind, Orestes no longer felt the uneasy presence of the pursuing Erinyes. He knew again the affection that he had known in his childhood before the days of his exile and before he had been commanded by the gods to do the dreadful deeds that he had done.

There was much indeed that brother and sister had to say to each other, but there was not the time nor the opportunity for much to be said. Orestes told her the reason why he and Pylades had come, how they had been instructed by Apollo to seize the statue of Artemis and bring it to Athens, and Iphigeneia, though she was herself the priestess of Artemis, could see no wrong in the deed, for Artemis was Apollo's sister and, once the statue was removed to Athens, it would no longer be worshipped with the savage ceremonies of human sacrifice. The difficulty was in how to

escape with the statue and with their own lives, for the temple was guarded by King Thoas' soldiers and at any moment the King himself might be expected to arrive in order to find out whether the sacrifice had been duly carried out. Meanwhile Orestes and Pylades were defenceless; for, though Iphigeneia had freed their hands, their weapons had been taken from them.

It was Iphigeneia herself who thought of a plan by which to deceive the King and to secure their escape. When, as she knew would happen, King Thoas came to the temple, she told him that a strange event had taken place—something which would make it necessary for the sacrifice to be postponed. She said that, when the two Greeks had been brought into the presence of the goddess, the holy statue itself had miraculously moved, turning away its head from them. Then, said Iphigeneia, she had questioned the two strangers and had discovered that they were men who had been driven out of Greece because they had been guilty of shedding a mother's blood. Thus they were impure and the goddess would never accept them as a sacrifice until they had been taken to the sea, washed in the sea water and been purified from guilt with the proper prayers. Only she, Iphigeneia, could perform this ceremony and, while she was doing it, all the inhabitants of the city must stay within the city walls, in case they too should be involved in the guilt which was being washed away from the two men. Only a few priests from the temple should attend on her to make sure that the prisoners should attempt no violent escape.

King Thoas listened to her with attention, since he believed that in matters that concerned religion she was much wiser than he. Iphigeneia then said that the holy statue itself had been polluted by the presence of these strangers and that it was necessary to take the statue also down to the sea so that it could be ceremonially cleansed from the stain. Here again King Thoas accepted her advice. He gave the orders that she had required him to give. He himself with all his troops remained within the city walls; the statue was brought out from the temple, and soon a small procession began to make its way down to the sea. Iphigeneia, as the priestess, carried the statue herself; Orestes and Pylades followed her and the temple attendants guarded them.

So they made their way along the shore until they had almost reached the place where the fifty-oared Greek ship lay at anchor, concealed behind a headland, and at this point Iphigeneia ordered the temple attendants to bind the hands of Orestes and Pylades and to wait there while she herself performed the proper rites over them. The attendants could not dispute the commands of the priestess of Artemis, nor did they see how two men, unarmed and fettered, could attempt to make an escape. So they remained behind while Iphigeneia, carrying the statue and followed by Orestes and Pylades, went on farther along the shore until they were out of sight.

Time passed and still the waiting attendants saw no sign of their priestess returning. At length they began to grow uneasy and decided to go after her to make sure that all was well. But no sooner had they gone round the next headland than they saw a sight to surprise them,—a Greek war-ship, with fifty men sitting at the oars. The anchor was being raised and the hawsers drawn aboard. In the stern of the boat stood the two strangers, no longer bound, and with them was the priestess of Artemis, holding the statue of the goddess in her arms.

With their wild barbarian cries the temple attendants rushed down towards the shore; but they had arrived too late and there were too few of them to be able to resist the crew of the Greek ship. Standing in the stern Orestes cried out to them: "Tell your King that it was by the will of the gods that I came here. I am Orestes, son of Agamemnon, a brother to this Iphigeneia, whom I am bringing back to her own home. Apollo himself preserves us and it was Apollo who commanded me to take this image of yours to Athens, where it will no longer receive the sacrifice of men's blood, but will be worshipped as the gods ought to be worshipped."

Then he shouted to the rowers and the rowers bent forward over their oars. Over the whitening foam the ship shot like an arrow from that savage shore, moving too fast for any pursuit. So Orestes brought back his sister to her own land and so he himself at last found peace after all that he had suffered.

HELEN

It is well known how Paris, the son of King Priam of Troy, was called upon, while he was watching his sheep on Mount Ida, to judge a competition of beauty between the three goddesses, Hera, Aphrodite and Athene. The goddesses, each anxious to be the winner in this contest, offered gifts to Paris. Hera offered power and Athene offered wisdom; but Aphrodite told him that, if only he would declare her to be the winner, she would give him Helen, the most beautiful woman in the world, to be his wife. It is known how Paris was persuaded to give to Aphrodite the prize for beauty and how, by doing so, he brought utter ruin upon the great city of Troy and death to many men, Trojans and Greeks alike. For he stole Helen from her own home and her own husband, Menelaus, the King of Sparta and the brother of the powerful King Agamemnon; and it was to win her back again that there sailed from Greece the great expedition which for ten years fought in the plains of Troy. There Hector lost his life, and Achilles and many other warriors until, in the end, Troy was taken and Menelaus regained his wife, a woman whose faithlessness had caused much blood to be shed.

This is the story of Helen as it is generally told. But there is another and a different story of her. According to this other story Helen was neither wicked nor faithless. She was the victim of jealousy among the gods and she most undeservedly suffered much before, in the end, she became happy as she ought always to have been. This second story is as follows:

Aphrodite wished certainly to keep her promise to reward Paris for having given her the prize for beauty. And Paris, when he sailed away from Sparta, carrying with him a lovely woman whom he called "Helen," was convinced that he had had his reward. In fact, however, this was not so. For Hera, in her anger at his having preferred Aphrodite to herself, had cheated him out of his real prize. She had given orders to the god Hermes to take Helen away from

Sparta and to hide her in a distant land. And to take the place of Helen she had created out of thin air a phantom whom Paris took with him to Troy, and it was for this phantom that the Greeks and Trojans fought for so many years. No one could tell the difference between the real Helen and the phantom. Paris all the time believed that it was Helen herself who was his wife. Menelaus too, when the war was over, believed that he was carrying back again in his ship the woman to whom he had once been married and who had left him. Yet all the Greeks and all the Trojans who had fallen in this great war had fallen for something which did not really exist, since all this time Helen herself had never been in Troy at all.

The real Helen had been taken up by Hermes in folds of air, carried far away from her home in Sparta, from her loved husband Menelaus and from her little daughter Hermione, and set down in Egypt, where she was entrusted to the care of the King of that land, Proteus, a man who, though not a Greek, was one who revered the gods and who would obey their commands. He had been told by Hermes to keep Helen safe in his kingdom until the time should come for her husband Menelaus to find her and to take her home again.

And so for year after year Helen lived in exile in the palace of King Proteus. She was kindly and courteously treated, yet all the time she longed for her home and for her husband who, with all the great warriors of the Greeks, was fighting beneath the walls of Troy in the mistaken belief that he was fighting, not for a phantom, but for his real wife.

King Proteus had married one of the nymphs of the sea and by her had had two children, both of whom grew up during the time that Helen was in Egypt. The son was called Theoclymenus. He was a brave warrior, though he had a rash and hasty temper. His sister was called Theonoe and to her the gods had given the power of knowing what was happening in any part of the world, however far away, and what also was destined to happen. Thus she was a great prophetess and spent her life in the pure service of the gods.

Now so long as Proteus was alive Helen lived peacefully in the King's palace, though unhappily enough, since she was separated from her husband and her friends and she knew that throughout the world the story of her was that she was a faithless wife who had brought on her people the horrors of a long war. It was difficult indeed to bear the thought of all the hatred that was so wrongly felt against her and she often wept when she reflected upon what the gods had done to her. She was the daughter of Zeus himself who, in the form of a swan, had visited her mother Leda. Her brothers were the twin Dioscuri, the children of heaven, Castor and Pollux, who were among the greatest heroes of the time. Her husband was a King. She herself had behaved well and worthily of her great position, and yet all her family must certainly think of her as a wicked and disgraceful creature. It was true that Hermes had told her that in the end, when the will of the gods had been accomplished, she would be reunited to her husband and would return to her home in Sparta. But in the meantime what might not happen? Men were dying for her sake every day and women were being worn out with sorrow for husbands, brothers and sons lost in the destructive war.

So for ten years in Egypt Helen lamented her fate. Yet she was at least well treated and her person was safe in the care of the good old King Proteus. But a time came when even this consolation was taken away from her. Proteus died and his young son Theoclymenus became King in his stead. Now everything was changed. So long as his father had been alive Theoclymenus had had to obey him. He had treated Helen with the respect that was her due and he had followed his father's hospitable way of welcoming all Greeks (there were not many of them) who came to Egypt from time to time and could tell the latest rumours, true or false, of the great war still raging in the plains of Troy. But now Theoclymenus cast off all restraint. He was determined to make Helen his wife, whether she liked it or not, and, lest there should be any hope of her ever seeing her husband again, he gave orders to his officers that all Greeks landing in Egypt should immediately be put to death.

It seemed to Helen that now there was no escape open to her in this life, no possible way of relief. She was resolved to remain faithful to her husband Menelaus and to refuse the marriage offered to her, or forced upon her, by the young King of Egypt. Yet she had no one to defend her and no means now even of meeting with those who might give her hope from the news that they might bring. She fled from her room into the open air in front of the great gateway and battlements of the palace. Here was the tomb of Proteus and at this tomb she sought refuge, since even Theoclymenus, she thought, would not dare to violate his father's tomb by dragging her away from it by force. Yet still it seemed to her that there was nothing in which she could rest her hope. She began to look forward to death and even to contemplate how best she could take her own life. She did not know that, at this very moment when she was the most vexed with terrible thoughts, her deliverance and her happiness were at hand.

Nor did she know that by this time, after its long siege, Troy had fallen and the victorious Greeks were on their way home. When finally she received the news it came to her in such a way as to make her even more unhappy than before. For one day a Greek who had fought in the Trojan war landed in Egypt and, not knowing that all Greeks were hated by the King of Egypt, made his way to the tall palace by the banks of the Nile. This Greek was Teucer, the famous archer and the brother of the great Ajax, who had been one of the foremost of all the warriors at Troy. In the end Ajax had met with a cruel fate. He had quarrelled with the other leaders of the Greeks and then the gods had taken away his right mind and made him mad. When once more he came back to his senses he was so ashamed that he took his own life. Teucer, his brother, had sailed home sorrowfully and when he reached his home in the island of Salamis that lies, shaped like a bean, off the coast of Athens, his father, King Telamon, treated him most unjustly. He blamed him, quite without reason, for his brother's death, and since he had come home without the great Ajax, no welcome was given to him and he was, after so many years of fighting abroad, driven out again into exile. Now, with a chosen company of men, he was on his way towards the eastern sea where he was to found a city, another Salamis, in the island of Cyprus. His ship had entered Egyptian waters undetected and had avoided the great storm in which, as we shall see, another of the Greeks had almost perished. So Teucer came to the palace of Theoclymenus, intending to ask for help and for guidance on his way.

The first thing that he saw was Helen standing by the tomb of Proteus, beautiful and distressed. He turned upon her and cursed her; not that he believed that she really was Helen, because he had seen with his own eyes that other Helen who was a phantom carried off from Troy by Menelaus. But he so hated the woman who had been the cause of all his sufferings that even to be reminded of her by one who, he thought, so closely resembled her, made him half-crazy with anger. Helen spoke to him gently. "Why do you blame me," she said, "for what I have not done?" And Teucer was moved by her words and by her manner. "Forgive me," he said, "for my sudden anger. But I and all the Greeks have suffered countless miseries because of a woman who looks so exactly like you that I can scarcely believe my own eyes." Then, still not knowing that it was to Helen herself that he was speaking he told her what he knew. It was, for her, a sad story to hear. Troy, he told her, had fallen after ten years of fighting in which many of the best of the Greeks had lost their lives. Menelaus had sacked the city and had taken away with him the faithless wife for whose sake the war had been fought. But a great storm had scattered the ships. Menelaus had never reached home and it was believed that he and all his ship's company had been lost at sea. At this news Helen could scarcely prevent herself from crying out, but she found courage to ask more questions and, as Teucer answered them, she became more wretched still. Her mother Leda, so Teucer told her, had hanged herself because of the shame she felt at her daughter's conduct. As for her brothers, the Dioscuri, there were two stories and Teucer did not know which one was true. Some said that they also had died because of the disgrace which their sister had brought upon them; but others said that, because of their virtuous and great deeds, they had been set in the heavens like shining stars and had joined the company of the gods. It was, as will be seen, the second of these stories which was correct.

Miserable as she was when she heard these words of Teucer, Helen was still able to control herself. She could not tell him who she was; for in the first place, he would never believe it; and, even if he did believe it, he would not be able to help her to return to Greece, for he himself was an exile. So she simply warned him to escape from Egypt as quickly as he could, since King Theoclymenus would kill every Greek whom he found in his kingdom. Teucer thanked her for her advice. "Indeed," he said, "though you have a face like Helen's, your heart is very different from hers. I pray that Helen may be drowned in the deep sea, but for you I wish every happiness that can come to you."

So he went on his way and left Helen more unhappy than she had ever been; for now it seemed that she had been betrayed by the gods and had nothing to live for at all. Till this moment she had still believed, or half believed, that somehow and some day her husband would return to her, but now, if what Teucer told her was true, Menelaus was dead and had died without ever knowing that she had always been faithful to him. It seemed that she was wholly lost. She could marry Theoclymenus and be a queen; but that she was resolved not to do. It would be better, she thought, to die, and she began to plan how she could take her own life. Indeed her fate was a sad one. To other women beauty had always brought happiness, or at least the opportunity for it, but in Helen's case, it was just this great beauty of hers that had ruined her life.

One thing she determined to do before she killed herself. Theoclymenus, she knew, was out hunting. So she would leave the sanctuary of Proteus' tomb, go into the palace and there consult the King's sister, Theonoe, the prophetess who knew everything, both the present and the future. She was good and, if she were earnestly besought, she would tell her whether Menelaus was still alive or whether he had been lost in the waves of the sea. Helen dreaded to ask the question, yet ask it she must; for she could not kill herself unless she was certain beyond all doubt that no hope, not even the faintest, remained to her.

And so, walking carefully, in case she might be seized upon by some guard set for her by Theoclymenus, she left the monument which was her refuge and she entered the great gates of the palace, knowing that, once she had made her way to Theonoe, she would be safe, since the prophetess was so holy that not even the King, her brother, would dare to disturb one who had placed herself under her protection.

But no sooner had she gone inside the palace than the very thing for which she had so long been waiting actually took place. Menelaus, her husband, returned. But he returned in a way that was unexpected and no one who saw him as he drew near the palace would have guessed that he was a great King. For he came in rags, with hair and beard unkempt. His face bore all the marks of suffering and privation, for he had long been driven by storms across the angry seas as he tried to make his way back from Troy, carrying with him in his ship that phantom woman whom he had seized from the captured city and whom he believed to be his real wife. And now, by the will of the gods, his ship had been wrecked on the rocks just by the very place where Helen herself had so long been waiting for him. Menelaus had escaped from the wreck and so had most of his crew together with that beautiful living image which they all believed to be Helen. It seemed to them that their case was desperate. They had lost their ship and were not even certain of what land they stood on. Menelaus had ordered his men to remain in hiding in a cave on the shore of the sea and there to guard his wife—for so he called the creature who had caused all his sufferings. He himself, seeing a great palace towering above the level plain, had determined to go there and, though a King, to beg for bread for himself and his company, and, if the people in this part of the world should prove hospitable, to ask for help as well.

So, just as Helen had gone inside the palace, terrified that she might be told by the prophetess that her husband was dead, Menelaus himself arrived at the palace gates, alive and strong, although instead of king's clothing he was dressed in wretched rags and instead of meeting with the reception due to a king he was forced to knock at the gate like any beggar.

As he knocked a woman servant half-opened the door, but refused to let him in. Seeing his miserable clothing she was at first for driving him away like a dog, but there was something in his bearing which impressed her and in the end she spoke to him kindly. When she discovered that he was a Greek, she warned him to escape at once. "In our house," she said, "no Greek is welcome," and when Menelaus asked her the reason for this, she replied, "It is because the daughter of Zeus, Helen, is living in this land."

Menelaus was astonished at the words. His wife,—the one whom he had just left in the cave,—could not have stolen away from there and reached the palace before him. "What Helen do you mean?" he enquired and the woman answered him calmly, "Helen of Sparta, who came here before the Greeks set sail for Troy."

Then she shut the door in his face and left him entirely bewildered. For how could he possibly believe what she said? He had fought in Troy for ten years and in the end had won back from that city a woman who to him and to everyone else was "Helen." He had just left her in the cave. Yet what was he to make of this maid servant's words? It occurred to him that perhaps in Egypt also there was a place called "Sparta" and in this Egyptian Sparta there had lived a woman called "Helen." It sounded improbable; but what other explanation could there be?

And now, while he was reflecting on the strange words which he had heard and was wondering what next he could do to help himself and his companions, the gates of the palace opened and Helen herself came out from them. At first she did not notice Menelaus, for she was smiling to herself and her eyes were fixed in thought upon the ground. She smiled because she had heard good news. The prophetess Theonoe had told her the truth which was that, though her husband had been shipwrecked, he was alive and he was very close at hand. So, as she came slowly forward from the palace, she was occupied in pleasing thoughts. "O when, when," she said to herself, "will he come, the husband whom I have waited for so long?"

Then she raised her eyes and saw standing in front of her, between her and the tomb of Proteus which was her sanctuary, a tall strong man, wretchedly dressed and with every mark of hardship upon him. Her first thought was that this must be some servant of Theoclymenus sent there to intercept her and to prevent her from reaching the safety of the tomb. In terror she sprang past him and began to run the short distance that separated her from her place of sanctuary. Menelaus called out to her not to be afraid of him, since he meant no evil to her, but she would not stop until she had reached the altar which stood by the tomb. There she knew that she was safe and there, clinging to the altar, she turned to look more closely at the man from whom she had fled. Menelaus also looked at her and he was astonished at what he saw. "Who are you?" he asked in amazement and now Helen, amazed too, since she saw beneath the wretched rags and all the marks of hardship the royal bearing which she knew, tremblingly replied, "I ask the same question. Who are you?"

"You look," said Menelaus, "exactly as Helen looks."

"And you," said Helen, "look to me like Menelaus." For, even though she knew him, she scarcely dared to believe in what she knew.

"Menelaus is indeed my name," he said. "And it is the name of a man who has suffered much."

At this Helen threw her arms about his neck. "O welcome!" she cried, "my husband! Welcome to your wife who has waited so long for you!"

But Menelaus unclasped her hands from his neck and stepped away from her. "Wife!" he said. "You are not my wife. I have a wife already, the woman whom I took from Troy. You look like my wife certainly, but the plain fact of the matter is that you are not."

Then Helen tried to explain to him what had happened, that it was only a phantom who had gone to Troy with Paris and that she herself, his real wife, had remained faithful to him all these years in Egypt. Menelaus listened to her, but still he could not believe her. He thought that this was some trick or sorcery that was being practised upon him. For how could he and all those others have fought and suffered so long at Troy for something which was only a figure of air, something that was not the real thing? So, though he had now at last discovered his real wife and could have known her as a much better woman than he had thought, he could not believe in the fact, so much was his mind dominated by what he had thought previously and by the long years of his hardship. Indeed he would have left her there and then, in spite of everything she might have said to him and in spite of the perfect beauty which was her own, if it had not happened that he now received some strange news which made him, finally, acknowledge the happy truth.

Just as he had dragged himself away from Helen's arms there came running to the palace gates one of his own company, an old soldier who had fought with him throughout the war and who had been his faithful servant ever since the time long ago when he had married Helen in his own land of Sparta. The old man came in a state of great excitement and at first did not notice Helen while he hurried to tell his surprising story. What had happened was this: soon after Menelaus had left the cave the woman or phantom whom he and all the others believed to be Helen had risen to her feet with a strange look in her eyes and had briefly spoken to the men who gathered about her. "Wretched Trojans," she had said, "and wretched Greeks, all of you who died for me in battle and on the high seas, thinking that you were fighting for Helen, when you were only fighting for me, a creature made by the gods for their own purposes out of thin air. Now my mission is over and I must go back into the air from which I was formed. I tell you that you fought for nothing and that Helen, the wife of Menelaus, is innocent." As she spoke these last words she melted away from their eyes into the surrounding air and the place where she had just been standing was left empty.

So the old man, bewildered and amazed, told his story to Menelaus. Then he noticed Helen herself standing in front of him and he became more puzzled than ever, since his first thought was that the woman who had so miraculously disappeared from the cave had now, in some equally miraculous way, reappeared in front of the palace. He did not know what to make of it. But Menelaus saw at once that this woman whom he had been on the point of rejecting was indeed his own wife, restored to him faithful and loving by the gods who had indeed treated both her and him cruelly but who had allowed finally the truth to be revealed. Joyful now indeed was their meeting, as they clasped each other in loving arms and each blessed the other for the happiness which they found together. As they began to speak and to tell each other of their fortunes, the old soldier, who had been bewildered at what he saw, began to understand what really had happened and he too rejoiced with them, for he remembered their marriage and, like a trusty servant, he honoured the good name of his master's house.

But now, after the joy of their recognition, the shadow of fear and of anxiety fell over them. For how were they to escape? Menelaus had lost his ship, so that the sea was closed to them. He and his men were brave warriors but they were too few to fight with the armies of the King of Egypt. Nor could they escape on land since Theoclymenus had chariots and horses which would overtake them. It was certain too that Theoclymenus, who desired Helen for his own wife, would kill Menelaus, in spite of the fame and glory he had won at Troy, if he ever suspected who he was. Moreover it seemed impossible for him not to know, because Theonoe, his sister, could never be deceived and she, partly from fear and partly from love of her brother, would tell him that Menelaus, the man whom he most wished to destroy, was in his hands.

And so, as they entered into their difficulties and dangers, their newfound joy gave way to sorrow, for indeed there seemed no hope of their ever escaping from Egypt and its King. Menelaus could think of no plan except to take his stand upon the tomb and there die fighting; Helen would die with him rather than fall into the hands of Theoclymenus.

It seemed that what they feared would take place almost at once; for now Theonoe, the prophetess, with the priests and priestesses of her religion accompanying her, came out of the palace. She recognised Menelaus at once, for she was filled with divine power. The gods had been speaking to her and she knew that among the gods themselves there was argument and debate as to whether Menelaus and Helen should be allowed to live or not. Hera, the wife of Zeus, who had made the phantom in Helen's shape, now wanted to reward Menelaus for his sufferings by giving him back his true wife. But Aphrodite wanted them both to perish in case it should be known that she had not been able to keep her word to Paris and that he had enjoyed the love, not of Helen, but of a creature made out of the air. Now it was for Theonoe herself to decide which of these goddesses should have her will. For, if once she told her brother that Menelaus was in his power, Menelaus, and Helen after him, would certainly die. Loyalty to her brother and fear for her own safety, if she should deceive him, made her incline to tell him the truth. But she listened to what Helen and Menelaus had to say to her. They reminded her that her father Proteus had been instructed to keep Helen safe and, in due time, to return her to her husband, and they begged her not to bring shame upon the memory of her good father, who had acted right-eously all his life, by betraying the trust which had been reposed in him. She herself, they pointed out, was the servant of the gods and how could it be right to serve the gods except by acting righteously?

As Theonoe listened to them her mind altered. She knew that it was wrong to betray innocent people to death and she determined that she would do right, even at the risk of her own life. She prom-ised them that she would not tell her brother of the presence of Menelaus; but beyond this she would not go. If they were to es-cape, they must manage the manner of their escape themselves. She would not offend her brother further by actively aiding them in the attempt.

And so she left them freed from one anxiety, but surrounded with others. At any moment King Theoclymenus might return from hunting and, even if he did not know who Menelaus was, he might put him to death simply because he was a Greek. Once more it seemed that nothing was left to them except to die bravely, and death would indeed have been their fate, had not Helen, who was as intelligent as she was beautiful, thought of a clever plan by which to deceive the King and, if all went well, to secure their safety.

Her plan was to go into the palace and there cut her hair short and put on black robes of mourning, for she was going to pretend that she had received news that her husband Menelaus had been drowned at sea. Menelaus himself was to pretend to be the man who had brought this news; he was to say that he was a sailor on the ship that had been wrecked and that he had actually seen Menelaus die. Helen would then tell Theoclymenus that, now that her husband was dead and would never return, she was ready to marry him; but she would ask him first to let her have a ship so that she might sail out a little distance into the sea and there make the proper sacrifices and offerings for those who had been drowned and whose bodies would never be placed in a tomb. She would ask for rich gifts to be given to the dead and she would ask that Menelaus and his men (whom Theoclymenus would think were the survivors from her dead husband's ship) should join her in making the offerings. Then, once they were at sea, they would fight the Egyptian crew for the control of the ship and, if they were successful, would set sail for Greece.

It was a daring plan, but it was the only plan that seemed to offer any hope. Menelaus sent his servant to tell his men to hold themselves ready and to hide the swords they carried underneath their garments, and Helen went into the palace in order to dress herself as though she were in mourning.

The plan had been made only just in time, for now Theoclymenus rode up to the palace, surrounded by his attendants, his hunting dogs and his horses. He was angry because he had been told that a Greek had escaped the notice of the guards whom he had posted along the coast and had entered the land of Egypt. He was determined to have this man's life and would have been more determined still if he had known that this Greek was none other than great Menelaus himself.

Soon, however, when he saw Helen come out of the palace, with her hair cut short and wearing black robes, his anger gave way to astonishment. She seemed no longer afraid of him but came quickly towards him with bent head and told him that she had now received certain news that her husband had been lost at sea, so that now she could accept the offer of marriage which Theoclymenus had made to her. At the same time she beckoned Menelaus to come forward (for he had hidden behind the tomb when he saw Theoclymenus approach). "This is the man," she said, "who has brought me the news of my husband. If it is news that pleases you, I beg you to reward him for it."

Theoclymenus was conceited enough to suppose that Helen really wanted to marry him. "You have done wisely," he said to her, "and you shall have the most splendid wedding. All the nobles of Egypt will be present and will bring you gifts. You must not grieve at losing your husband. You will find me a much better man than Menelaus was. And as for this stranger" (and here he turned to Menelaus) "since he has brought me such good news, his life shall be spared, he shall be given decent clothes to wear and I shall even invite him to my wedding banquet."

Helen was pleased to find that Theoclymenus was so stupid and vain as to have fallen into the trap which she had laid for him. Next she asked him to show his love for her by granting her a request and Theoclymenus willingly agreed. "There is a custom," said Helen, "among the Greeks which is that, when a man is drowned at sea, his nearest relatives sail out in a ship and hold a funeral ceremony for him, even though his body is lost. I beg you to let me do this for my husband Menelaus."

Theoclymenus at once agreed to let her have a ship for the performance of this ceremony. Being a barbarian, he was naturally impressed by Greek customs and asked Helen exactly what offerings were required for the dead. Helen replied that, for a man of the high rank of Menelaus, the ship should be loaded with clothing and armour and food of all kinds, together with animals for sacrificing. "And then," she added, "it would be a good thing if this stranger here" (and she pointed to Menelaus) "were to be put in command of the ship, since he and his men know the right way of making the sacrifices and how far exactly in the sea the ship ought to go."

To this also Theoclymenus agreed. In a way he was pleased that Helen seemed so anxious to perform all the proper rites for her dead husband, for, in his vanity, he thought that she would have an equal respect for him as soon as she had married him. And so he gave orders to fit out a swift ship of Sidon and to provide all the gifts and offerings which Helen had asked for. Menelaus meanwhile was taken inside the palace where he was given a bath and presented with fine clothes. When he came out again, with all the marks of travel and of the shipwreck washed away, dressed as he ought to be and girt with his own sword, there was something so royal in his bearing that anyone less vain and opinionated than Theoclymenus would have marvelled at it and would have thought twice before handing over to such a man the woman whom he desired to be his wife. But Theoclymenus was so busy in making arrangements for holding his own wedding feast that it never occurred to him that there was any danger that this feast might never be held.

And now the rest of Menelaus's ship's company arrived, strong tough men, with fierce and eager eyes, veterans of the Trojan war. Each had his sword hidden under his garments and each was ready to fight grimly to win a way home again to the land they loved.

So Theoclymenus told the captain of his Egyptian crew to obey the orders of the man he called "the stranger" until the sacrifices were over and then to bring back to him the woman who was to be his bride. "Do not mourn too much," he said to Helen. "Remember that you will soon have a husband who is a King."

"That also is my prayer," said Helen as she looked at Menelaus. Then Theoclymenus left them, and the animals and rich gifts were loaded on to the ship. The Egyptian rowers took their places at the oars; the sails were hoisted up; Helen and Menelaus went down the gangway and after them came the Greek sailors who sat together in the prow, waiting, tense and eager, with their faces fixed on Menelaus. Menelaus ordered the helmsman to steer the ship out to sea and, when they had gone some distance from the shore, he told his men to lift out of the hold the great bull which had been brought for sacrifice. Then he drew his sword and stood in front of the bull ready to cut its throat. The Egyptian rowers and officers waited, expecting that he would make some prayer for the dead man whom they believed that they were there to honour. But instead of this Menelaus lifted up his voice and cried out: "O great Poseidon, god of the sea, grant my prayer. After all our sufferings, bring me and my wife home to Hellas and to Sparta." Then he plunged the sword into the bull's throat and the blood spurted out directly into the sea, an omen which seemed to show that his prayer would be granted.

The Egyptians were dismayed. "There is treachery on this ship," they began to say. But Menelaus shouted out to his men: "Now, my comrades, show these foreigners how you fought at Troy. Strike them down and hurl every one of them into the sea." He himself sprang forward, dealing great blows with his sword, and his men followed him like wolves. As for the Egyptians they fought back with oars, with pieces of timber and with every weapon that came to hand, but they could not long resist these trained soldiers of the Greeks fighting to regain their native land. Only one of them escaped the slaughter and he, swimming in the sea, was picked up by another ship and taken back to land where he told King Theoclymenus that his bride had been stolen away from him and that "the stranger" who had outwitted them was great Menelaus himself.

The anger of Theoclymenus was unbounded and it turned at once against his sister Theonoe who had known that Menelaus was present in the land and who had concealed her knowledge. In spite of all that his counsellors could do or say, Theoclymenus determined immediately to put his sister to death; but, as he was actually on his way to do this evil thing, he was prevented by the gods. For there suddenly appeared in front of him two shining figures like stars, strong and beautiful young men riding upon white horses. These were the Dioscuri, the brothers of Helen, who had not died but had been taken up into the heavens to join the gods. Theoclymenus was abashed by their presence and he listened humbly to their words. They told him that what had happened was the will of Zeus. It was right that Helen should be reunited with her husband, and Theonoe had done rightly in reverencing the commands that had been given to Proteus. Theoclymenus therefore must lay aside his anger and look elsewhere for a wife.

As he listened to the divine beings Theoclymenus felt the passion in his heart decline. He was glad that he had been prevented from committing a crime and he blessed Helen. "For," he said, "she is altogether exceptional among women, being not only beautiful, but also wise and faithful."

As for Helen and Menelaus, fair winds carried them on their way over the green and the blue of the sea. After so many years of pain they were happy and happily they lived in Sparta. Nor did they ever know death, for when their years on this earth were over, the gods carried them to the Islands of the Blessed, a place where no keen winds come, no snow or storms of rain; gently the waves break on those sunlit shores and the mild air they breathe there keeps them young for ever in this garden that the gods have made for them. Here they know no sorrow and no toil, but live easily like the blessed gods themselves.